MALIGNANT NEGLECT

MALIGNANT NEGLECT

JOSEPH H. HIGHLAND, MARCIA E. FINE,
ROBERT H. HARRIS, JACQUELINE M. WARREN,
ROBERT J. RAUCH, and ANITA JOHNSON
of the ENVIRONMENTAL DEFENSE FUND
and ROBERT H. BOYLE

ALFRED A. KNOPF   NEW YORK   1979

Grateful acknowledgment is made to the following for permission to use previously published material:

Academic Press: Portions of "Cancer Etiology and Prevention" by John Higginson, in *Persons at High Risk of Cancer,* Joseph F. Fraumeni, Jr., ed. Copyright © 1975 by Academic Press. Used by permission of Academic Press and John Higginson.

Cold Spring Harbor Laboratory: Graphs from Sidney M. Wolfe, "Standards for Carcinogens: Science Affronted by Politics," and a graph by Robert H. Harris in *The Origins of Human Cancer,* copyright © 1977 by Cold Spring Harbor Laboratory. Used by permission of Sidney M. Wolfe, M.D., Robert H. Harris, and Cold Spring Harbor Laboratory.

Dr. Michael Greenberg: An extract from "The Special Distribution of Cancer Mortality and High and Low Risk Factors in the New Jersey–New York–Philadelphia Metropolitan Regions, 1950–1969" by Dr. Michael Greenberg. Distributed by The State of New Jersey Department of Environmental Protection, Trenton, New Jersey, Program on Environmental Cancer and Toxic Substances. Used by permission of Dr. Greenberg.

Medical Publications, Inc.: An extract from the August 1943 issue of *Industrial Medicine* by Dr. Leonard Greenburg. Used by permission of Medical Publications, Inc.

New England Journal of Medicine and Dr. Anita Bahn, M.D., Sc.D.: An excerpt from a letter by Dr. Anita Bahn to the *New England Journal of Medicine,* August 19, 1976, vol. 295, No. 8. Reprinted by permission of the *New England Journal of Medicine* and Dr. Anita Bahn, M.D., Sc.D.

The New York Academy of Sciences and Dr. Joseph Wagoner: Excerpt from the keynote address to the 1975 New York Academy of Sciences symposium on Occupational Carcinogenesis, published in the Annals of the New York Academy of Sciences, 1976, Vol. 271. Used by permission of The New York Academy of Sciences and Dr. Joseph Wagoner.

The Royal Swedish Academy of Sciences: An excerpt from "The PCB Story," by E. Helle, M. Olsson, and S. Jensen, which appeared in *Ambio,* vol. 5, No. 5–6, pp. 261–3, 1976. Used by permission of The Royal Swedish Academy of Sciences.

Library of Congress Cataloging in Publication Data
Environmental Defense Fund.
    Malignant neglect.
    Bibliography: p.
    Includes index.
    1. Carcinogenesis.   2. Environmentally induced diseases.   3. Cancer—United States.   I. Highland, Joseph H.   II. Boyle, Robert H.   III. Title.
RC268.5.E59   1979   616.9′94′071   78–20373
ISBN 0–394–41070–X

Manufactured in the United States of America
Published May 22, 1979
Second Printing, July 1979

For Frances Highland, Jane Sanger Boyle,
Ruth T. Fine, and Susan Warren Sossin

CONTENTS

PREFACE

Over the past two decades there has been an enormous increase in scientific knowledge and understanding about the nature of cancer. Most important, we have learned that cancer is not an inevitable disease of old age nor an infectious disease nor one caused by a particular virus. Instead, cancer results from exposure to chemical and physical agents present in our environment. Curiously, this increase in scientific knowledge has not been reflected in increased public understanding or in effective efforts at cancer prevention. Rather, as more information on the causes of cancer has been made available, the public has responded first with concern, then with anger, and finally with dazed and cynical complacency as it has come to perceive all chemicals, and everything we do, as causing cancer. It is our aim to dispel this growing cynicism.

Cancer is a complex mixture of diseases with an equally complex etiology. Many factors, including synthetic chemicals, ionizing radiation, diet, and cigarette smoke are strongly implicated as causative agents. While the exact extent to which each of these factors currently influences cancer rates remains unclear, it is absolutely certain that if voluntary and involuntary exposure to environmental carcinogens continues, cancer rates will soar even higher. If we remain on our present course, we are not simply inviting disaster; we are rushing to embrace it.

However, we *can* utilize our newly expanded knowledge to avert such a calamity. Through appropriate regulatory policies and altered life styles, we can take positive steps to prevent cancer in the future. We are not under the illusion that what we do today to reduce our exposure to carcinogens will be immediately felt in lower cancer rates. But we owe our children more than the clothes we buy them, the food we feed them, and the education we provide for them. We also owe them an environment that will not cut their lives short through the most feared disease in modern history.

For the more than ten years of its existence, the Environmental Defense Fund staff has been amassing expertise on environmental health issues, particularly cancer. Staff members have contributed their special knowledge on each of the subjects covered in this book. In addition, such a volume would not have been possible without the assistance of all the EDF staff, trustees, and members of the science advisory board who reviewed, typed, and proofread our work. Further, we would like to offer our sincere thanks to Charles Elliott and Elizabeth Catenaccio for their editorial and technical assistance. We are also indebted to the George Gund Foundation for its financial support, which was indispensable to the work of this project.

MALIGNANT NEGLECT

CHAPTER 1
THE NATURE
AND SCOPE
OF THE PROBLEM

There is great misunderstanding by the public about the nature and causes of cancer, a disease which has now reached epidemic proportions in the United States. Cancer is not caused by some inexplicable miasma, although it may seem that way to the uninformed. *Instead, most scientists now agree that the overwhelming majority of cancers are environmentally caused.* As such they are largely preventable. But failure by the public, industry, and government to recognize this fact and *act* on it is why we have a cancer epidemic today, and why that epidemic may become even worse in the years ahead.

Consider the scope of the epidemic. Of the 216 million Americans alive now, 54 million—one of four in the population—will suffer from cancer during their lifetime. Two out of three persons who contract the disease will die from it. In 1977 more than 380,000 Americans died from cancer, and the annual number of fatalities far exceeds the number of combat deaths the U.S. suffered in World War II or in the Korean and Vietnamese wars combined.

About one-half of all cancer deaths in the U.S. occur before the age of 65. Cancer is the leading killer of women between 30 and 40 years of age, and after accidents it is the chief killer of all Americans under 35. Among children between the ages of 1 and 10, cancer is the leading cause of death.

In American men lung cancer leads in rate of incidence. It has increased almost twentyfold in the last forty years. In men lung cancer is followed in rate of incidence by cancers of the prostate, colon and rectum, and bladder and stomach. Among American women breast cancer leads, followed by cancers of the colon and rectum, uterus, lung, and ovary. The 300,000 or more cases of skin cancer which occur each year are not included in these statistics.

In 1900 cancer ranked eighth as the cause of death in the U.S.; tuberculosis was first. Cancer now stands second after heart disease as the leading killer. Although the jump in cancer mortalities can be accounted for in part by population growth, increased longevity, improved prevention and treatment of infectious diseases, and more accurate reporting on causes of death, there has been a true and significant increase. Between 1930 and 1975, correcting for changes in the age distribution of the population, the national cancer rate increased from 116.7 deaths per 100,000 people to 130.9 deaths per 100,000. Cancer and chronic obstructive pulmonary diseases are the only major causes of death that have not shown a long-term decline.

Besides the suffering it inflicts on the victim, cancer can also cause disruption among the surviving members of a family, who can be left emotionally and economically destitute. Overall, the cost of cancer is estimated to range from $15 billion to $25 billion a year in the U.S. and this excludes the costs associated with factors such as pain and suffering. It is a mark of the times that an American Family Corporation subsidiary specializing in cancer insurance recently took a full page ad in *Time* magazine to announce that "we are growing at a faster rate than any other life insurance company in America." The company's rate of return after taxes as a percentage of sales was 12.9 percent in 1976, better than that achieved, the ad noted, by the Columbia Broadcasting System, Coca-Cola, or Dow Chemical.

Despite the high toll cancer takes, it would be folly to consider the disease inevitable. Not "everything" causes cancer. The reason why we are presented periodically with the announcement of a new cancer threat, such as polychlorinated biphenyls, saccharin, vinyl chloride, or Tris, is due in large part to our carelessness in the marketing, use, or disposal of products that have not been adequately tested for long-term toxic effects prior to their introduction into the marketplace. Also, advances have been made in developing and refining the analytical techniques needed to identify carcinogens (cancer-causing agents) and to detect their presence, even in minute amounts, in the human body or the world around us. It is not beyond our ability to deal with the causes of cancer. Indeed, it is possible to be optimistic, if we examine the problem willingly and intelligently and apply solutions. But we had better get on with the job, because if we do not, the cancer rate is likely to rise even higher.

What are the facts? The principal fact is that cancer is largely an environmental disease. For years physicians commonly assumed that cancer was an inevitable accompaniment of old age, but in 1964 the World Health Organization reported that on the basis of available evidence, 60 to 80 percent of all cancer cases were caused by natural and man-made carcinogens in the environment. Cancer may be caused by carcinogens in the polluted air we breathe, the contaminated water we drink, or the kind of food we eat. Cancer may also be caused by occupational or personal exposure to chemicals, cigarette smoke, sunlight, or X rays. Thus the incidence of cancer can be reduced by diminishing or eliminating human exposure to carcinogens. Prevention, not "cure," is the key. Although the federal government has lavished more than a billion dollars on attempts to find a cure, following passage of the National Cancer Act in 1971, few if any cancer researchers expect to find a miracle cure.

There are two other important facts to bear in mind about cancer:

1) Exposure to any carcinogen presents some risk. As the Ad Hoc Committee on the Evaluation of Low Levels of En-

vironmental Carcinogens reported to the surgeon general in 1970, "no level of exposure to a chemical carcinogen should be considered toxicologically insignificant for man."

2) Cancers have a latency period, or lag time. For most cancers the latency period is from five to forty years between the time of initial exposure to a carcinogen and the time the disease makes itself noticeable. Like a ticking bomb, cancer takes time to explode. Consequently, the great majority of present cancer cases originated between the end of World War II and the mid-1950s.

Actually, cancer is not one disease but the collective name for more than one hundred clinical diseases that can affect various sites in the body in different ways. All cancers, however, have one factor in common: the diseased cells multiply in uncontrolled fashion. Most forms of life, both plants and animals, are vulnerable to cancer, but there is no evidence that it is communicable. The ancient Egyptians, Greeks, and Romans were acquainted with the disease. Several mummies show signs of cancer of the bone or the nasopharynx, and Hippocrates, the father of medicine, was familiar with cancer of the mouth, uterus, stomach, breast, and skin. The name *cancer* stems from *karkinos,* the Greek word for "crab," because cancer was likened to a crab's groping claws. In all likelihood, many cancers in ancient times were caused by carcinogens found in the natural environment. For centuries Egyptian farmers working in the Nile have been infested by a parasitic fluke, *Schistosoma haematobium,* which lives in a snail during part of its life cycle. The fluke penetrates the human body through the skin and often becomes encysted in the bladder wall. There it may produce chronic changes that can cause cancer. Other carcinogenic agents found in the natural environment are aflatoxins, the metabolic products of *Aspergillus flavus,* a mold that can grow on food staples—for example, peanuts, corn, and lentils—stored under conditions of high temperature and humidity.

Although John Hill, a London physician, reported on six cases of "polypusses" in his *Cautions Against the Immoderate Use of Snuff* published in 1761, Percivall Pott, a surgeon at

St. Bartholomew's Hospital in London, is generally acknowledged as the first to recognize that an environmental agent could cause cancer in man. Pott studied the high incidence of cancer of the scrotum in chimney sweeps, and in 1775 he attributed the disease to the accumulation of soot in the folds of the scrotum, which was usually not washed.

Other research was long in coming. In 1875 a German researcher, Richard von Volkmann, linked scrotal cancer in workers to the production of paraffin by the distillation of coal tar, and in 1918 two Japanese scientists, Katsusaburo Yamagiwa and Koichi Ichikawa, demonstrated that the continuous application of coal tar preparations to the ears of rabbits over several months would cause skin cancer. Following the Japanese research, Dr. Peyton Rous, of the Rockefeller Institute in New York, similarly painted the ears of rabbits with coal tar preparations. To identify the rabbits, Rous punched small holes in their ears, and he was astonished to find that cancer appeared around the punch holes far sooner than expected as compared with animals whose ears had not been thus assaulted. In London during the 1920s and '30s, Sir Ernest Kennaway identified and isolated, and found to be carcinogenic, polycyclic hydrocarbons such as benzo(a)pyrene in coal tar. In the 1940s Dr. Isaac Berenblum, currently at the Weizmann Institute of Science in Israel, rubbed the skin of mice with benzo(a)pyrene. Based on previous tests, the dosage he applied was not supposed to cause any effect. He then rubbed the skin of the mice with croton oil, an irritant. The mice quickly developed skin cancer. Berenblum showed that a dose of a carcinogen too low to produce a significant effect in a small group of animals could cause cells to become premalignant and stay that way, only to turn cancerous when promoted by another agent perhaps years later. This was the first demonstration that otherwise safe chemicals could interact with carcinogens to enhance their effect.

In the 1940s benzo(a)pyrene was found in cigarette smoke. In 1950 Dr. Ernst L. Wynder, at Washington University in St. Louis, began to investigate smoking and produced evidence that it was involved in the rapid increase of lung cancer cases. Two skeptics, Dr. Daniel Horn and Dr. E. Cuyler Hammond of the American Cancer Society, both cigarette smokers themselves, began their own study of 187,766 middle-aged male smokers; by the time they were halfway through analyzing the results, both of them had stopped smoking. Published in 1954, the Hammond-Horn study demonstrated that lung cancer and heart disease went hand in hand with cigarette consumption.

Much of what we know about cancer comes from studies of the workplace. Although industrial representatives have long claimed that only 1 to 5 percent of cancer incidence results from occupational exposure, HEW Secretary Joseph Califano, referring to a 1978 study by the National Cancer Institute and the National Institute of Environmental Health Sciences, stated that ". . . at least twenty percent of all cancer in the United States—and perhaps more—may be work related."

In Germany in the 1890s Paul Unna linked skin cancer in sailors and farmers to excessive exposure to ultraviolet radiation from sunlight, and Ludwig Rehn, a surgeon, discovered an inordinate rate of bladder cancer in workers in the aniline dye industry. Dr. Wilhelm Hueper, who emigrated to the U.S. from Germany in 1923, and was an outstanding pioneer in occupational and environmental cancer research, worked for du Pont but was fired when he pointed out that beta-naphthylamine could cause bladder cancer in company dye workers. In his classic book *Occupational Tumors and Allied Diseases,* published in 1942, Hueper wrote that "environmental agents, some of them man-made, represent significant sources of carcinogenic exposure in men. Therefore, they are one of the main causes of cancer in men." Joining the National Cancer Institute in 1948, Hueper attempted to do epidemiological studies on workers exposed to carcinogens, but as he wrote later, "I was actively discouraged by the official advice that it was undesirable to arouse resentment of the chemical companies involved by conducting such investigations." Frustrated by government, Hueper outraged some of his colleagues by granting interviews to the *Police Gazette.* "The workers didn't read the *Journal of the National Cancer Institute,*" Hueper says, "but they did read the *Police Gazette* at the barber shop. If you don't get a public response, you don't get any action." Now in his eighties and retired from the National Cancer Institute, Hueper is—at last—honored as a prophet.

To mark the two-hundredth anniversary of the discovery of occupational cancer by Pott, the New York Academy of Sciences held a symposium in 1975 on occupational carcinogenesis, and in the keynote address Dr. Joseph K. Wagoner reported that thousands of coke oven workers in the steel industry are inhaling substances of the same class that caused scrotal cancer in Pott's chimney sweeps "and, as a result, are dying of lung cancer at a rate 10 times that of other steel workers." Thousands of uranium miners were still working, as of 1971, in environments where radiation dangers were "of such magnitude as to triple their prospects of dying from lung cancer." Eighty years after Rehn discovered that German dye workers were getting bladder cancer from aromatic amines (and 30 years after Hueper was dismissed from du Pont for pointing out the hazards of beta-naphthylamine) "thousands of American workers were still literally sloshing in them. . . . Indeed as recently as 1973, 50 percent of the former employees at one benzidine plant in the United States were reported to have developed bladder cancer." And in 1975, "130 years after the observation of scrotal cancer in copper smelters exposed to inorganic arsenic, fully 1.5 million workers in the United States are inhaling the very same substance, and many occupational groups exposed to inorganic arsenic are known to be dying of lung and lymphatic cancers at two to eight times the national average." Wagoner noted, "We now know that children living near copper smelters have unusually elevated levels of arsenic in their urine and hair"—a most important point, because carcinogens can spread from the workplace to the general populace, and this problem is greater, more prevasive, and more subtle than is generally recognized.

There is no clearer example of the spread of a carcinogen

from the workplace into the general environment than that of asbestos. In the 1960s Dr. Irving J. Selikoff, of the Mount Sinai School of Medicine in New York, found that exposure to asbestos was responsible for the disastrous cancer rate later suffered by men who had worked in the Union Asbestos & Rubber Company plant in Paterson, New Jersey, during the 1940s and early 1950s. Additional studies linked asbestos fibers to cancers diagnosed in persons living near asbestos factories and in members of the workers' families who were exposed to fibers in the clothes worn home. In demonstration of the spread of asbestos into the environment at large, Wagoner noted that "We now know that virtually 100 percent of all urban dwellers coming to autopsy show the presence of asbestos in lung tissue."

Studies of migrants have also been of assistance in documenting the environmental causation of cancer. In 1968 William Haenszel of the National Cancer Institute reported that within two generations after migrating to the United States, cancer patterns in Japanese immigrants changed. These people suffered a fourfold increase in cancer of the rectum, a rare cancer in Japan, and women acquired a breast cancer rate almost as high as that of American women. At the same time, the normally high incidence of stomach cancer found among native Japanese declined to levels comparable to those of white Americans. These changes in cancer patterns, attributed to changes in diet, demonstrate that environmental agents are of great significance. Genetic change is simply not rapid enough to account for these reversals in cancer patterns. Epidemiological studies of English immigrants to South Africa and Australia and of Poles to the United States make the same point. According to J. Staszewski's *Epidemiology of Cancer of Selected Sites in Poland and Polish Migrants,* published in 1976, the more Poland becomes industrialized and urbanized, the more closely its cancer rates approximate those of the urban-industrial nations of North America and Europe.

In the U.S., cancer mortality rates differ not only by occupation and ethnic background but by geography as well. Some regions of the country have much higher cancer rates for specific body sites than do others, a fact made compellingly evident in 1975, when the Epidemiology Branch of the National Cancer Institute (NCI) published the *Atlas of Cancer Mortality for U.S. Counties: 1950–1969,* showing geographical variation in cancer death rates among whites throughout the country. Sixteen common cancers were mapped on a county-by-county basis, while nineteen other cancers were plotted by "state economic area," defined as a single county or group of counties with similar economic and social characteristics. Two general maps show the prevalence of all cancers throughout the U.S. for white males and white females.

As Dr. Robert Hoover, an author of the *Atlas,* has written, "For various cancers, the maps reveal a surprising number of clusters or 'hot spots.' " Different cancers between men and women in the same area are suggestive of occupational factors, whereas the same pattern for both sexes in the same area indicates the possibility of carcinogens distributed in the environment.

In the Northeast—New Jersey, southern New York, Connecticut, Rhode Island, and Massachusetts—cancers of the colon and rectum, believed to be related to diet and other environmental factors, were present at above-average rates in both men and women. The same held true for men and women in Buffalo, Cleveland, Detroit, Chicago, and Milwaukee—all on the Great Lakes. By comparison, cancers of the colon and rectum were low in the southern and central U.S. The incidence of breast cancer followed similar geographical patterns, suggesting that breast cancer may share a causative factor with cancers of the colon and rectum. The *Atlas* reports, "Since colon cancer is generally more common in populous areas, a cluster of high rates in rural areas would arouse suspicion. Such a cluster occurs for both sexes in some southeastern Nebraska counties. The aggregation may be due to chance, to unusual demographic factors (e.g., socioeconomic, ethnic), or to environmental exposures indigenous to this rural area."

Men in the Northeast had high rates for cancers of the

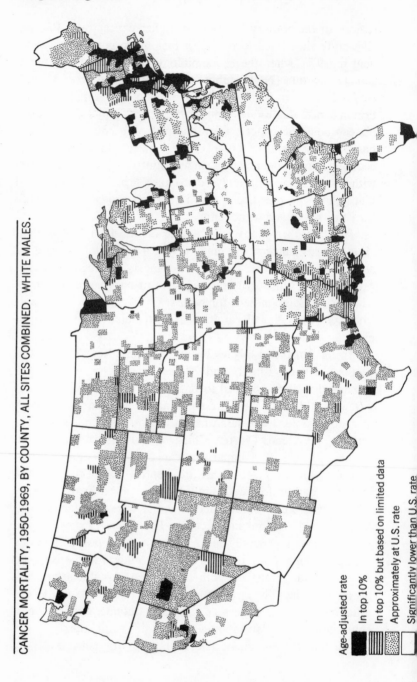

CANCER MORTALITY, 1950-1969, BY COUNTY, ALL SITES COMBINED. WHITE MALES.

Age-adjusted rate

In top 10%

In top 10% but based on limited data

Approximately at U.S. rate

Significantly lower than U.S. rate

CANCER MORTALITY, 1950-1969, BY COUNTY, ALL SITES COMBINED. WHITE FEMALES.

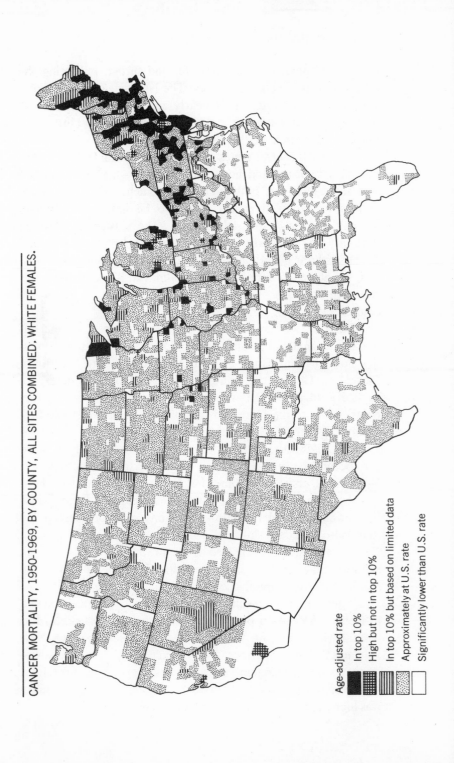

Age-adjusted rate

■ In top 10%

▦ High but not in top 10%

▥ In top 10% but based on limited data

⋮ Approximately at U.S. rate

☐ Significantly lower than U.S. rate

bladder, esophagus, larynx, mouth, and throat, indicating the influence of occupational factors. The NCI scientists who compiled the *Atlas* wrote, "It is nearly certain that industrial exposures have produced the striking geographical clusters of bladder cancer in males" in the Northeast.

The north-central states—North and South Dakota, Minnesota, Wisconsin, and northern Michigan—had high rates of stomach cancer for both men and women. "The geographic pattern for stomach cancer seems to be influenced strongly by ethnic factors," the *Atlas* notes. "The clusters of elevated mortality, in both sexes in the North Central States correspond closely with the geographic concentrations of persons from Austria, the Soviet Republics, and Scandinavia. These findings are consistent with the increased risk of stomach cancer in the countries of origin."

Thirteen Louisiana counties were in the top 1 percent nationally for male lung cancer deaths. So were seven other counties along the Gulf Coast and the Atlantic Coast from northern Florida to Charleston, South Carolina. "Further studies are needed to identify the environmental and demographic factors contributing to the increased risk of lung cancer in these predominantly rural and port areas."

The *Atlas* revealed that melanoma, a rare form of skin cancer, occurred primarily among whites in the southern states. By contrast, rates were somewhat lower in areas in the Southwest bordering Mexico. Exposure to sunlight is a major cause of skin cancer, and fair-skinned persons are more susceptible than those with dark skin.

There was an unexpected concentration of above-average rates for cancers of the lip and mouth/throat in women in the South. The causes are unknown.

Other patterns revealed scattered high rates for leukemia in men in the central part of the country from Texas to Minnesota. The clustering for women was similar. Eastern New England had elevated rates of Hodgkin's disease for both sexes. Among women Hodgkin's disease caused excessive mortalities in Minnesota and the Dakotas, whereas among men mortality was high in parts of Kansas, Nebraska, and South Dakota.

Female bone cancer showed "a prominent pattern of excess mortality" stretching from Oklahoma eastward through the South into Appalachia. The bone cancer pattern for men was less pronounced, but scattered high rates occurred in Pennsylvania, West Virginia, Virginia, Kentucky, Louisiana, and Kansas. In 1976 the National Cancer Institute brought out a similar *Atlas* for U.S. nonwhites—blacks, American Indians, Chinese, and Japanese. It noted,

For all [body] sites combined, the geographic patterns among nonwhites [as shown below] resemble to some extent those among whites, with generally high rates in the Northeast and low rates in the South. This pattern applies especially to cancers of the esophagus, colon, rectum and breast. Cancers of the larynx, bladder and ovary show a northern excess for nonwhites, although not as consistently as for whites. Both racial groups have high rates for lung cancer in northern urban areas, but the striking clustering of elevated mortality among white males along the Gulf and Southeastern Atlantic coasts is not seen among nonwhites.

This may reflect the fact that whites have been occupationally exposed for a longer period of time than nonwhites to "hazardous" industries in these areas.

Drs. Robert Hoover and Joseph F. Fraumeni, Jr., two of the authors of the *Atlas,* carried geographical analysis of cancer mortality a step further by studying 139 counties where the chemical industry is most highly concentrated. They found excess rates for bladder, lung, liver, and certain other cancers among males in those counties, and they wrote, "The correlation could not be explained by confounding variables such as urbanization, socioeconomic class, or employment in nonchemical industries. If the excess cancer mortality in these areas is due to industrial exposures, the actual risk of cancer among certain chemical workers must be very high." In addition, Hoover and Fraumeni reported, "Of particular note are the elevated rates of (1) bladder cancer in counties manufacturing cosmetics, industrial gases, and soaps and detergents; (2) lung cancer in counties producing pharmaceutical preparations, soaps and detergents, paints, inorganic pigments, and synthetic

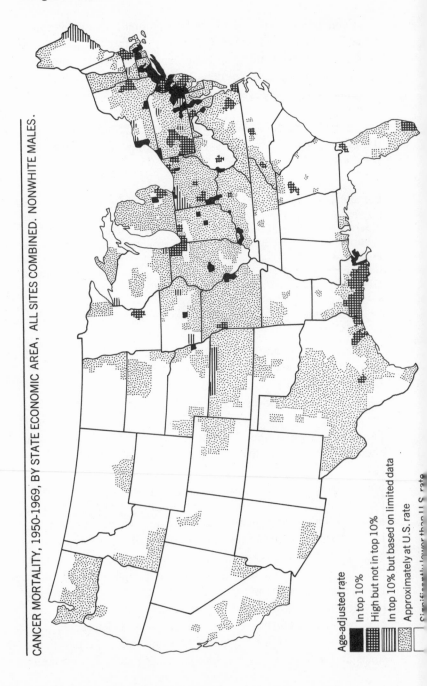

CANCER MORTALITY, 1950-1969, BY STATE ECONOMIC AREA, ALL SITES COMBINED. NONWHITE MALES.

Age-adjusted rate

In top 10%

High but not in top 10%

In top 10% but based on limited data

Approximately at U.S. rate

Significantly lower than U.S. rate

CANCER MORTALITY, 1950-1969, BY STATE ECONOMIC AREA, ALL SITES COMBINED. NONWHITE FEMALES.

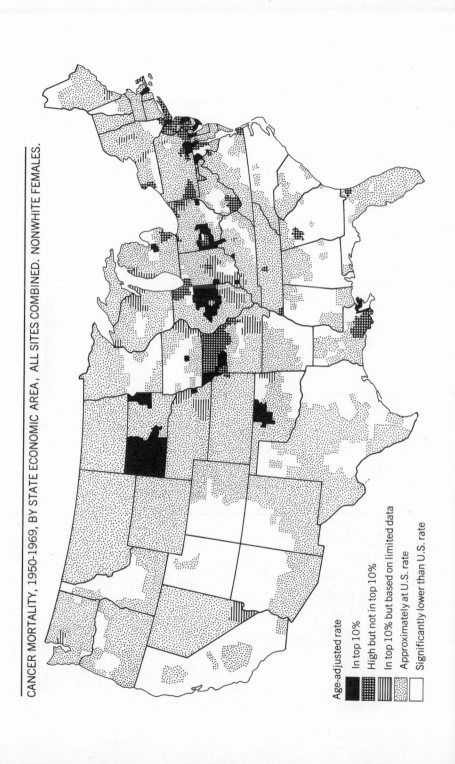

Age-adjusted rate
In top 10%
High but not in top 10%
In top 10% but based on limited data
Approximately at U.S. rate
Significantly lower than U.S. rate

rubber; and (3) liver cancer in counties manufacturing cosmetics, soaps and detergents, and printing inks."

Publication of the *Atlas* caused a furor in New Jersey, which has the highest cancer rate overall of all fifty states. Long proud to be known as the Garden State, New Jersey found itself with the unwelcome nickname of Cancer Alley. The state is highly industrialized, with approximately 1,200 chemical and allied plants, employing 130,000 persons and generating annual sales of $10 billion.

There are a variety of carcinogens in the air, soils, and waters of New Jersey. Trichloroethylene has been found in soil near Edison and in the air in Paterson, Bound Brook, and East Brunswick. Vinyl chloride has been detected in the air in Passaic and Clifton. Chloroform has been found in drinking water taken from the Toms River and Passaic Valley, and chloroform, pesticides, and inorganics have been found in the ground water at various localities. Eighteen of the twenty-one counties in the state have male bladder cancer rates in the highest 10 percent in the U.S. Salem County, in the southwestern part of the state, had the highest rate of bladder cancer in the U.S., with an average of 16.1 deaths per year per 100,000 population between 1950 and 1969. Approximately one-fourth of the men in Salem County work in chemical plants and allied industries, but environmental as well as occupational exposure is indicated by the fact that the bladder cancer rate for white *women* in Salem County was also 50 percent above the national average.

Publication of the first *Atlas* prompted the New Jersey legislature to establish a special commission that, in turn, proposed a bill to set limits for the emission of chemicals known to cause cancer and to shut down offending factories. The commission also proposed another bill to ban products that contain carcinogens in dangerous amounts. Neither bill ever got off the ground because of industry opposition. "We don't think responsible operators in the chemical industry have any uncontrolled or unknown emissions which might be causing a problem," said Christian A. Hansen, vice-chairman of the Chemical Industry Council of New Jersey.

A third bill, which did pass because it was considered non-controversial, required the state Department of Health to establish a registry for cancer incidence. Furthermore, publication of the *Atlas* prompted Governor Brendan Byrne to establish, by executive decree, a Cabinet Committee on Cancer Control.

The committee has taken a number of steps, some of which are discussed in chapter 11, but one move that bears notice here was the commissioning of Dr. Michael R. Greenberg, a geographer at Rutgers University, to do a study of the spatial distribution of cancer mortality and of the high-risk and low-risk factors in the state.

Greenberg's study area encompassed forty-five counties, including all those in New Jersey and nearby portions of New York, Pennsylvania, Connecticut, and Delaware. He found that "the highest [risk] white male counties lie along the urban/industrial corridor: New York City, Hudson, Essex, Middlesex, and Philadelphia. The highest [risk] white female counties are also generally found in the corridor but also include Monroe and Putnam Counties. Overall, all cancers are strongly correlated with ethnic groups, occupations, and local ambient environmental factors common to the region's urban/industrial corridor."

Epidemiological studies such as Greenberg's deal with mortalities from cancers initiated years ago. What about the future? Here we must take a brief step back into time by examining the graph presented below. The open circles and triangles show the rates of increase in per capita cigarette consumption for men and women in England and Wales from the turn of the century on. The closed circles and triangles show the rates of increase in lung cancer incidence for these men and women over the same period. It is clear that the increased rates of lung cancer follow the increased per capita consumption of cigarettes by twenty to twenty-five years—the latency period for lung cancer.

Cigarette smoking is hardly the sole menace. For instance, since World War II, the chemical industry has undergone a tremendous boom, led by petrochemical production, which has increased by more than 2,000 percent since 1945. Within the last decade U.S. production of synthetic organic chemicals

CIGARETTE SMOKING AND LUNG CANCER

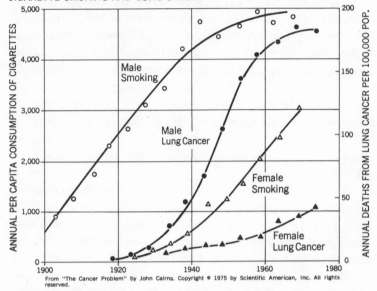

alone has increased 255 percent. More than two million chemicals are known, nearly thirty thousand are in use, and about five hundred new chemicals are put into use each year in this country. Next to nothing is known about the hazards these chemicals might pose because little testing has been done. Most of them may be harmless, but some may be carcinogenic, mutagenic (capable of causing genetic change), teratogenic (capable of causing birth defects), or simply acutely poisonous.

The fact that the cancer rate is increasing is ominous to many scientists who are particularly concerned about chemicals in the environment. Through general pollution of the environment we may have locked ourselves into a cancer growth curve that could, in five, ten, or twenty years, make us look back upon the present as the good old days. Plotted below are production curves for the manufacture of pesticides, plastics, and synthetic rubber from 1940 until the present. Many of the chemicals found in these commodities and their by-products are carcinogenic. Although production does not reflect human exposure, it is a good surrogate in light of our almost complete failure to regulate the use, discharge, and disposal

CANCER MORTALITY RATES AND CHEMICAL
PRODUCTION AS A FUNCTION OF TIME

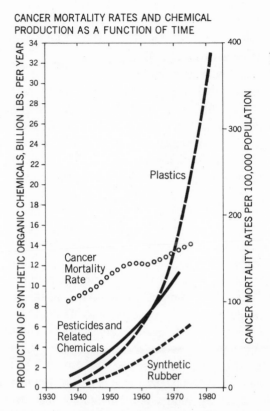

of these chemicals in the environment. Exposure to these carcinogens may well cause an increase in the national cancer rate in the near future in much the same way that cigarette smoking in the 1930s and 1940s foretold the rate of incidence of lung cancer in the 1950s and 1960s.

As Dr. Bruce Ames, of the University of California at Berkeley and a member of the president's National Cancer Advisory Board, recently said: "We haven't seen the effects in terms of carcinogenicity of the modern chemical world. That is going to hit us in the 1980s because of the 20-to-25-year lag period. We'll pay something for it. But whether that's relatively small or relatively large, no one now knows."

Many industrial concerns engaged in the manufacture and sale of chemicals and chemical products, of course, dispute not only Dr. Ames' statement that in the future we will "pay" for our past use of chemicals but also that cancer incidence rates today are actually increasing. The du Pont Company, for example, has argued that if lung cancer incidence rates are subtracted from total cancer incidence rates, then overall cancer rates are in fact declining. Such an argument is not only misleading but factually incorrect. The rationale for subtracting lung cancer rates is that its incidence reflects the impact of smoking on public health and is not related to exposure to synthetic chemicals. Although smoking clearly is a causative agent in many cases of lung cancer, it is not the sole factor by any means. As discussed later in this book, other factors such as air pollution are also believed to play a significant role. Therefore, one cannot discount the total incidence of lung cancer as being non-chemically related. Furthermore, the age-adjusted cancer incidence rates for 1970–1975 compiled by the National Cancer Institute show that for all races and sexes in the U.S., the incidence of bladder, rectum and colon cancers, and among females uterine and breast cancers, have increased, while the incidence of stomach and cervical cancer has gone down. Overall cancer incidence rates for this period, including or excluding lung cancer rates, have increased.

It is easy to detect signs of trouble in fish and wildlife, which can serve to sound environmental alarms. Alarm bells have been ringing since 1962, when Rachel Carson roused the public to the menace of chlorinated hydrocarbon pesticides with the publication of *Silent Spring*. Although industry scientists and agribusiness interests attacked her thesis—that pesticide residues posed serious threats, including the threat of cancer—a 1963 President's Science Advisory Committee supported her. The committee report said, "Elimination of the use of persistent toxic pesticides should be the goal."

Still, in some ways conditions in the natural environment are even worse than Rachel Carson would have supposed. Since 1966 the Smithsonian Institution has maintained a Registry of Tumors in Lower Animals. Evidence indicates that in recent years tumors have become more prevalent in fish as waters have become more polluted. Dr. R. A. Sonstegard of the University of Guelph in Ontario examined a collection of goldfish-carp hybrids captured in 1952 off the mouth of the River Rouge in Detroit. None had tumors, but collections Sonstegard made some 20 years later of hybrids at the same geographic site "revealed tumor frequencies as high as 100 percent in older males." Even fish that look normal can be contaminated with chemicals. In September 1976, after New York State prohibited anglers from possessing coho salmon, Chinook salmon, smallmouth bass, and four other species of fish from Lake Ontario because of contamination by an insecticide called mirex, the National Water Quality Laboratory in Duluth, Minnesota, prepared a list of chlorinated organic chemicals detected in a single fish, a herring identified as "Lake Ontario alewife sample number NWQL-72416." Besides mirex, a carcinogen, the herring contained detectable quantities of trichlorobenzene, tetrachlorobenzene, pentachlorobenzene, hexachlorobenzene, heptachlorostyrene, octachlorostyrene, pentachloroaniline, tetrachloroanthracene, DDT, DDD, DDE, chlordane, nonachlor, octachloronaphthalene, and eleven homologues of polychlorinated biphenyls (PCBs).

Several of these chemicals—DDT, hexachlorobenzene, chlordane, and PCBs—are carcinogenic. Had the herring also been tested for polynuclear aromatic hydrocarbons, the list of compounds—and carcinogens—found might have doubled. Although the number of synthetic chemicals in the herring might seem overwhelming, the American people are not far behind in chemical contamination of their own bodies. Among the chemicals detected thus far in the adipose (fatty) tissues of Americans are PCBs, aldrin, dieldrin, heptachlor, heptachlor epoxide, endrin, mirex, oxychlordane, transnonachlor, hexachlorobenzene, DDT, DDE, DDD, BHC, and lindane.

Why should this be? The answer is that federal and state governments have failed to protect both the environment and citizens from a flood of hazardous substances, including carcinogens. Even when legislation has required federal agencies to take steps to protect citizen health and the environment, the responses of the Environmental Protection Agency, the Food and Drug Administration, the Occupational Safety and Health Administration, and the Consumer Product Safety Commission have been slow and weak. The promulgation and enforcement of the implementing regulations that make the laws effective have often come late, and in many cases only in reaction to public pressure. Programs have foundered because of a lack of direction. Industry pressure from those companies most directly affected by proposed regulations has too often gone unopposed. The commonly held belief that government is "protecting the public" shows a failure to understand the true nature of the regulatory situation.

Regulation, on those occasions when it has been attempted, has often proceeded in a limited manner. Chemical carcinogens have not been regulated by classes but rather on an individual basis, thus resulting in large and expensive duplications of effort. Moreover, the current governmental structure fragments responsibility among agencies, and even among divisions within agencies, in such a way that action on one front to protect the public health may or may not be supported by commensurate action on another. There is, in sum, no unified federal approach to the control of carcinogens.

For example, the EPA is responsible for regulating the discharge of PCBs into waterways. So far the agency has limited the discharge of PCBs from capacitor and transformer manufacturing plants that drain their effluent into navigable waterways. Meanwhile the EPA ignores discharges from other industrial sources along these same bodies of water. The agency is also responsible for setting PCB standards for drinking water and direct air emissions, but it has yet to do so. Similarly, the FDA's regulation of PCBs in food and food-packaging materials has been incomplete and inadequate.

At least a half-dozen federal agencies specifically deal with cancer. First and foremost of these is the National Cancer Institute. Founded in 1937, the NCI is one of the components of the National Institutes of Health. In 1971, after cancer had become an attractive political issue, the NCI shot to the fore. In his State of the Union address that year

President Richard Nixon declared that "the time has come when the same kind of concentrated effort that split the atom and took man to the moon should be turned toward conquering this dread disease." Many scientists strongly question this moon-shot approach. As Dr. Robert A. Good, president and director of the Sloan-Kettering Institute for Cancer Research, pointed out: "It's ridiculous to compare the conquest of cancer with putting a man on the moon. At the time the Apollo project was initiated, we knew all the basic information we had to know in order to go to the moon. We simply do not have that information about cancer." Dr. Ruth Sager, professor of cellular genetics at Harvard Medical School, made the same point more vividly: "It is as if there had been a huge government program to put a man on the moon in 1920 before missiles were invented. Contracts would be given to cannon manufacturers, ladder builders, and many, many administrators to set up committees, support facilities, and backup teams, but there would be no support for missile research."

With the passage of the National Cancer Act in 1971, the NCI became a major research entity unto itself, with the director reporting directly to the White House. The NCI also began to receive massive infusions of money. Within six years the budget tripled to $815 million. As spending increased, so did the annual age-adjusted cancer death rate, rising from 129.9 per 100,000 in 1971 to 132 per 100,000 in 1976.

Critics contend that one reason more progress has not been made in preventing cancer is that the NCI has lavished its money on programs directed at *curing* cancer, and consequently neglected efforts at finding the *causes* of cancer, such as testing chemicals to determine whether or not they are carcinogenic. While today the NCI's bioassay testing program is running more smoothly, it is still underfunded for the amount of work that needs to be done. The current budget allows for only 50 to 60 new chemicals to be tested each year, and because of bureaucratic delays coordinated toxicological testing between the NCI and other government agencies is still not a reality.

Compared to several years ago, when Representative David R. Obey of Wisconsin charged that the "program is in shambles," things have improved—although not as much as they should have. But the past performance of the bioassay program is rather bleak. In fact, in April 1976 Dr. Umberto Saffiotti resigned as associate director for carcinogenesis at the NCI in protest against a lack of support from his own institute. Saffiotti, who remained on the staff of the NCI to do research, said that, among other reasons, he resigned because the NCI did not give him sufficient manpower and money to review and publish bioassay results on some two hundred chemicals tested for carcinogenicity. "I cannot accept any longer," he wrote, "a situation which in fact deprives the regulatory agencies, industry, labor, consumers and the scientific community of data of urgent public health value: it is *people* who are now exposed to toxic agents and who are not protected because the necessary support was not provided in time."

Like the NCI the National Institute for Occupational Safety and Health (NIOSH) is a research institute in the National Institutes of Health in the Department of Health, Education and Welfare (HEW). Established by Congress in 1970, NIOSH develops standards to safeguard the health and safety of workers and forwards them to the Occupational Safety and Health Administration and other appropriate regulatory agencies.

NIOSH has done some excellent work, but HEW officials in the Nixon and Ford administrations kept the NIOSH budget so low that the institute was understaffed. In fact, Representative Obey once remarked that "The heart of the NIOSH research effort is located in Cincinnati in a building so antiquated and inadequate that the whole operation might well be shut down if federal employees were protected by the Occupational Safety and Health Act." Speaking on the problem of lack of support for NIOSH several years ago, Obey said, in words that still ring true at this writing: "One reason is that not enough high-level government officials understand the importance of the problem. Not many are scientists or environmentalists. Another is simply because the chemicals question has not become a sexy political issue. Nothing generates a politician's awareness of a question quite so much as an indication that the public is interested in it. And the problem is that today the American public is simply not aware of the potential seriousness of the problem." •

NIOSH forwards its recommendations to the Occupational Safety and Health Administration (OSHA), a regulatory agency in the Department of Labor. Responsible for the health and safety of some 60 million workers, OSHA came into existence along with NIOSH in 1970 when the Nixon administration was courting the labor vote for the 1972 presidential election. The legislation sailed through Congress with the support of both labor and the White House. After all, no one could be against an agency such as OSHA that was created to eliminate or reduce hazards that caused annually, by 1970 official estimates, 14,200 deaths from occupational accidents, 390,000 new cases of work-related illness, and 10 to 20 million on-the-job injuries.

Unfortunately OSHA has not lived up to its original promise. It has pursued such trivial issues as the shape of toilet seats and the space between rungs on ladders but ignored major hazards. Politics appears to have played a part. Indeed, as much as the Nixon administration used the creation of OSHA to woo labor, it then sought to use the muzzling of OSHA to attract business.

In April 1972 a Ralph Nader study group charged, in a report entitled *Occupational Epidemic,* that the Department of Labor had shown "an unbelievable disdain" for the legislative history that brought OSHA into being and, furthermore, that the department was in "a frantic rush to turn the Occupational Safety and Health Act into a farce" by giving "maximum relief to employers." George Guenther, a Pennsylvania executive who was serving as an assistant secretary of labor and OSHA's first head, refused to comment on the Nader group's charges.

Guenther had reason to keep quiet. As the Senate Watergate Committee records later disclosed, Guenther was soon busy citing internal curbs on OSHA as "a sales point" to raise money from business to re-elect President Nixon. Guenther outlined his ideas on June 14, 1972, in a memorandum to Undersecretary of Labor Lawrence Silberman, who had asked how department programs "could contribute to the President's re-election." Guenther replied, "While promulgation and modification activity must continue, no highly controversial standards (i.e., cotton dust, etc.) will be proposed by OSHA or by the National Institute of Occupational Safety and Health." Guenther wrote that while he had noted "the great potential of OSHA as a sales point for fund raising and general support by employers, I do not believe the potential of this appeal is fully recognized." Guenther added, "Suggestions as to how to promote the advantages of four more years of properly managed OSHA for use in the campaign would be appreciated."

When the Guenther memorandum came to light, in July 1974, Dr. Sidney M. Wolfe, the head of Nader's Health Research Group, wrote to Watergate Prosecutor Leon Jaworski noting that OSHA had not implemented new standards for thirteen substances cited by NIOSH. Some five million workers were exposed to skin and lung carcinogens, neurotoxins, and other dangers, including arsenic and inorganic lead. "A look at the record from 1972 through the present," Wolfe wrote,

suggests that with the exception of the asbestos standard, issued only after OSHA was petitioned by the AFL-CIO, none of the other criteria documents transmitted from NIOSH to OSHA has resulted in the issuance of a new standard.

In brief it is clear that the present dilatory tactics of OSHA are perfectly consistent with the promise of the Guenther memo. Although the standard answer may be that it is just bureaucratic inertia, the memo offers a rare glimpse into the mechanism whereby bureaucratic inertia is financed.

While campaigning in New Hampshire in 1976, President Ford told businessmen that he knew they would like "to throw OSHA in the ocean." Although OSHA-imposed fines averaged only thirteen dollars in 1974 and 1975 for an overwhelming majority of violations, Ford said he knew some businessmen had "experienced difficulty at the not-always-tender hands" of OSHA and that he, the president of the United States, would not "tolerate the unnecessary and unjustified harassment of citizens." Ford issued an executive decree requiring that OSHA and other health and environmental agencies draw up so-called inflationary impact statements detailing estimates of the cost to industry of each new major regulation.

At present, OSHA is under the direction of Dr. Eula Bingham, whose new and forceful leadership appears aimed at altering OSHA's policies. Under Bingham's leadership, OSHA has proposed a sweeping change in the regulation of carcinogens in the workplace (see Chapter 11). In addition, in 1978 OSHA eliminated some 1,100 trivial regulations for workplace safety.

The Food and Drug Administration (FDA), a regulatory agency in the Department of Health, Education and Welfare, is supposed to protect the public against unsafe and impure foods, drugs, cosmetics, and medical devices. In 1958 Congress passed the Food Additives Amendment to the Food, Drug and Cosmetic Act; it includes the so-called Delaney Clause, named after Representative James J. Delaney of New York, who chaired a special House committee investigating chemicals in food in the 1950s. The Delaney Clause prohibits the intentional addition of a carcinogen to human food. Moreover, the clause states that no food additive shall be deemed safe "if it is found to induce cancer when ingested by man or animal," or, if the FDA deems appropriate, when taken into the system by means other than ingestion. The term *food additive* is defined very broadly so as to include "any substance intended for use in producing, manufacturing, packing, processing, preparing, treating, packaging, transporting, or holding food; and including any sources of radiation for such use." In 1960 Congress inserted the same Delaney Clause language into the Color Additives Amendments.

Only on rare occasions has the FDA invoked the Delaney Clause to ban an additive in food. In the spring of 1977 the FDA curiously invoked the Delaney Clause to announce a ban on saccharin, curious because the general safety provisions of the Pure Food, Drug and Cosmetic Act would have done the job. Sherwin Gardner, the acting FDA commissioner, misled the public by implying that to get cancer a person would have to drink eight hundred cans of diet soda with saccharin per day. Instead of saccharin becoming a scientific issue, the Delaney Clause became an emotional and political issue, leading Senator Edward Kennedy, chairman of the Senate Subcommittee on Health and Scientific Research, to remark at a hearing on saccharin, "The cavalier manner in which the initial FDA announcement was made did little to generate public understanding of what is a crucial policy problem. Instead, it created a firestorm of criticism, with the potential to do great harm, to completely dismantle a protective barrier against cancer—the Delaney Amendment—without having a better replacement or any replacement at all." Fortunately, the new FDA commissioner, Dr. Donald Kennedy, started putting the facts before the public.

Under the law the FDA is also empowered to set "tolerance levels" for hazardous substances inadvertently added to human food and shipped in interstate commerce. The agency has the power to seize foods that exceed the tolerance level. As we note in chapter 7, the FDA record in this regard is severely deficient.

The Environmental Protection Agency (EPA) was established as an independent regulatory agency in 1970. To quote from the official *United States Government Manual*, "In all, EPA is designed to serve as the public advocate for a liveable environment." The EPA administers a number of important laws, such as the amended Federal Water Pollution Control Act of 1972, the Clean Air Act of 1970, the Safe Drinking Water Act of 1974, the Resource Conservation and Recovery Act of 1976, and the Toxic Substances Control Act of 1976. The agency's record in carrying out these laws has been—as this book makes clear—deficient, to say the least. Perhaps the EPA approach to the problem of carcinogens in the environment is best summed up by Dr. William M. Upholt, a former agricultural entomologist who rose in the bureaucracy to become director of health effects and science policy in the Office of Water and Hazardous Materials before his retirement. In 1976 Upholt told *Newsday,* "I'm predicting that in the next 10 years people will come to the conclusion that cancer isn't the worst thing in the world. Bad as it is, it isn't the worst thing that can happen to somebody."

As a bureaucratic entity, the EPA has been dismal and disorganized. In 1976 the EPA's three top pesticide lawyers resigned, and so did the principal cancer pathologist, because the agency had failed to exert its authority, in part for fear of riling industry. According to Jeffrey Howard, one of the resigned lawyers, the agency made no effort to establish priorities on the relative hazards of toxic substances.

In November 1975 the Congressional Research Staff of the Library of Congress, in a report entitled "Effects of Chronic Exposure to Low-Level Pollutants in the Environment," concluded that

it is clear that Federal policy is still based on responding to specific episodes. EPA, created to bring a comprehensive viewpoint to environmental protection, has failed in this area. In part, the failure lies in the fragmented nature of the statutes dealing with pollution and other routes of exposure. In part, however, the failure appears to lie within the Agency—exemplified particularly in the criticism of its research program and its apparent inability to set defensible standards to control low-level toxic pollutants. Only when an adequate research and monitoring program is mounted can the problem of low-level pollutants be truly defined and the possible need for revised control authorities delineated. In the meantime, the fragmentation of research and controls—largely undertaken in response to newly discovered hazards—can be expected to continue. At issue is whether this largely ad hoc, fragmented policy can adequately protect health and the environment in today's advanced industrial society.

In March 1976 the National Research Council of the National Academy of Sciences scored the EPA. A study by the council called for more scientists with experience in environmental problems in the agency leadership, termed monitoring of water and air pollution uncoordinated, inefficient, and inflexible, and found that the EPA was inevitably dependent on the industries it regulates for much of the information it uses in making decisions.

The EPA has ten regional offices in the U.S., and they vary in effectiveness. The Region V office, in Chicago, has an excellent reputation, but the Region II office, in New York, until recently handed out "permits to pollute" to industries under terms of the Federal Water Pollution Control Act Amendments. To cite only one instance, Region II gave the Hooker Chemical & Plastics Corporation in Niagara Falls a permit to dump up to 950 pounds of unspecified chlorinated hydrocarbons a day into the Niagara River, which flows into Lake Ontario. Under such a broad permit the government retained little or no control over the highly toxic contaminants that could enter the river and eventually pollute the lake.

The results of a recent study, *Troubled Waters: Toxic Chemicals in the Hudson River,* make it very clear that the kind of permit granted to the Hooker Corporation was the rule rather than the exception. Of more than 250 municipal and direct dischargers into the Hudson River studied, none had provisions in their permits for adequate control of the release of hazardous wastes. In most cases no regulations existed to control the discharge of toxic pollutants into the Hudson River.

The Consumer Product Safety Commission (CPSC), established as an independent federal regulatory agency in 1972, has the authority to set safety standards to reduce unreasonable risk of injury to consumers from products. In fact the CPSC has the authority to ban products it finds hazardous. Thus far, however, the CPSC has an appalling record of ineffectiveness. It has drawn fire from consumer groups, the General Accounting Office (an investigative arm of Congress), and members of the Consumer Subcommittee of the Senate Committee on Commerce, Science, and Transportation. In April 1977 Senator John A. Durkin of New Hampshire said, "Plans for reorganization and next-to-worthless product profiles have split the commission apart. Morale is very low and turnover is ridiculously high. As a result, the commission is paralyzed." The then commission chairman, S. John Byington, a Michigan Republican appointed by Gerald Ford, admitted to the subcommittee on which Durkin served that "I do not believe that this agency has lived up to the expectations of many." In May 1977 the same subcommittee accused the CPSC of "inordinate delays" in banning Tris, a carcinogen used in children's sleepwear as a fire retardant.

No one example—such as the CPSC's delay in the banning of Tris, or the EPA's granting of a broad permit to pollute, as in the case of the Hooker Corporation—is sufficient to create a true understanding of the ineffectiveness of past governmental action to protect citizens from environmental carcinogens. But preventing cancer involves more than changes in governmental policies. It involves changes in attitudes and, even more immediately, changes in individual life styles. It is the aim of this book to show the direction and shape these changes should take.

CHAPTER 2
THE BIOLOGY
OF CANCER

If an understanding of cancer is ultimately to be achieved, the experimental oncologist will have to explain why cancer cells divide persistently and in an unrestrained manner in their hosts and why such cells invade underlying normal tissues and metastasize to distant sites, while growth of all normal cells is precisely regulated.

—Armin C. Braun
The Biology of Cancer, 1974

Cancer is a disease of cells. Plants, animals, molds, in fact all living things, are composed of cells. The simplest organisms, such as amoebas and paramecia, are composed of only one cell. Higher forms of life are multicelled. In higher organisms cells function together to form a total being. Human beings, for example, are composed of billions of cells, each carrying on its own function. Red blood cells bring oxygen to the tissues of the body and carry wastes away. White blood cells fight invading disease-carrying organisms. Bone cells compose a skeleton, which serves as a support for the organs of the body. Each cell or group of cells continually does its job toward supporting the whole.

In no case is this a stagnant process. New cells are being

formed every minute, and old cells are dying and being discarded. A red blood cell normally lives 120 days, whereas a bone cell may live for several years. Whenever an old cell dies, it is replaced by an identical new cell. If this were not the case, there would be no order, no logical maintenance of life. Under normal conditions the entire process is precise and well regulated. However, when cells become cancerous, all of this changes.

Because cancer is a disease of cells, it is equally capable of expression in all higher organisms, such as plants, frogs, birds, and numerous mammalian systems, including humans. Although clinically there are more than one hundred distinct types of cancer, each having a unique set of specific symptoms, cancers can be generally subdivided into four major categories.

Carcinomas are by far the most important and common form of human cancers, accounting for over 85 percent of the observed malignancies. Carcinomas are solid tumors derived from epithelial cells. These cells make up the tissues that are the internal and external body surface coverings and therefore are the cells most readily exposed to environmental carcinogens. Skin, glands, nerves, and the linings of the respiratory, gastrointestinal, urinary, and genital systems are all composed of epithelial tissue.

Leukemias are the second major category of cancers. In leukemias abnormal numbers of white blood cells are produced by the bone marrow. The increased production of white blood cells is very similar to the body's normal response to infection, but in leukemias most of the white blood cells do not mature to a functional state. Leukemias are among the most common malignancies of childhood, but they strike people of all ages. They are also one of the classes of cancers that have been most successfully treated during the last ten years. Even so, less than 50 percent of those treated remain in remission after five years. According to data published by the American Cancer Society in 1978, leukemias accounted for approximately 4 percent of the

690,000 cases of cancer, not including non-malignant skin cancers and *in situ* uterine cervix cancers, diagnosed in 1977.

Abnormal numbers of white blood cells are also involved in the third class of cancers, lymphomas. However, in lymphomas the spleen and lymph nodes produce the abnormal numbers of white blood cells. Hodgkin's disease is the best-known form of lymphoma. It is estimated that lymphomas accounted for approximately 6 percent, or more than forty thousand cases, of the diagnosed malignancies in 1977.

Sarcomas fall into the fourth major category of cancers. These are solid tumors that are derived from certain embryonic tissues, such as cartilage, bone, muscle, connective tissues, and fat. Although sarcomas are frequently observed in studies of carcinogenicity in laboratory animals, they themselves account for only 2 percent of human malignancies.

In addition to being classified into four major categories, the more than one hundred clinically identifiable cancers share several common properties that distinguish them from normal cells. A tumor cell, whether benign or malignant, is a persistently altered cell that reproduces true to type and over which the host has no adequate control mechanism. This uncontrolled proliferation of cells is termed neoplasia and perhaps represents the single most important characteristic of tumor cells, since without neoplasia there would be no tumors. It would appear that when a normal cell becomes a tumor cell, it undergoes a permanent change that allows it to determine its own activities irrespective of the laws that carefully regulate the precise growth of all normal cells. In addition to growing independently, without reason or control, tumor cells take on structural characteristics similar to basic fetal or embryonic cells common to the earliest stages of life. This change in cell type is termed anaplasia. Anaplastic cells have no logical connection or relation to the parent tissue. Instead of maintaining an orderly spatial arrangement, their distribution is often jumbled or apparently random, usually resulting in cells piling up upon each other.

The terms *malignant* and *benign* are often used to distinguish between types of tumor cells. In general, we feel relieved if a tumor is diagnosed as benign rather than malignant because we understand the term to mean that the growth is contained and is not spreading throughout the body. However, in some cases, depending on where it is located, a benign tumor can be of concern too. This is true of benign tumors associated with the use of synthetic hormones. These benign tumors, which occur in the liver, can rupture, causing massive bleeding and death. Both benign and malignant tumors represent a drastic alteration in cellular activities, and distinguishing between them can often be a difficult task. While some tumors will remain benign, this is not always the case.

Malignant tumors have the capacity both to invade underlying tissues and to detach small groups of cells from the tumorous mass, which can then spread, or metastasize, through the blood and lymph vessels to distant sites, touching off the growth of new tumors. The capacity of malignant cells to metastasize throughout a host is what makes cancer such a dangerous and often incurable disease. However, not all malignant tumors invade and metastasize. Certain tumors that deeply invade underlying normal tissues rarely metastasize, while others become widely distributed in their host despite a minimum of local invasion. Further, the ability to invade and metastasize may be acquired relatively late in the life of a tumor, and may be overlooked in a diagnosis of a tumorous condition.

It must be remembered, too, that how a tumor develops may depend on the place and conditions under which it is growing. This characteristic is particularly well illustrated by studying the conditional or hormone-dependent tumors that occur in both animals and plants. Conditional prostate or breast tumors of mammals, which may be highly malignant, grow only so long as they are being stimulated by the appropriate hormone. Without the hormone, growth of the tumor stops and in many cases regresses. However, when the stimulus is restored, tumors will reoccur in the same place and with the same characteristics. Over the course of time many conditional tumors reach a hormone-independent state, in which case the presence or absence of the hormonal stimulus is no longer of importance.

The study of cancerous cells has revealed quite detailed information on the biochemical changes that take place when a normal cell becomes transformed to a cancerous one. These include changes in the cell membrane, in the levels of particular enzymes, and in the extent of cell differentiation. But the critical biochemical event (or events) that transforms a cell from normal to cancerous appears to involve an alteration of the cell's basic genetic constituents. Possibly a change occurs in certain proteins or other cellular components, but the latest scientific evidence suggests that the key change is in the cell's genetic material.

What is this genetic material? How can a change at this very basic level lead to the transformation of a cell from normal to cancerous?

Every cell in the human body, with the exception of the sex cells, contains a full set of genetic material—forty-six chromosomes. Every chromosome is, in turn, composed of genes, and it is the genes that convey the information needed for development and growth.

Genes are composed of building blocks called nucleic acids. There are four basic building blocks that when linked together in groups of three spell out "words" in the genetic language. Each word has only three letters, although four letters are actually available. The average gene contains approximately three hundred letters, or nucleic acid bases, and spells out one hundred words. These words, when read together, determine such characteristics as eye color, hair color, and height, as well as providing the informational or directional orders for life.

As development proceeds and more and more cells are produced, differentiation occurs so that some cells become specialized and begin to function together as blood vessels, while others begin to make a heart, and so on. Each of these specialized cells still retains a copy of the full set of genetic material contained in the original single-celled zygote. For some as yet unknown reason, however, only a small portion of this information is used in each cell—the information that details the specialized instructions needed by that cell in order to function properly. This selective process is carefully regulated, and it may best be understood by an analogy to the daily reading of the newspaper. One person may read the news section first, then the sports section, and finally the comics. Another may read the financial section first, the entertainment section next, and finally the news. Each one has the entire newspaper, but each chooses to read only certain sections, ignoring others, and routinely reading them in a certain order.

The normal process of life, therefore, is precisely controlled and regulated. Each cell does its job in harmony with all the other cells of the body. The division of cells to produce new cells, also a part of the normal process of life, is likewise carefully regulated and controlled. Each time a new cell is formed, it inherits a complete complement of genetic material, a complete set of chromosomes and genes. This new set of chromosomes and genes is made by copying those in the original cell. As with any other system, mistakes can happen. When a mistake in copying occurs and the wrong nucleic acid base is inserted into a gene, one of two things can occur. Either the body's repair systems can fix the mistake by cutting out the wrong base and inserting the correct one or the mistake can go unrepaired. In this latter case the change becomes permanent and is inherited by all new cells, which then derive their genetic complement from this altered, or "mutated," cell. The effect of a mutation—a change in a nucleic acid base, or "letter," in the genetic code —may be inconsequential or it may be highly significant, depending on which base is changed. To understand why such a change can be either inconsequential or significant and how it can relate to the change in a cell from normal to cancerous, one must know how the words of the genetic code are read.

As stated earlier, each nucleic acid base, or "letter," in the genetic code is not read individually. As in human language, letters are read in groups, or "words." The genetic language is quite simple in this respect. Each word contains only three letters. Thus, a single genetic message may contain three hundred letters, which are read as one hundred different words. As in any language, some words that look and sound alike mean the same thing. For example, the word *gray* sounds like, looks like, and means the same thing as *grey*. The only difference is that in one case the word is spelled with the letter *a* and in the other, the letter *e*. When reading either word in a sentence, the meaning is clear. However, if another letter were changed, the entire meaning of the word would be altered. By changing *g* to *p*, the word changes from *gray* to *pray*, and the meaning of a sentence containing the word drastically changes.

The same holds true with the letters of the genetic alphabet and the words they spell. In the language of genes the word GA*G* means the same as GA*A*. However, GA*U* means something entirely different. Therefore, the small change of a *G* to an *A* will make essentially no difference to the meaning of the word or of the genetic sentence in which it appears. However, the equivalent small change of *G* to *U* entirely changes the meaning of the word and may alter the meaning of the entire sentence. To further understand what the ultimate effect of a change in a single word can mean, one must understand what the genetic sentence is saying. Most genetic sentences specify the same type of information—information that determines the structure of cellular proteins. It is proteins that help determine cellular characteristics and provide the directional orders for life.

Each protein is composed of individual building blocks called amino acids. Each three-letter genetic word specifies a particular amino acid. Therefore, each genetic sentence specifies the order of a series of amino acids that, when linked together, make a protein.

Since there are only four nucleic acid bases, or genetic

letters, and they are used in combinations of three letters per word, there exist only sixty-four possible genetic words. There are only twenty-one amino acids that can act as building blocks for proteins. It follows, therefore, that some genetic words identify the same amino acids. This explains why the change in the genetic word GAG to GAA is inconsequential. Both GAG and GAA specify the same amino acid, glutamic acid. However, GAU specifies aspartic acid. Similarly, a change from GAG to GCG (again, only a one-letter change) changes the meaning of the genetic word from glutamic acid to alanine.

Clearly, a change in a single letter of a genetic word can change the meaning of that word and the meaning of the genetic sentence it appears in. An altered genetic sentence can lead to an altered protein, which can have a major effect on the function of a cell. For example, a single change in a nucleic acid base is responsible for sickle-cell anemia. Individuals with this disease have altered red blood cells that cannot carry oxygen to the cells of the body as efficiently as normal red blood cells. The name for the disease comes from the fact that the affected red blood cells are sickle-shaped in appearance instead of being concave. When biologists isolated the altered protein in this disease, they found that only *one* amino acid had been changed, but that one change was sufficient to cause a functional change in the protein and bring about the change in shape of the red blood cell. Understanding sickle-cell anemia is a simple task compared with understanding the change or changes responsible for cancer, but there are several theories as to what changes take place when a cell becomes transformed.

The most straightforward and least complicated explanation of the carcinogenic process is that it is a direct and permanent alteration of the nucleic acid bases that comprise the genes, in much the same way that a nucleic acid change leads to sickle-cell anemia. It has been known for some time that exposure to ultraviolet radiation, which increases the risk of skin cancer (see chapter 8), can cause direct damage to the cell's nucleic acid bases. In particular, two adjacent bases can be joined together, causing a localized distortion, as a result of the accumulation of energy derived from exposure to ultraviolet light. This distortion can signal the body's repair system to cut out the distorted bases and replace them with normal unjoined bases. The body has enzymes that specialize in cutting out the segment of the altered gene, reforming the correct sequences of bases, and rejoining the chain together. When the body's repair system fails, the damage becomes permanent. It is believed that such a permanent change may be the initial step in the carcinogenic process.

Gene damage is not caused solely by ultraviolet light. Other forms of radiation, such as X rays, can cause damage to the cells, including actual breaks in the chain of bases. Moreover, chemical carcinogens that contaminate the environment are known to interact with the nucleotide bases. They usually do this by chemically joining with a nucleic acid base in a process known as alkylation or by joining with two nucleic acid bases and forming a bridge between them in a process known as cross-linking. As with damage caused by radiation, it is believed that these or similar unrepaired alterations may be the first step in the carcinogenic process.

It is a common misconception that any chemical when ingested or inhaled in large enough amounts is carcinogenic. Not "everything" can cause cancer. Although increasing exposure will increase the carcinogenic risk from chemicals that are truly carcinogenic, it will not make non-carcinogenic chemicals active carcinogens. Moreover, the results of a study sponsored by the National Cancer Institute suggest that *most* chemicals are *not* capable of causing a carcinogenic response. In this study 120 chemicals, including 104 pesticides, judged to be potential carcinogens by their structure and chemical similarity to known carcinogenic pesticides were tested for carcinogenicity in carefully controlled animal experiments. Less than 10 percent of the chemicals tested actually proved to be carcinogenic. Over 90 percent showed no evidence of carcinogenicity based on the results obtained.

Not only are most chemicals non-carcinogenic, but not

every exposure to a chemical carcinogen touches off the carcinogenic process. The interaction of the chemical carcinogen and a nucleotide base reflects the final outcome of a series of cellular events. We know that the entry of the chemical carcinogen into the cell is not a random, uncontrolled process but one regulated by the cellular membrane through which the carcinogen must pass. We also know that many chemicals must first be altered or metabolized to a different form in order to make them reactive and capable of interacting with nucleotide bases. Therefore, in only those cases where the proper sequence of events occurs does exposure lead to a definite interaction, and the beginning of the carcinogenic process. Although there may be many steps and each may occur with different probabilities in different individuals, increased exposure to chemical carcinogens obviously increases one's risk of cancer.

As noted, many chemicals that are ultimately carcinogenic must first be modified, or "metabolized," to an active form. The human body has a series of enzymes capable of activating them. Activation of a precarcinogen to an ultimate carcinogen is not usually a one-step process. In many cases several metabolic steps are required.

For example, the chemical carcinogen acetylaminofluorene (AAF) produces liver tumors in male rats that ingest AAF in their diet. AAF is termed a precarcinogen, because without metabolic activation by enzymes in the liver it is not carcinogenic. However, AAF can be metabolized to N-hydroxy-AAF and then to N-sulfate-AAF. Enzymes termed *oxidases,* which are present in the liver, carry out the first conversion, AAF to N-hydroxy-AAF, while other enzymes known as *sulphotransferases* are responsible for the second conversion, N-hydroxy-AAF to N-sulfate-AAF. Tests have shown that N-hydroxy-AAF, like AAF, is not carcinogenic, and that it must be further metabolized before it can produce a carcinogenic response. N-hydroxy-AAF is therefore termed a *proximate carcinogen*. The conversion of N-hydroxy-AAF to N-sulfate-AAF produces what scientists believe is the ultimate carcinogen. Through a series of internal rearrangements N-sulfate-AAF becomes reactive and can directly bind to and alter guanine, a nucleotide base present in the genes. Unrepaired, this nucleotide alteration may be the first step in the carcinogenic process.

N-sulfate-AAF, like many other ultimate carcinogens, can react not only with the nucleotide bases of the genes but also with other critical molecules of the cell. Some theories of the carcinogenic process focus upon these other interactions. However, many of these other theories still postulate an ultimate effect on the nucleotide bases of the gene. Rather than being a direct effect caused by the interaction of a nucleotide base and the ultimate carcinogen, it is an indirect effect mediated through the interaction of the ultimate carcinogen with another critical molecule of the cell.

None of these theories has been proven. However, many scientists favor a genetic explanation because the direct modification of a gene is the simplest possible mechanism. Moreover, a genetic explanation provides the most rational explanation for preservation of the necessary information during the prolonged period between the exposure to the carcinogen and the appearance of the tumor. In humans this period may be from five to forty years. Since generations of cells will have lived and died in that time, a modification that can be passed on from one cell generation to another is apparently needed. An alteration of a nucleotide base in the cell's genes provides such a permanent change.

Once initiation of the carcinogenic process occurs, several intermediate steps are thought to occur before the growth of a tumor. Many chemicals, although not initiators of the carcinogenic process themselves, directly influence the events that follow. For example, in 1941, Dr. Isaac Berenblum showed that an application of croton oil, an irritant, to the skin of animals treated with a weak solution of benzpyrene, a known chemical carcinogen, greatly enhanced the carcinogenic response. Berenblum was here observing the *cocarcinogenic,* or promoting, action of certain chemicals.

A number of chemicals are now known to be promoters, or cocarcinogens; petroleum fractions, catalytically cracked oils, phenolic compounds, anthranilin, 1-fluoro-2,4-dinitrobenzene, and some tobacco constituents have all been shown to have promoting effects. Not all cocarcinogens, however, are separately identifiable chemicals. Even viruses can modify the tumorigenic process. Although no human cancer virus has been identified, experiments with animals suggest that viruses may, in some cases, either play a cocarcinogenic role or be the sole agent responsible for starting cancer growth. If viruses do play a role in human cancer, it would appear to be a very limited one.

What is the biochemical nature of promotion? How do promoting agents and modifying factors affect the carcinogenic process? In most cases the answers remain unknown. In some cases effects on cell division have been suggested; in others effects at the level of the cell membrane are believed to be important. Whatever the exact nature of these actions, it is clear that many factors can alter the progression of the carcinogenic process from initiation to tumor formation.

In addition to the myriad external factors that affect the carcinogenic process, an individual's own genetic makeup can play a very important role. Just by looking at people we see that no two people are alike. Some are taller, some are fatter, some have red hair, whereas others have blond, brown, gray, or white hair—or they are bald. All these variations reflect differences at the genetic level—differences in genes. In exactly the same way, no two people produce identical amounts of enzymes in their cells; the amounts we produce of different enzymes in different tissues vary from individual to individual. Because these levels vary, our response to carcinogens also varies.

For example, a recent study of former heavy cigarette smokers found that those who did *not* get lung cancer generally had lower levels of aryl hydrocarbon hydroxylase, the enzyme needed for the metabolic activation of a chemical carcinogen, benzpyrene, present in cigarette smoke. In much the same way we have learned that women whose mothers or sisters suffer from breast cancer are themselves at greater risk of developing this disease. This increased susceptibility is believed to be genetically related.

There is no way to know ahead of time when such differences exist, nor is there currently any reason to believe that these differences afford people a true protection against cancer. Although some people may not have a sufficient quantity of the necessary hydroxylating enzyme present in their lung tissue to activate a chemical carcinogen in cigarette smoke, this doesn't mean that cigarette smoking is safe for them. They may suffer statistically less lung cancer, but the cigarette smoke may effectively act as a cocarcinogen in a different carcinogenic process. Witness the increased bladder cancer rates recently reported for men who used saccharin and smoked cigarettes, compared to those who only smoked. It is currently impossible to predict which individuals are at greater or lesser risk from exposure to any given chemical carcinogen, because our understanding of the biological events relating to the carcinogenic process is incomplete. A broad spectrum of susceptibilities exists, and public policy must be made to account for this.

Although cancer can occur in a variety of organisms, it does not necessarily occur the same way in each organism. Indeed, sometimes what is carcinogenic to one species may not be carcinogenic to another. For example, the metabolic activation of AAF occurs in male rats. Female rats of the same strain do not have the same susceptibility to liver tumors when fed AAF. Although the necessary oxidase enzymes for the conversion of AAF to N-hydroxy-AAF are present in the liver cells of the females, the sulphotransferase enzymes are present in such low quantity that the conversion of N-hydroxy-AAF to N-sulfate-AAF occurs very infrequently, and thus AAF does not induce a carcinogenic response. Similarly, in the guinea pig no tumor formation is observed following AAF ingestion, because this animal does not have the necessary oxidase enzyme to convert AAF to N-hydroxy-AAF. However, a guinea pig fed N-hydroxy-AAF will develop tumors, because it has the necessary sulphotransferase enzyme to convert N-hydroxy-AAF to an active carcinogen.

Clearly the most accurate information on the magnitude of the carcinogenic risk posed by human exposure to a carcinogenic chemical would come from epidemiological studies—statistical investigations of exposed human populations. Retrospective studies are done "after the fact." They measure the results of occupational or inadvertent exposure that occurred before there seemed to be a reason for concern.

In 1974, before an epidemiological study revealed that workers exposed to vinyl chloride were dying from a rare and incurable form of liver cancer called angiosarcoma, Dr. Cesare Maltoni, of the Institute of Oncology and Tumor Center in Bologna, Italy, showed that rats exposed to vinyl chloride died of the same disease. It took a record of human suffering and death to bring about recognition of this problem and regulation of occupational exposure to this chemical carcinogen.

The evidence in this case was compelling because angiosarcoma is rare, and the common occupational exposure of all those involved was to vinyl chloride. Most other cases are not so clear. Exposure may not be limited to one specific chemical, and the cancer induced may be of a common kind. In cases like this the correlation between human exposure and increased carcinogenesis is difficult to establish.

Take, for example, the case of benzene, the most widely produced synthetic organic chemical. Each year more than twelve billion pounds of benzene is produced in the United States alone, and used for a wide range of industrial solvent and feedstock applications. For years, studies have suggested that human exposure to benzene causes an increased rate of leukemia. However, each epidemiological study that reached this conclusion was qualified by the fact that those exposed to benzene had also been exposed to other synthetic organic chemicals. Furthermore, the increased incidence of leukemia over the normal background rates, although significant, was not exceptionally high. As late as 1976 the National Academy of Sciences, reviewing the literature on cancer incidence and benzene exposure, concluded that benzene as yet only appeared to be associated with leukemia and must therefore be considered no more than suspect as a leukemogen.

Then, in 1977, a more complete epidemiological study was reported. Seven of 748 workers in an Ohio Goodyear Tire and Rubber Company plant who had been exposed solely to benzene developed leukemia—a rate significantly higher than would be normally expected. The Occupational Safety and Health Administration, which is responsible for worker protection, issued an emergency temporary standard to limit further occupational exposure to benzene, declaring: "The available scientific evidence establishes that employee exposure to benzene presents a cancer hazard—specifically the hazard of developing leukemia."

Epidemiological studies are certainly valuable. They are very limited, however, because not only do they require human exposure to a carcinogen plus cancer induction, which can take years to be manifested, but they are also subject to a variety of interfering factors that can cast doubt on the conclusions. What is the alternative, then, for judging whether a chemical poses a carcinogenic risk to humans? The traditional alternative is to test for the carcinogenicity of a chemical in long-term animal experiments. Under development now are simplified short-term tests conducted either in cell culture, on bacterial plates, or under other appropriate laboratory conditions.

Although animals, mice, rats, dogs, and guinea pigs may respond differently from humans to a potential carcinogen, there is an excellent correlation between the carcinogenicity of chemicals in these test species and that in humans. Below, in Table 1, are some of the chemicals known to be carcinogenic to humans and the type of cancer induced. Species of animals that showed a carcinogenic response when exposed to these chemicals are also listed, along with the site of tumor induction.

All but one of the chemicals so far identified as a human carcinogen—arsenic—have proven to be carcinogenic when appropriately tested on laboratory animals. In not every case is the site of cancer the same in the test animals as it is in humans. For vinyl chloride and asbestos, the primary site of

TABLE 1

Chemical	Tumor Site in Humans	Animal Species	Tumor Site in Animals
Aflatoxin	Liver	Rat	Liver, kidney
		Trout	Liver
		Duck	Liver
		Monkey	Liver, lung
4-aminobiphenyl	Bladder	Mouse	Bladder, liver
		Rat	Bladder, mammary gland
		Rabbit	Bladder
		Dog	Bladder
Asbestos	Lung	Monkey	Lung
		Guinea pig	Lung
Auramine	Bladder	Mouse	Liver, leukemia
		Rat	Liver
Benzene	Leukemia	Mouse	Leukemia
Benzidine	Bladder	Dog	Bladder
		Rat	Liver
		Hamster	Liver
		Mouse	Liver
Bis(chloromethyl)-ether	Lung	Mouse	Lung, skin
		Rat	Lung
Cadmium oxide	Prostate	Mouse	Lung
N,N-bis(2-chloroethyl)-2-naphthylamine	Bladder	Mouse	Lung
Chromate	Lung	Mouse	Lung
Diethylstilbestrol (DES)	Vagina	Mouse	Vagina, cervix, breast
		Hamster	Mammary
2-naphthylamine	Bladder	Dog	Bladder
Nickel	Lung, nasal cavity	Rat	Lung
		Mouse	Lung
Vinyl chloride monomer	Liver	Mouse	Liver, lung, breast
		Rat	Lung, bone, skin

action in the test animals and in humans is the same. For auramine and bis(chloromethyl)ether, the sites are different. Clearly, the results of experiments with test animals are an excellent predictor for the human experience.

The National Cancer Institute has established a standard protocol for testing the carcinogenicity of a chemical compound. Two species of animals are used, generally the mouse and the rat. Both males and females of each species are exposed to the chemical under investigation. The route of administration is usually oral, because it is the simplest and least costly. In some cases inhalation or skin absorption is selected, especially when most human exposure is via one of these two routes.

The animals are divided into several groups. Some are kept

as controls and not exposed to the potential carcinogen at all. Others are fed a level of the chemical defined as the "maximum tolerated dose," or MTD. As the name implies, this is a level of the potential carcinogen that is the most the animal can tolerate without showing significant signs of overt toxicity. A third group of animals is also exposed to the potential carcinogen usually at a dose equivalent to one-half the MTD. Exposure begins after weaning and continues for the life of the animal. In most cases after two years of exposure the animals are sacrificed and diagnosed for tumor formation. By comparing the incidence of tumors in the treated animals with those in the controls, scientists are able to tell whether, under the conditions of the test, the chemical is carcinogenic.

How accurately do the results of such tests predict the true risk to humans exposed to these chemicals? Might the results of these tests underestimate or overestimate the real risk to man? Does a person, as has been suggested, really have to drink eight hundred cans of diet soda a day to be at risk of cancer from saccharin, or use twenty-five bottles of hair dye a day to be at risk of cancer from this product?

Because of the expense involved in a typical study the number of animals tested is kept to a minimum. An average test with only three hundred animals now costs approximately $250,000 to conduct. Because the number of animals exposed to the potential carcinogen is very small, it is usually necessary to feed the animals doses that greatly exceed those predicted for human exposure. If this were not done, the carcinogenic effect of many chemicals would not be seen.

In addition to being high enough to cause an increased incidence of tumors, the dose of a carcinogen must be high enough so that the increase that is seen can be judged to be statistically significant. Any event has some probability of occurring by chance. If tumors are seen in one group of animals and not in another, it is necessary to be sure that they result from exposure to a carcinogen and not by chance. The smaller the group of animals, the greater the difference in incidence of tumors must be between two groups before it can confidently be said that it reflects exposure to a carcinogen. In the standard NCI test a finding of four animals with bladder tumors among fifty exposed to a chemical carcinogen such as benzidine compared with zero in a control population of animals not exposed to benzidine would not be considered statistically significant, even though it represents an 8 percent increase. Such an increased incidence of bladder tumors among workers exposed to benzidine would be catastrophic, but because of limitations in experimental design, the increase would not be considered statistically significant. In addition to compensating for the small number of animals used relative to the potential human population at risk, large doses are employed to compensate both for the shorter life-span of animals as compared with humans and the relatively faster rate of metabolism and excretion that test animals have.

For chemical carcinogens there is a dose-response relationship—the higher the dose, the greater the incidence of tumor formation. Since even at high doses most chemicals will not cause cancer, an experimental design with doses far in excess of normal human exposures is considered scientifically proper and valid. Therefore, it is not true that an individual would have to drink eight hundred cans of diet soda or use twenty-five bottles of hair dye to be at risk of cancer from these products. *Normal* use of these products will increase one's risk of cancer.

Having determined that a particular chemical poses a carcinogenic risk to a given animal species lets us know that a risk to humans likely exists too, but says nothing about exactly *how great* that risk is. Establishing the magnitude of the risk is not an easy task. Two basic questions must be answered. First, what is the level of risk to the test animal at doses that approach or equal human exposure levels? Second, how does one convert from the risk to a test animal at a given exposure level to a risk in humans at that same exposure level?

Several mathematical models can be used to estimate the carcinogenic risk at exposure levels comparable to those of normal exposure, given the incidence of tumors produced in experimental animals at higher doses. Although the models are quite different and complex, they are all compatible with the premise that any level of exposure to a carcinogen produces a risk of cancer—that is, that there is *no safe level of exposure*, no threshold for activity. This concept is quite different from what is observed of other toxic effects exhibited by chemicals. Arsenic, for example, is both acutely toxic—it will kill you immediately if ingested in large enough amounts—and carcinogenic. However, if one dilutes an arsenic-containing solution far enough, the risk of immediate death from poisoning can be eliminated, but the risk of cancer can only be decreased. It can never be eliminated, no matter how small the dose.

Using an appropriate mathematical model, one can calculate the incidence of cancer that would be expected at any dose level, given the incidence at other dose levels. But any attempt to relate such a calculated level of risk in an animal to actual human risk at the same dose level is fraught with difficulties. First, there is the question of differences in species sensitivity. Humans are not mice, but do they react to the same extent to exposure to a given carcinogen? Past experience tells us that variations in sensitivity are to be expected. In the case of thalidomide one-hundredth of the dose that caused no observable effects in test animals caused birth defects in humans. We were more sensitive than expected. Second, test animals are bred to be genetically homogeneous—that is, to be as identical as possible; we are not. Some of us are bound to be more sensitive and vulnerable to a given carcinogen than others, but how much more sensitive and how many of us this applies to remains unknown. Third, exposure of test animals starts after weaning, whereas our exposure to many carcinogens begins at the very critical and sensitive time during *in utero* development and infancy (see chapter 10). Exposures at these times may be of greater consequence than comparable levels of exposure later in life. Recent experiments performed by Dr. Cesare Maltoni of the Institute of Oncology and Tumor Center in Bologna support this conclusion: Maltoni compared the lifetime cancer incidence of two groups of rats, both exposed to 6,000 parts per million of vinyl chloride for four hours a day, five days a week, for five weeks. The only difference was that one group of rats started when they were one day old and the other group started when they were thirteen weeks old. Over 30 percent of the rats started at one day got cancer, while none of those started at thirteen weeks did.

Fourth, unlike laboratory animals, which are healthy and well fed, many of the humans exposed are sick and poorly nourished. Fifth, and perhaps most important, we are exposed to many carcinogens and promoting agents all at once, each having its own effects, and many possibly acting together to increase our risk. Because such factors cannot be quantified, extrapolation from risks in animals to risks in humans is currently very limited. In many cases the assumption is made that humans and test animals are equally sensitive. Such an assumption may in some cases overestimate the risk. More important, it is likely in other cases to underestimate it.

Although animal tests are costly, take years to complete, and are difficult to use as a precise yardstick of human vulnerability, they currently provide the best indication of potential human risk, short of good epidemiological studies. However, in recent years a new series of tests have begun to emerge that promise to develop even more rapidly in the near future and that have the potential for providing rapid, inexpensive, and highly accurate methods of determining carcinogenic risk.

The Ames test, developed by Drs. Bruce Ames and Joyce McCann, of the University of California at Berkeley, is today the most advanced of these tests. It is conducted by exposing populations of *Salmonella* bacteria to potential carcinogens and observing whether or not the chemical is mutagenic, altering the genes of the bacteria. To mimic as closely as possible the metabolic changes likely to occur when animals or humans are exposed to these chemicals, extracts isolated from animal or human livers are added to provide for necessary metabolic activation. On a plate no bigger than four inches in diameter, several billion bacteria can be grown. Therefore, the likelihood of seeing a change occur at any given dose of chemical is much greater than when only 50 rats or mice are used.

Of course, bacteria are not humans. Yet, like humans, bacteria contain chromosomes and genes, genetic material similar to our own. If the transformation of a cell from normal to cancerous involves an alteration of the cell's genetic material, then an alteration of the bacteria's genetic material that is readily measurable can serve as a test system for potential carcinogenic activity. Indeed, Dr. Ames and his colleagues have shown that for hundreds of known carcinogenic chemicals the results in their bacterial system agree in more than 90 percent of the cases. For chemicals believed to be noncarcinogenic the bacterial test is also in good agreement. These results have been validated by two separate laboratories, one in England, one in Japan. Work by Ames and others continues to improve the test, making it more reliable and predictive. Although its results correlate highly for several classes of carcinogens and are even able to distinguish between carcinogenic and noncarcinogenic members of the same chemical class, it has, to date, not been shown to be a good predictor for such classes of carcinogens as metals, hormones, and polychlorinated organic chemicals such as PCBs and DDT. However, other tests have also been developed, not all using bacteria (one uses cells from hamster embryos). A number of these "short term" tests are now available as predictors of carcinogenicity and are being used by many industrial concerns. Governmental agencies have begun to incorporate them into regulatory policies.

Much remains to be learned about the biology of cancer. The critical change (or changes) that induce a cell to turn cancerous have eluded research scientists' efforts to find them. Attempts at cancer cure with either radiation or chemotherapy have met with only limited success. But our ability to detect potential carcinogens has improved enormously, providing us with a real opportunity to prevent human exposure—and thus cancer itself—before it occurs.

CHAPTER 3
PCBS:
A CASE IN POINT

During the House debate on the Toxic Substances Control Act in 1976, Representative Gilbert Gude, a Maryland Republican, called polychlorinated biphenyls—PCBs—a "mad dog" of the environment. Out of the seas of chemicals that surround us PCBs alone were singled out by name. The Toxic Substances Control Act prohibits the manufacturing, processing, and sale of all PCBs in the United States starting in 1979. As extraordinary as this ban might seem to some, it does not even begin to answer the problem.

In many ways our experience with PCBs can serve as the model for the situation that exists for hundreds of chemicals that now contaminate the environment and man. Their careless spread is a horrifying lesson in what can happen when government fails to regulate the use of toxic substances. The U.S. will continue to pay the price of PCBs for years: some of the higher chlorinated PCBs may persist for decades.

PCBs are probably the most widespread chemical contaminant known to mankind. They are tough chemical cousins of DDT, but unlike DDT they have not been sprayed on purpose but have instead entered the world through the back door, by discharge, vaporization, leaks, and spills. They are carcinogenic in laboratory rats and mice.

Widely used by industry because of their resistance to heat, PCBs are toxic to a wide range of life, including humans. Ingestion of PCBs has caused a host of afflictions, including numbness of limbs, deformities of bones and joints, and stillbirths. Thanks to the ignorance and recklessness of industry and government, PCBs have even been found in animals 11,000 feet down in the North Atlantic.

Fish and wildlife in many parts of the United States are sodden with PCBs. Many of the fish stocks of most of the Great Lakes and numerous river systems are now officially too dangerous to eat because they contain 5 parts per million (5 ppm) or more of PCBs, the Food and Drug Administration's current "temporary tolerance" level for fish products. Moreover, as of this writing, the FDA has proposed reducing the temporary tolerance to 2 ppm. This will eventually mean the loss of even greater supplies of fish.

PCBs are literally almost everywhere in the United States. Indeed, the U.S. Environmental Protection Agency calculates that 91 percent of all Americans have detectable levels of PCBs in their adipose tissues, and 40.3 percent have at least 1 ppm.* Both the percentage of Americans showing detectable levels of PCBs and the extent of contamination have been increasing over the last several years.

PCBs did not become a matter of urgent national concern until 1975, even though they had been in use for almost fifty years. In 1927 Theodore Swann, of the Federal Phosphorus Company, set up a pilot plant to supply biphenyl for use as a heat transfer fluid in the refining of lubricating oils. Biphenyl is a derivative of benzene, a liquid aromatic hydrocarbon found in coal tar. By 1929 Swann developed polychlorinated biphenyls, and in 1930 Monsanto took over production. PCBs

---

* Populations in some other countries have higher levels. The Israelis are reported to have an average of 2.75 ppm of PCBs in their adipose tissues, the Austrians 3.5 ppm, and the Germans 6.8 ppm (in Cologne) to 10 ppm (in Munich).

are made by controlled chlorination of biphenyl with anhydrous chlorine, with iron filings or ferric chloride serving as a catalyst. When biphenyl is chlorinated, chlorine atoms replace the hydrogen atoms. Since each biphenyl has ten hydrogen atoms, as shown in the illustration, PCBs may have any number of chlorine atoms up to ten.

BIPHENYL MOLECULE

Monsanto, which discontinued production in 1977, has sold PCBs under the trademark name of Aroclor. In its Aroclor line of PCBs Monsanto used numerical designations, such as 1221, 1232, 1242, 1248, 1254, 1260, 1262, and 1268. The first two digits—12—indicate the twelve carbon atoms in the biphenyl structure, while the last two digits describe the percentage of chlorine. Thus Aroclor 1254 means a polychlorinated biphenyl with twelve carbon atoms and 54 percent chlorine by weight. There was one exception in the Aroclor line—1016. It really should be called 1241-plus, because it has twelve carbon atoms, not ten, and contains slightly more than 41 percent chlorine, not 16 percent. It is very similar to Aroclor 1242, with which it has sometimes been confused in analytical work.

PCBs have also been manufactured abroad under different trade names, such as Pyralene and Phenoclor in France, Fenclor in Italy, Clophen in West Germany, and Kanechlor and Santotherm in Japan. In addition, chemical plants in Czechoslovakia and the Soviet Union have produced PCB mixtures.

PCBs are among the most stable organic compounds known to science. Their very hardiness gladdens industrialists and depresses ecologists. Highly chlorinated PCBs are able to persist in the environment for years because enzymes are essentially unable to shear the bonding between the chlorine atom and the biphenyl structure. There are only two feasible methods known to destroy PCBs. One is to burn them in a special incinerator generating temperatures in the range of 2,000 to 3,000 degrees Fahrenheit. The other method is to expose them to ozone and ultraviolet light. Of course, neither of these methods can be used to eliminate PCBs dispersed in the environment.

Because of their low flammability, high heat capacity, and low electrical conductivity, PCBs have had obvious advantages as dielectric and heat transfer fluids. Other properties regarded as favorable by industry include low solubility in water and low vapor pressure. PCBs are also resistant to acids, alkalies, and corrosive chemicals. They are insoluble in ethyl alcohol and water but soluble in fats. Hence, they tend to become stored in the fatty tissues of organisms.

Because of their industrial properties PCBs have been used in an extraordinary variety of products, so broad that almost no one in the U.S. populace has escaped contact. In 1975 Karl E. Bremer, of the Environmental Protection Agency Region V office in Chicago, listed the past and present uses of PCBs. These uses include:

—In transformer and power capacitors
—As hydraulic fluids
—As a diffusion pump oil
—In heat transfer applications
—As plasticizers
—As adhesives in the manufacture of brake linings, clutch faces, and grinding wheels
—As a laminate of ceramics and metals
—In the making of washable wall coverings and upholstering materials
—In adhesives for envelopes and tapes
—In coatings for ironing board covers
—As a delustering agent for rayons
—As a flameproofer for synthetic yarns

—In waterproofing canvas
—As additives for paints and varnishes
—In film casting solutions
—In insulating tapes
—In protection lacquers
—In the making of plastic bottles
—In epoxy resins for protective coating of metals
—As an additive in sealants, such as caulking compounds and putty, in concrete and asphalt, as well as in fireproofing sealants for floors, doors, ceilings, and partitions
—In the making of "carbonless" carbon paper
—As a coating for papers used in thermographic duplicating machines
—As an additive in the xerographic transfer process (in Xerox toner)
—As a plasticizer for printing plates and flexographic plates

In addition to deliberate uses, PCBs also turn up accidentally. They are a by-product of paper recycling. They have also been found in toilet soaps, barrier creams, hydrated lime used to manufacture glass, water-treatment chemicals, primer paints, coloring compounds, industrial degreasers, additives in zinc alloys, and waxes used in the tool and die-casting process.

Since 1930 Monsanto has produced 1.4 billion pounds of PCBs at manufacturing plants in Anniston, Alabama, and Sauget, Illinois. Of this, 150 million pounds was exported, leaving 1.25 billion pounds in U.S. sales. In addition, 3 million pounds was imported for sale. Out of this total, 758 million pounds is currently in service, 55 million pounds is presumed to have been destroyed, 290 million pounds is in dumps and landfills, and 150 million pounds is in soil, water, and air. According to EPA calculations, 10 million pounds of PCBs contaminates the environment each year through vaporization, leaks, and spills.

In 1971 Monsanto announced it would restrict PCB sales to so-called closed-cycle systems, such as capacitors and transformers. U.S. industry manufactures more than 100 million capacitors a year for use in air-conditioning units, refrigerators, television sets, and fluorescent light ballasts. PCBs can be and have been directly discharged into rivers and streams, municipal sewage systems, and the atmosphere during the production of capacitors and transformers. When any of these products are discarded, they are ordinarily taken to dumps, where the chance exists that PCBs can leach through the ground into water or vaporize into the air. In New York and Michigan several companies drained PCBs from old transformers, mixed them with crankcase oil, and sold them to municipalities as a dust suppressor on roads. It is worth noting that street dust collected in Washington, D.C., has contained PCBs.

Apart from such practices, transformers and capacitors can rupture or leak. Here are some typical examples. On March 8, 1973, a transformer being trucked through Kingston, Tennessee, sprang a leak, and 630 gallons of PCBs was spilled. The contaminated soils were placed in 11,500 drums and sealed in concrete at a cost of $1.7 million. This was paid for by General Electric, which was shipping the transformer. In addition, local residents brought suit and received $120,000 in damages.

On Friday, March 13, 1974, the U.S. Air Force got involved in a Catch-22 PCB episode when an electrical transformer fell off a pier in Seattle and 265 gallons of PCBs bled into the Duwamish River. An army supply depot in Tooele, Utah, had crated the transformer, destined for an air force radar station in Shemya, Alaska, and shipped it to a government warehouse in Seattle, where it was to be loaded onto a barge under contract to the U.S. Navy. Usually such six-foot-square transformers are equipped with metal ears for hoisting, but the army packers had encased the transformer in wood and placed it on four-by-four-inch pine skids. Instructions on the crate read: "Lift by case only." When the case was two feet off the ground, one of the skids broke, the case fell, the transformer ruptured, and PCBs spilled into the river. The Department of Defense refused responsibility, and so did the Coast Guard, which claimed that PCBs are not among the chemicals it is required to recover. The EPA had to hire divers, who recovered 70 to 90 gallons of PCBs and contaminated river bottom sediments, and only a little less than a year later did the Defense Department agree to pay the cost of this diving operation, $148,000. Defense also paid $8,000 to ship 215 barrels of contaminated matter to Twin Falls, Idaho, where the PCBs were "entombed" in a former Titan missile silo.

On April 16, 1976, Dr. Ward B. Stone, an associate pathologist in the New York State Department of Environmental Conservation, took soil samples from two electric lighting poles in Dutchess and Putnam counties, New York, after their Westinghouse capacitors ruptured. "My calculations indicate that each Westinghouse capacitor contains about 15 pounds of PCBs," Stone wrote in a memo to his superiors.

From the cases reported above, the cans became swollen and the seams ruptured and most of the PCB fluid drained out. At Castle Point, Pole #1866, one capacitor failed so that I would estimate the PCB contamination to be 12–15 pounds at that site. At Cold Spring Pole #59156, two capacitors failed and the estimate of loss is 24–30 pounds. . . .

I think we can account for 36 to 45 pounds of PCB 1016 spilled in a relatively small geographic area and that numerous other discharges of this type have occurred recently, and are occurring, in other parts of this state, nation and world. This all adds to the PCB contamination of the world and increases the likelihood of fish and wildlife management problems and potential animal and human health problems.

As far back as the 1930s medical reports showed that PCBs were detrimental to the health of workers. As Dr. Barry Commoner, of Washington University in St. Louis, has written, "There is much irony—and tragedy—in the PCB story, for it shows that had the scientific community given enough attention to its earlier effects on workers, the present ecological hazard could have been avoided and the long-term effects of industrial exposures would now be much better understood."

In a paper published in 1936 in the *Archives of Dermatology and Syphilology,* Drs. Jack W. Jones and Herbert S. Alden, of Atlanta, reported on the case of "O.D.," a twenty-six-year-old Negro who began working in the distillation of chlorinated diphenyl (biphenyl) in April 1930. In three years "O.D." developed a severe skin disease, chloracne, and his body was covered with pustules. By October 1933 twenty-three of the twenty-four men working in the manufacturing plant had acneform eruptions on the face and body. In December 1933 "O.D." complained of lassitude, loss of appetite, and loss of libido, now classic symptoms of PCB poisoning, but as Drs. Jones and Alden reported, "On examination he seemed in good general health. His complaint of lassitude was not borne out by anything more than the usual temperament of the Negro toward work."

In the August 1943 issue of *Industrial Medicine* Dr. Leonard Greenburg, executive director of the Division of Industrial Hygiene of the New York State Department of Labor, reported on outbreaks of chloracne among workers handling electrical equipment containing PCBs and the chemically related chlorinated naphthalenes. "During the past year," Dr. Greenburg wrote, "the Division of Industrial Hygiene of the New York State Department of Labor has conducted an investigation in two cable plants using chlorinated naphthalenes and diphenyls. In this investigation, a large number of cases of dermatitis were found, and several deaths due to liver damage among workers in the industry." One of Dr. Greenburg's main conclusions was that "chlorinated naphthalenes and diphenyls are in general highly toxic compounds and must be used with extreme care. Industrial hygienists should make every effort to see that such exposures are controlled, in so far as humanly possible." Nothing was done.

Although PCBs began entering the environment soon after they were first manufactured, they were not detected in the environment until 1966. The detection took place not in the United States but in Sweden. In 1964 the Royal Swedish Commission on Natural Resources asked Dr. Sören Jensen, an analytical chemist at the University of Stockholm, to determine the levels of DDT and other chlorinated pesticides in human fat and in wildlife. Using gas chromatography, in which peaks traced on a graph represent individual chemical components,

Dr. Jensen soon discovered, by his own account, "numerous peaks whose retention times did not agree with any of the known chlorinated pesticides." None of these peaks was described in any of the literature, and so Jensen had to play detective.

He asked the assistance of ecologists at the Swedish Museum of Natural History. They collected fish, in this instance pike, from the south of Sweden and from Lapland, in the relatively unpolluted north. All the pike showed traces of the unknown compounds, but the farther north the samples of pike, the lower the levels of residues. Reasoning that the compounds might possibly be unknown metabolites of pesticides, Jensen tested this hypothesis by analyzing single feathers from white-tailed eagles collected by the museum from 1888 to the present. The unknown compounds were found in the feather of an eagle collected in 1942 and subsequent years, but since chlorinated pesticides had not been introduced until 1945, Jensen knew that the compounds could not be their metabolites.

By chance a white-tailed eagle was found dead in the Stockholm archipelago, and Jensen had the opportunity to examine the whole bird. He discovered that it contained enormous amounts of the unknown compounds. He injected a solution containing an extract of fat from the muscle into a combined gas chromatograph–mass spectrometer, and, as he reported, "The mass numbers equal to the molecular weights of the unknown peaks could be read to 324, 358, 392 and 426. Astonishingly enough, the molecular differences were constantly 34 mass units. This constant difference for the first time showed that there was a relationship in the origin of the unknown substances."

Jensen was able to recognize the presence of chlorine from the unusual isotopic pattern, and by using a series of equations he was able to determine the molecular weights of the parent hydrocarbons. Given the molecular weights, the most plausible formula for the parent hydrocarbon was biphenyl. Logically, then, the unknown substances were polychlorinated biphenyls. He confirmed the identification by injecting a PCB mixture into the mass spectrometer. Gas chromatographic studies also showed that the mixture gave peaks "with retention times identical to those of the unknown peaks from the white-tailed eagle and the other species investigated." Jensen published his findings in *New Scientist* in 1966.

After the appearance of Jensen's paper, scientists in the Netherlands, England, Scotland, and the U.S. began their own investigations. Dr. Robert Risebrough, of the University of California at Berkeley, did important work on West Coast peregrine falcons. A paper of his prompted Monsanto to issue a statement scoffing at both his research and Jensen's. "The conclusions of these scientists are puzzling from several aspects," Monsanto said. "Polychlorinated biphenyls are stable chemical compounds which are essentially insoluble in water. Their use does not make them easily released into the natural environment. . . . It has also been implied that polychlorinated biphenyls are 'highly toxic' chemicals. This is not true."

In the January–February 1970 issue of *Environment,* Risebrough published an article summarizing knowledge to date about PCBs. He called for the establishment of tolerance levels of PCBs in food, and he warned, "The possible PCB hazard, like so many environmental hazards, is one of long-term, low-level exposure and perhaps of effects from its combination with other poisons. There is also the more indirect, but no less real danger of destroying other forms of life—part of the vast interconnected web of species of which man is but one part and on which he depends."

Risebrough took particular note of the ability of PCBs to stimulate or induce the production of enzymes in the livers of birds and rats. "Induction of these enzymes would be one of the expected effects of the polychlorinated biphenyls in people," he wrote.

Normally the lifetime of the induced enzymes is short. The foreign, water-insoluble compounds that act as inducers are usually converted to water-soluble derivatives that can be excreted by the kidney. Enzyme activity falls as the inducers are metabolized in this way. The polychlorinated biphenyls, however, particularly those with greater amounts of chlorine, are relatively resistant to biological breakdown. They might therefore persist as inducers without being broken down themselves. As the enzymes are continually induced, hormones and perhaps other classes of molecules as well might therefore be metabolized at rates faster than normal over the whole life span of the organism. The long-term significance of this phenomenon is as yet unknown.

In the early spring of 1970 John R. Clark, then assistant director of the U.S. Marine Gamefish Laboratory at Sandy Hook, New Jersey, suggested to Robert H. Boyle, a senior writer at *Sports Illustrated,* that the magazine have the eggs and flesh of coastal gamefish tested for residues of DDT and other chlorinated hydrocarbon pesticides. It was high levels of DDT in Lake Michigan coho salmon that caused Clark's concern. Boyle spoke to the editors at the magazine, and they assented. The WARF (Wisconsin Alumni Research Foundation) Institute in Madison, Wisconsin, a leading analytical laboratory, agreed to test the fish, and in May 1970 *Sports Illustrated* correspondents collected fish from the Atlantic, Gulf, and Pacific coasts and shipped them to the WARF Institute. As a result of reading Risebrough's PCB article in *Environment,* Boyle asked the WARF Institute to check the flesh and eggs for PCBs. He also asked that the flesh be tested for methyl mercury.

The October 26, 1970, issue of *Sports Illustrated* carried a long article by Boyle reporting on the findings of the WARF Institute. The tests revealed that a number of fish species contained PCBs. Striped bass from the Hudson had especially high levels. They averaged 11.4 ppm of PCBs in their eggs and 4.01 ppm in the flesh.

Because Boyle held a scientific license to seine fish from the Hudson River, he was required to make an annual report to the state conservation department, and on February 17, 1971, he wrote to Carl Parker, chief of the Bureau of Fish, and reported on the levels of PCB and DDT in the striped bass eggs. "These are grim figures," Boyle wrote, "and I certainly think the state should warn fishermen not to eat striped bass eggs." He also informed Parker that the levels in the flesh were "not great reading" and suggested he read the article in full. In reply, Parker scoffed at the WARF findings as unproven allegations.

Despite Parker's response, documents later obtained from

the Department of Environmental Conservation (DEC) revealed that the state had begun collecting Hudson River fish as early as the summer of 1970, although PCB analysis was not conducted until 1972. Tests conducted then showed that eleven of twenty-nine largemouth bass from the Hudson had PCB levels in excess of 5 ppm in their flesh. One largemouth had 53.81 ppm of PCBs. Other 1972 findings included a smallmouth bass with 17.58 ppm of PCBs, a striped bass with 10.48 ppm, a northern pike with 17.78 ppm, and four sturgeon with levels ranging from 5.73 to 7.03 ppm. Out of fifteen white perch tested, seven had excessive levels. Not a word was said to the public.

In April 1973 the DEC collected twenty-two striped bass from the Hudson near the Tappan Zee Bridge. The fish were tested in 1974, and eighteen of the twenty-two stripers had excessive residues of PCBs. The highest level was 49.63 ppm. Again not a word was said to the public.

In May 1975 six striped bass were taken from the Hudson near the Tappan Zee Bridge. Four of the six proved to have excessive levels, with the highest 37.80 ppm.

The September 29, 1972, issue of *Science* carried a paper by Dr. Donald J. Lisk and Carl A. Bache, of the Pesticide Residue Laboratory at Cornell University, and two other Cornell scientists, reporting that all lake trout tested from Cayuga Lake contained PCBs. Eighty percent of the trout more than twenty-two inches long had PCB levels in excess of 5 ppm. A nine-year-old laker had the highest level, 30.4 ppm, and the Cornell scientists noted that there was a "highly significant" correlation between the levels of PCBs and the age of the fish. They wrote, "The fish were netted in October 1970. Their ages were accurately known because the fish are annually stocked as yearlings and distinctly marked as to year class." Although Cayuga Lake is well known in New York for its lake trout fishing, no one in the DEC bothered to call the Cornell scientists to ask about their findings. Indeed, the only call Bache remembers receiving came from a representative of a chemical company, not Monsanto, who wondered where the PCBs were coming from.

The conservation department suppressed information on excessive levels of PCBs detected in Lake Ontario coho and Chinook salmon in the early 1970s. In 1975 a scientist, who requested anonymity (and thus received the code name of Deep Trout), gave Boyle copies of analyses performed on the salmon by the department's Rome Pollution Laboratory between December 23, 1971, and September 26, 1973.

The first report dealt with seven Chinook salmon collected in the fall of 1971. The PCB residues ranged from 15.29 to 39.48 ppm. Another report on fifteen coho salmon collected in 1971 noted that PCB levels ranged from 6.93 to 21.43 ppm. Still another report, dated September 26, 1973, reported that of twenty Chinook salmon tested, only one had less than the FDA limit. It had 4.92 ppm of PCBs, just under the standard. The other levels in the nineteen Chinook ranged from 6.30 to 12.97 ppm. The report specifically noted that "all PCB levels except one fish are in excess of the 5.00 ppm tolerance level established by FDA." There was not a word from the state to anglers. The DEC was busy extolling the wonderful salmon fishery it had established for anglers in Lake Ontario.

Undoubtedly there were other reasons why the state did not go public about PCB contamination of waters in New York. For one, it might hurt license sales, and the DEC is dependent upon fishing license revenues for income. For another, the truth of the situation might have reflected poorly on Governor Nelson A. Rockefeller and other members of his administration, who had promised in 1965, after voters approved the billion-dollar "Pure Waters" bond issue, that all the waters of the state would be clean by 1972.

Throughout all this there was one recalcitrant scientist within the conservation department, later grandly renamed the Department of Environmental Conservation (DEC). Wildlife pathologist Dr. Ward B. Stone had warned his superiors for years that PCBs were a menace. He had fired off warnings as far back as 1970, but despite all his memos, his efforts were, in Stone's word, "futile," and there were times when he wondered if he were crazy and the rest of the department sane. "No one really cared," says Stone. In one very typically blunt memo, he advised: "I hope the department begins to take some of these toxic problems seriously . . . because it is doubtful these problems can be put off. In fact, they already have been put off far too long." The state continued to put off the problems.

In May 1974 the U.S. Environmental Protection Agency held a hearing on toxic pollutant effluent standards; PCBs were a major issue. By now industry was beginning to have second thoughts about PCBs, and some indication of the threat that PCBs pose to the environment and human health can be gleaned from an answer given by Dr. James H. Wright, a chemical engineer with the Westinghouse Electric Corporation. Asked by EPA attorney Alan Eckert, "When you took these steps to prevent the discharge of PCBs, did you attempt to flush out or clean sewers contaminated with PCBs from old operations?" Dr. Wright answered, "I would be the most frightened man in the world to recommend the flushing out of old lines and old drains."

Dr. Wright's startling reply drew no public attention, but the answers given by the next industry witness, Dr. Edward L. Simons, who appeared for General Electric, eventually helped give rise to national public alarm.

In the course of his testimony Dr. Simons testified that a GE transformer plant in Rome, Georgia, was discharging PCBs into the Oostanaula River "on the order of one pound per day." The effect on organisms living in the river was not known because, as Dr. Simons admitted, "We have made no measurements of biota for any facility of the General Electric Company."

Simons also testified that another GE transformer plant, in Pittsfield, Massachusetts, released PCBs into the Housatonic River. In the vicinity of the outfalls, according to "occasional samples" by GE, the river's water contained between 1 and 3 ppb (parts per billion) of PCBs, while levels in the river sediments varied from 130 to 1,300 ppm. At "a distance of something between one and six miles" downstream, PCBs were "not detectable" in the water, but PCB levels in the river sediments were between 30 and 60 ppm. Simons pointed out that the Pittsfield plant was releasing an average of only 0.1 pound per day of PCBs into the Housatonic, with "occasional excursions as high as 0.8 pounds per day." He noted, "To put that 0.1 pound per day in a possibly more illustrative format, that would correspond to a small jigger of whiskey, about one ounce, so we are not talking about a major spill. This is a relatively small volume of liquid." Later Dr. Simons testified that "a loss of something on the order of one ounce during the day's operation is, we think, a very creditable performance. I don't know of any other really heavy manufacturing operation which handles fluids in which that kind of level of control is displayed."

These answers were horrendous enough to anyone acquainted with the toxic properties of PCBs, but the most dramatic moment in the hearing came when Eckert asked Simons about two GE capacitor plants at Fort Edward and Hudson Falls, New York, on the Hudson River. The Fort Edward plant began operating in 1942 and the Hudson Falls plant in 1951. Eckert inquired about the PCB discharge to the Hudson, and Simons replied that the two plants were discharging twenty-five to thirty pounds a day to the river on the average. Eckert was so taken aback that he had to ask for a brief recess. "Your Honor," he said, "I think I have a good deal more questioning for Dr. Simons."

This was to be the breakthrough nationally on PCBs, although GE's dumping of PCBs into the Hudson had to undergo more bureaucratic twists and turns. In a memo dated May 31, 1974, Sandra P. Kunsberg, an attorney in the Water Enforcement Branch of the EPA Region II office, in New York City, wrote to Dr. Richard Spears, chief of the Surveillance and Analysis Division,

Following the [toxic pollutant effluent standards] hearings [at which GE admitted dumping PCBs], in a memorandum from Alan Eckert to Meyer Scolnick, the Office of Enforcement and General Counsel in New York recommended that this office undertake a careful investigation of PCB discharges from the Fort Edward and Hudson Falls facilities to determine whether or not there exists a health hazard within the meaning of Section 504 of the FWPCA [Federal Water Pollution Control Act].

Section 504 authorizes the administrator of the EPA to sue to restrain persons whose pollution of waters causes "substantial endangerment to the health of persons or to the welfare of persons, where such endangerment is to the livelihood of such persons." Dr. Royal J. Nadeau and Robert F. Davis, of the Region II EPA Laboratory, conducted the recommended investigation, and they reported, based on GE figures, that the Fort Edward plant was discharging up to 30 pounds a day of PCBs into the Hudson River, while the Hudson Falls plant was discharging up to 17.6 pounds. Minnows they collected below the GE discharge averaged 78 ppm of PCBs, while a rock bass contained 340 ppm of PCBs. Nadeau and Davis wrote, "The PCB level in the rock bass is greater than the maximum level documented for fish taken from any industrial river in the U.S. . . . This represents a new record for PCB contamination of fresh water fish." They noted that youngsters from Fort Edward fished areas downstream and that "ingestion of these fish by the populace would certainly lead to contamination of specific tissues in their bodies."

Nadeau and Davis submitted their report to the EPA Region II office, but effective action was very slow in coming. Richard Flye, the chief of the Region II Water Enforcement Branch, apparently saw little reason to raise a fuss. As he remarked afterward, "From some of the evidence I've seen, you can eat PCBs just like an ice cream cone."

Months passed, but the Nadeau-Davis report was not forgotten. It shocked scientists at the EPA National Water Quality Laboratory in Duluth, Minnesota, and when no action was forthcoming, Dr. Gilman Veith of the lab wrote a "review" of the Nadeau-Davis report on July 7, 1975.

This field investigation has revealed the largest source of PCBs into the aquatic environment that I know of. . . . It is my opinion that this report has been written in a conservative manner and does not by itself adequately describe the significance of the G.E. discharge into the Hudson River. . . . The river for many miles downstream from the G.E. discharge could be contaminated with PCBs at levels one hundred times over the 10 ppt [parts per trillion] guideline set forth by EPA in 1972 and a thousand times higher than the recommended water quality criteria [of 1 ppt].

Veith's review was forwarded to the Region II office, and the bureaucrats there finally realized that the Nadeau-Davis report was too explosive to contain. The regional administrator, Gerald Hansler, thereupon finally passed it on to Ogden R. Reid, the new commissioner of the Department of Environmental Conservation.

The report astounded Reid, who began a preliminary investigation of his own. He soon learned that the department had known for several years that striped bass from the Hudson and coho and Chinook salmon from Lake Ontario were heavily contaminated by PCBs. Reporter Richard Severo, of the *New York Times,* persuaded Reid to give him the story, and on August 8, 1975, Severo broke it on the front page. In the story Reid warned the public against eating stripers from the Hudson or salmon from Lake Ontario because they contained more than 5 ppm of PCBs, the FDA's temporary tolerance for fish. With the appearance of that warning on the front page of the *New York Times,* PCBs at last became a national issue.

Even after Reid's warning, EPA bureaucrats were less than helpful. Thomas Whyatt and John Harris-Cronin, of the Hudson River sloop *Clearwater,* began an investigation. When Harris-Cronin went to the EPA office in Manhattan to request a copy of the Nadeau-Davis report, Richard Flye told Harris-Cronin he would have to submit his request in writing. Aware of EPA runaround tactics, Harris-Cronin had had the foresight to bring stationery with him, and he immediately wrote out the request on the spot. Flye looked at the letter and then said to Harris-Cronin that under the Freedom of Information Act "we have 10 days to decide whether or not to honor your request, and the tactic we're going to employ with you is to use them all."

In Albany, Commissioner Reid learned, to his shock and

dismay, that the New York State Department of Health had given the GE plants a water quality certification in 1971, and in 1973 none other than the chief of the enforcement section of the Division of Pure Waters in the DEC had done the same. Still Reid had the DEC bring a complaint against GE, accusing the company of violating state water quality standards and the Environmental Conservation Law. Professor Abraham Sofaer, of Columbia University Law School, served as the hearing officer in the case, which began in the fall of 1975.

The case did not go well for GE. In an affidavit the company admitted that 65 employees had become ill in the two plants in the course of a fifteen-year period under conditions that "may have been caused or aggravated by exposure to PCBs." Of approximately 1,300 employees, 49 had complained of "allergic dermatitis," and 16 others had reported suffering from fungus, nausea, asthmatic bronchitis, and nasal and eye irritations. Another setback for GE came when Dr. Gerald J. Lauer, vice-president of Ecological Analysts Inc., later characterized by Professor Sofaer in his decision as "a firm that engages for profit in preparing testimony for corporations in environmental litigation," testified that the average concentrations of PCBs in the edible portions of fish sampled from the river were well below the FDA guideline of 5 ppm. During cross-examination by Sarah Chasis, of the Natural Resources Defense Council, and Philip Gitlen, of the DEC, Lauer admitted that there had been some omissions and errors in his data. The fish sampled had been tested by Woodson-Tenent Laboratories in Memphis, Tennessee, and as Lauer put it, "I got most of my data over the phone." He admitted that levels in four fish were well over the FDA limit of 5 ppm, with levels of 66 ppm, 75 ppm, 112.1 ppm, and 143.2 ppm. GE's lawyer, N. Earle Evans, Jr., was so taken aback at "the cloud" over the data that he offered to consent to a withdrawal motion of the data. GE also agreed to request that Woodson-Tenent prepare a complete analysis of all its Hudson River samples. The laboratory did, and several fish had more than 100 ppm in their edible flesh, while concentrations in what GE called "non-edible" tissues reached as high as *1,178 ppm!*

In February 1976 Professor Sofaer rendered his decision and found GE guilty of violating state water quality standards. "PCBs are toxic substances," Sofaer wrote in his decision, "capable in sufficient quantities of causing skin lesions, destroying cells in vital body organs, adversely affecting reproduction, and inducing cancer and death."

A new hearing was ordered to determine what steps the company should take to rid the Hudson of an estimated five hundred thousand pounds of PCBs lodged in the riverbed silt and backwaters. The case was settled by Reid's successor, Peter Berle, in September 1976, when GE agreed to pay the state $3 million in cash and contribute an additional $1 million in research. The DEC for its part agreed to contribute $3 million of its own, making the total clean-up package $7 million.

Inasmuch as estimates for dredging the entire contaminated section of the upper Hudson now range up to $204 million, $7 million might seem a paltry sum. But legally pursuing the case further posed problems, since the state itself was culpable for having given GE water quality certifications. Moreover, pollution cases, as exemplified by Reserve Mining's pollution of Lake Superior with asbestos fibers, can drag on for years in the courts, and since PCBs were flowing over the Troy Dam from the upper Hudson and entering the tidal Hudson at the rate of ten thousand pounds a year, action was deemed imperative.

GE agreed to discontinue the use of PCBs at Hudson Falls and Fort Edward on or before July 1, 1977. Independent scientists and environmentalists were appointed to serve on an advisory board to explore ways to rid the river of PCBs, but barring some miracle, the Hudson will not be free of PCBs for decades.

A number of the fish species in the Hudson migrate in and out of the river system, and a fish can quickly become contaminated by PCBs by taking in bottom sediments, eating lesser organisms that are polluted, or simply swimming through water that contains PCBs. PCBs bioaccumulate in fish, so that the levels of contamination can become far higher than the PCB concentrations to which the fish were exposed. Dr. Ian Nisbet, of the Massachusetts Audubon Society, author of EPA's 1976

Criteria Document on PCBs, has calculated that some fish could concentrate up to nine million times the PCB levels found in surrounding waters. Fish exposed to PCB-contaminated waters accumulate the chemical in a very brief period of time, twenty to thirty days, at which point the concentration reaches a "steady state." If the PCB contamination is increased, accumulation resumes.

Little is known on if or how contaminated fish rid themselves of PCBs, but reduction in levels in a fish apparently depends upon growth. If, for example, a five-pound striped bass had 30 ppm of PCBs (a reasonable figure for a Hudson fish) it would have 15 ppm when it reached ten pounds in weight and 7.5 ppm at twenty pounds, provided it did not reenter contaminated waters, simply because of dilution. However, inasmuch as striped bass spawned in the Hudson regularly return there to spawn as adults, the levels are not likely to drop at all.

Interestingly, stripers that spawn in the Hudson—and the Hudson is the most northerly spawning ground on the East Coast of the U.S. for stripers—migrate as far north as Massachusetts, possibly Maine, and as far south as New Jersey, possibly Delaware. The Oak Ridge National Laboratory has estimated that Hudson-spawned stripers constitute from 50 to 90 percent of the bass caught in Long Island Sound and off the south shore of Long Island and the northern New Jersey coast. These Hudson fish pose a threat, then, to fishermen, who may eat them after they are caught in supposedly "clean" waters far from the Hudson.

There are other species involved, such as the menhaden, an "industrial" fish through which PCBs can reach humans by indirect routes. In a report submitted to the Rockefeller Foundation in 1975, biologist William L. Dovel, of the Boyce Thompson Institute in Yonkers, New York, wrote that

the Hudson estuarine system makes a major contribution to the menhaden industry of the northeast. Larval and juvenile stages develop in the Hudson and move toward the sea, where they represent the most valuable commercial fish species taken along the North Atlantic coast. Menhaden are ground into protein meal and oil to form additives for poultry and cattle feed, margarine, paint, lubricants, resins, putty, caulk-ing, linoleum, soap, fertilizers, ink, electrical cables, and antibiotics. The cost of poultry probably would be prohibitive were it not for the rapid growth attained by adding high-protein meal to chicken and turkey feed. Fish meal is a richer source of protein than soybean meal, its most im-portant competitor. It contains amino acids not yet found in vegetable protein and a yet unknown growth factor which makes its use in feed formulas particularly desirable.

Although the Hudson is the most dramatic case of PCB pollution, there are numerous other bodies of water with se-vere problems. The U.S. Fish and Wildlife Service, which re-gards the presence of one-half part per million (0.5 ppm) in a fish egg as a source of biological trouble, maintains one hun-dred monitoring stations across the United States, and trouble spots have ranged from the Merrimack River in Massachusetts to the Saint Johns River in Florida on the Atlantic Coast, from the Apalachicola in the Florida panhandle to the Río Grande on the Gulf Coast, and from the Sacramento to the Columbia and the Snake on the Pacific Coast. Inland drainage systems, such as the Mississippi, Missouri, and Ohio system, have their trouble spots. Even the Yukon River in Alaska is affected, and so are parts of the Atlantic, Gulf, and Pacific coasts.

Much of the Great Lakes system, the single largest supply of fresh water in the world, is contaminated. The Great Lakes states restricted the use of DDT in 1970, and by 1975 DDT levels had dropped 87 percent in Lake Michigan fish. By con-trast, PCB levels have remained ominously high. According to scientists at the EPA National Water Quality Laboratory in Duluth, all Lake Michigan trout and salmon greater than twelve inches in length exceed the FDA limit of 5 ppm of PCBs.

PCBs can enter Lake Michigan by various routes, of which atmospheric transport is probably the most important. Dr. Thomas J. Murphy, of DePaul University, estimates that almost half the estimated 2,800 pounds of PCBs that contaminate the lake each year enter through precipitation. Up to 0.20 ppb of PCBs have been found in snow falling on Milwaukee.

Even Lake Superior, which has the largest surface acreage of any freshwater body in the world and relatively little industry along its shores, has a PCB problem. Large lake trout often contain more than 5 ppm of PCBs. Two-thirds of the Superior basin is the lake itself, and the belief is that PCBs are entering the lake via atmospheric transport.

The Canadian Wildlife Service has done extensive monitoring of PCBs in the eggs of herring gulls from two colonies on each of the four Canadian Great Lakes. The main conclusions thus far are that the levels are high in the Great Lakes (especially in Lake Ontario, where the eggs contain from 70 to 180 ppm of PCBs, wet weight) and that there has been no evidence of a decline in PCB levels despite restrictions on use. "It is concluded that substantial amounts of PCBs are still entering the Great Lakes and/or that the stability of these compounds is so great that the half life of the higher chlorinated isomers should be reckoned in terms of decades."

PCBs are a problem in the Saint Lawrence River, which drains the Great Lakes. Fifteen harbor seals from the Saint Lawrence River averaged 9.2 ppm of PCBs in their blubber. Seals and mink are two mammals in which females suffer reproductive failure because of PCB contamination.

Swedish scientists, concerned about the low reproductive rate of ringed seals in the Baltic Sea, recently correlated pathological changes in the uterus with PCB levels. About 40 percent of the female seals examined had their uterine horns closed by constrictions and occlusions.

Enlarged blood vessels were found at the place of the stenosis or occlusion. The closed horn of the uterus usually contained a waterlike, reddish liquid. However, in some specimens the liquid was turbid, and in some cases the horns contained a material which was mustardlike in consistency and color. The enlargement of the blood vessels in the uterine wall may be a result of an earlier implantation followed by a resorption of the fetus. Grey seal and harbor seal found dead in the Baltic proper and off the Swedish west coast also showed these pathological changes.

In addition to PCB contamination of fish and wildlife the U.S. Food and Drug Administration and the U.S. Department of Agriculture have reported numerous specific incidents of PCB contamination of food. For instance:

In 1970 the Campbell Soup Company detected high levels of PCBs in chickens raised in New York State. As a result, 146,000 chickens were destroyed.

In July 1971 the Monsanto Chemical Company informed the FDA that large amounts of fish meal might have become contaminated with PCBs during pasteurization from a leak in a heating system in Wilmington, North Carolina. The FDA discovered that the leak began in April and continued through July. More than 123,000 pounds of egg products and 88,000 chickens had to be destroyed.

In 1971 the FDA also learned that high levels of PCBs, up to 20 ppm, had been found in turkeys by the USDA and Swift and Company. About 50,000 birds were kept from market.

The December 1975 issue of the *Journal of the National Cancer Institute* published a study by Dr. Renate Kimbrough and a team of investigators from the Center for Disease Control in Atlanta, the EPA, the National Cancer Institute, and the Johns Hopkins School of Medicine in which they "concluded that the polychlorinated biphenyl Aroclor 1260 had a hepatocarcinogenic [causing liver cancer] effect in female Sherman strain rats when fed in the diet."

Specifically Kimbrough and her colleagues reported that 26 of 184 rats fed 100 ppm of Aroclor 1260 for approximately twenty-one months developed hepatocellular carcinomas. Only 1 out of 173 control rats developed this lesion in the same period of time. Moreover, 144 of the 184 experimental animals—but none of the controls—had neoplastic nodules of the liver.

Earlier the World Health Organization reported that Aroclor 1254 and Kanechlor 500 are carcinogenic in mice. Both compounds induced benign and malignant cell tumors following oral ingestion.

Research of the utmost significance has been done by Dr. James R. Allen and his colleagues at the University of Wisconsin Medical School. This research, which has been underway for several years, involves the use of rhesus monkeys, non-human primates, as the test animals, and their close relationship to man is of importance. Allen and his colleagues fed six rhesus monkeys food containing 25 ppm of Aroclor 1248 for two months. The monkeys developed facial swelling, loss of hair, including their eyelashes, and acne lesions within a month. One of the monkeys died from PCB intoxication two months after going off the PCB diet.

In another experiment the scientists fed two groups of female rhesus monkeys food containing 5 ppm and 2.5 ppm of Aroclor 1248. Within two months both groups of monkeys had lost hair from the face and neck, and their skin was of "a sandpaperlike texture." Both groups developed acne, although the 2.5 ppm group developed the lesions later in time as the PCBs accumulated.

In six months' time all the monkeys in both groups were bred to control males that had not been fed PCBs. Six of the eight 5 ppm females became pregnant. Four of the six pregnant females aborted or resorbed the fetus, one gave birth to a stillborn, and one to a very undersized infant. All eight monkeys in the 2.5 ppm group became pregnant, and of these, two resorbed the fetus, one aborted, and five gave birth to undersized infants.

These five infants and the one survivor of the 5 ppm group were permitted to nurse on their mothers. The survivor of the 5 ppm group and two of the 2.5 ppm infants died while nursing. After weaning, the three remaining infants exhibited both behavioral and learning disabilities. They were hyperactive and did not learn various tasks as well as control monkeys under the same conditions.

The female rhesus monkeys who were fed diets containing 2.5 ppm and 5 ppm of PCBs were placed on a PCB-free diet for one year, and then they were rebred. The infants born were small at birth and had detectable levels of PCBs in their tissues. After nursing, the infants from those mothers who had previously been on a 5 ppm diet were hyperpigmented. After a year these infants showed learning and behavioral deficits. Allen measured the range of PCB concentrations in the milk of these mothers, and calculated the dose level that the nursing infants were receiving from the milk. The infants, some of which showed clinical signs of PCB intoxication following nursing, had received 5 to 20 milligrams of PCBs per kilogram of body weight.

The Environmental Protection Agency began testing the milk of human mothers in 1976. Preliminary results indicated that essentially all samples of mother's milk had detectable levels of PCBs. Indeed, the average, 1.8 ppm, gives an infant seven times the amount permitted in cow's milk by the Food and Drug Administration. One nursing mother in Michigan had 10.6 ppm of PCBs in her milk, and that dosage approaches the levels that caused learning disabilities and hyperactivity in two groups of monkeys studied by Allen.

No one knows what effect PCBs may have as an additive or synergist with other contaminants widely present in mother's milk, such as aldrin, dieldrin, or hexachlorobenzene. Indeed, any level of any carcinogenic agent in a nursing infant or any other human should be viewed with concern.

PCB poisoning became a fact of life in Japan in 1968, when residents of the island of Kyushu ingested rice oil contaminated with Kanechlor 400, a PCB mixture, which leaked from a factory pipe during processing. The rice oil contained 1,000 to 3,000 ppm of PCBs. Authorities officially declared 1,291 persons as having *yusho* (rice oil) disease, but estimates of those affected reach 15,000.

Yusho symptoms include chloracne and comedolike eruptions; dark pigmentation of the skin, nails, and mucous membrane of the eyes and mouth; cheeselike discharges from the eyes; loss of hair; loss of libido; fatigue; numbness of the extremities; stomachache; headache; nausea; dizziness and forgetfulness; menstrual disturbance; deformities of joints and bones; and poor development of teeth in children.

A number of newborn children suffered from dark skin pigmentation and were nicknamed "Cola babies," after the soft drink. The majority of the infants were smaller than the national average. There were also stillbirths. Examination of one stillbirth showed abnormal skin and hair development.

In November 1975 Dr. Masanori Kuratsune, of the University of Kyushu, told the National Conference on Polychlorinated Biphenyls in Chicago that nine out of twenty-two deaths of *yusho* victims had been caused by malignant neoplasms, "suggesting a possible excess of deaths from cancer."

In August 1976, in a letter to *The New England Journal of Medicine,* Dr. Anita K. Bahn, of the University of Pennsylvania, reported on "a possible new carcinogenic hazard" of Aroclor 1254, a PCB "used by a petrochemical plant in the Northeast in certain processes during a nine-year period ending in the late 1950's." Dr. Bahn noted,

Of a total of 31 men believed to have been heavily exposed to this agent, two malignant melanomas are known on the basis of a person–year analysis and with use of the Third National Cancer Survey incidence rates as the standard only 0.04 malignant melanomas would be expected. . . . An additional melanoma is also known from one of 41 employees in another group believed to have less exposure.

Although the data are based on small numbers and the study is still in progress, there are biologic grounds for assuming an association between PCB and malignant melanoma. . . .

Further study of this possible carcinogenic association is warranted. Because early detection of malignant melanoma may markedly affect survival rates, surveillance for melanoma among those exposed should be considered.

In June 1978, Horomu Koda and two colleagues on the Faculty of Medicine at Kyushu University reported that as of the end of 1977, 51 victims of *yusho* had died. Of 31 victims whose cause of death was confirmed, 11 of them, or 35.4 percent, had died from neoplasms. "This rate is substantially higher than the 21.1 percent which is the mortality rate from neoplasms in the same prefecture this year," Koda wrote. "However, it would be premature to conclude that this high mortality bears association with PCB poisoning."

Under the Toxic Substances Control Act, which became law in the fall of 1976, PCB sale, manufacture, or use in anything but closed systems in the U.S. was prohibited in 1978, and for all uses in 1979. But this ban, as we noted previously, does not even begin to answer the problem. The federal regulatory agencies are still asleep. There is, for instance, no comprehensive national recovery program for the 758 million pounds of PCBs currently in use. There is no program to deal with the 290 million pounds in dumps and landfills and the 150 million pounds in soils, water, and air. The EPA has even needlessly delayed action it proposed to take months ago under the Toxic Substances Control Act.

A number of agencies are remiss in affording more immediate protection to the public. In 1973 the Food and Drug Administration set temporary tolerances for PCBs in food and food packaging materials. In light of current scientific evidence on the carcinogenicity of PCBs and their effect on nonhuman primates, these action levels must now be considered woefully obsolete. In more recent times the FDA has been reviewing the latest scientific information to determine if the action levels should be revised, and the agency in 1977 put forth the proposal that the action level in fish be reduced from 5 ppm to 2 ppm. No final action on this proposal has been taken. In addition, 2 ppm of PCBs would still be unsafe. Even existing FDA coverage must be considered incomplete. There is, for example, no standard for PCBs in beef, or in water used in food or drug manufacturing.

For several years the EPA has been aware of air pollution problems occurring from the use of PCBs, but to date the agency has taken no action to curtail emissions. Neither has the EPA taken action to set standards with respect to the level of PCBs permissible in human drinking water. Even with the passage of the Toxic Substances Control Act, the EPA continues to lack an aggressive regulatory approach. That is being kind —the EPA has suggested that it *not* regulate the disposal of approximately 150 million pounds of PCBs in small capacitors and light ballasts.

Given the record of government failure and industrial negligence, PCBs are free to poison the environment and human beings for decades to come. A new and vigorous approach to the problem is imperative. After two thousand years it is time we learned a lesson from Ovid: "Ill habits gather by unseen degrees. As brooks make rivers, rivers run to seas."

CHAPTER 4
DRINKING WATER
AND CANCER

The rapidly increasing pollution of many bodies of fresh and salt water with [such] carcinogenic agents and the inabilities of the presently used filtration equipment to remove adequately such contaminants from the drinking water supply has created conditions that may result in serious cancer hazards to the general population.

Drs. Wilhelm Hueper and W. W. Payne,
American Journal of Clinical Pathology, 1963

This warning by the former head of the National Cancer Institute's Environmental Cancer Section and his associate could have been written today. But it was not. It appeared nearly a decade and a half ago, before many persons were concerned about what many state and local officials are fond of characterizing as the "low levels" of carcinogens in drinking water supplies.

A year after Hueper and Payne's warning, a special committee advised the World Health Organization that effective measures were needed to prevent the introduction of carcinogenic industrial wastes into water supplies. In good part, these warnings were triggered by rising concern about the literally thousands of new chemicals synthesized since World War II.

Many of these chemicals have become components of consumer and industrial goods and are discharged widely in industrial waste streams. Yet the vast majority of these chemicals have never been tested for adverse health effects such as cancer. Reports from Scandinavia and Great Britain, dating from the early 1950s, suggested an association between cancer mortality rates and the source of water supplies, but follow-up studies were never conducted. The massive fish kills in the lower Mississippi River, caused by the pesticide endrin, made news in the 1960s, while the concern expressed by Dr. Lucia Dunham, of the National Cancer Institute, that the excessive bladder cancer rates in New Orleans might be caused by carcinogens in the drinking water the city drew from the Mississippi River went largely unnoticed.

Dr. Dunham's worries were stimulated by earlier studies by Dr. Hueper, who had demonstrated that organic extracts taken from Kanawha River drinking water in Nitro, West Virginia, were carcinogenic in laboratory mice. Among 163 metropolitan areas in the U.S. during the years 1959 through 1961, New Orleans had the third highest rate for kidney cancers and the sixth highest rate for cancer of the bladder and urinary tract. The bladder cancer rate, usually low in southern cities, was three times higher in New Orleans than in Atlanta or Birmingham. Indeed, the New Orleans cancer rates for 1959 through 1961 were so embarrassing that city officials afterward refused for years to assist the National Cancer Institute in compiling cancer data.

There were other hot spots. In 1967 Drs. Galen Cook and Frances Watson, at the Cancer Research Center in Columbia, Missouri, observed a clustering of counties with unusually high cancer incidence along the Missouri River. Although Cook and Watson suggested that carcinogens in drinking water drawn from the Missouri might be responsible for the increased rates, they were unable to interest federal or state funding agencies in sponsoring further investigations. Similarly, Dr. William H. Brooks, of the University of Kentucky Medical School, was unsuccessful in attracting support to investigate why there was an excess of brain tumors along major tributaries of the polluted Kentucky and Licking rivers in Kentucky.

Despite these ominous indications, and even though discharge rates were growing exponentially, little progress was made toward understanding the implications of industrial discharges of toxic and carcinogenic chemicals into water. Pollution abatement efforts in the United States continued to focus exclusively on the treatment of traditional pollutants, such as disease-causing microorganisms in human sewage and the oxygen-consuming substances in the wastes from pulp and paper mills, dairies, canneries, and other industries. The aim of water purification efforts was to lower bacteria counts and quantities of organic material and suspended solids in order to prevent infectious waterborne diseases and to allow fish and other aquatic life to thrive. Completely ignored were such synthetic chemicals as carbon tetrachloride, vinyl chloride, PCBs, and the hundreds of other by-products of the chemical and petrochemical industries that mushroomed after World War II. Traditional waste treatment plants and water purification facilities were not designed to remove these new pollutants. Indeed, politicians, engineers, and most public health authorities ignored the menace posed by chemicals, even though they were expending enormous sums of public funds on the construction of sewage treatment plants that had no facilities whatever for the removal of synthetic chemicals.

Moreover, little or no effort was made to prevent, monitor, or even note the discharge of toxic chemicals; so these poisons were free to disrupt aquatic food webs, accumulate in fish, birds, and wildlife, or end up as a chemical alphabet soup in a glass of drinking water or the morning cup of coffee of citizens who mistakenly believed their drinking water had been purified. Scandalously neglected, nearly seven hundred industrial and agricultural chemicals have so far been identified and continue to be present in drinking water across the country.

By the mid-1960s signs of this chemical pollution were causing increased complaints from citizens along the lower Mississippi River in Louisiana. Fishermen reported they were unable to sell their catch because of an off-taste in the fish, and people who drank the foul-smelling and foul-tasting water were driven to bottled water in increasing numbers. As a result the Federal Water Pollution Control Administration, which later became part of the Environmental Protection Agency, in 1967 initiated a monitoring study to investigate the presence of chemicals in industrial effluents in the Mississippi—and, by extension, in the drinking water served to more than one million Louisianians. This number included residents of New Orleans, who depend entirely upon the river as a water supply.

The Mississippi drains nearly 40 percent of the agricultural, urban, and industrial lands in the U.S. Mark Twain accurately called it the "colon of America." No less than fifty of the nation's largest chemical and petrochemical manufacturing and process plants spew their wastes into the 130-mile stretch of the river between Baton Rouge and New Orleans alone.

Not until 1972 did the EPA issue its report on the results of the monitoring study. Citing data that indicated that three of the chemicals identified in the drinking water—chloroform, benzene, and bis(2-chloroethyl)ether—were carcinogens, the EPA concluded, "The trace organics in the Mississippi River drinking water supplies are a potential threat to the health of 1.5 million people who consume this water, particularly the elderly, those who are ill, and children."

Newspapers and television focused attention on the EPA findings. Surprised at the furor, EPA officials joined with New Orleans authorities to calm public fears by declaring that the problem was not as serious as it appeared and that an ongoing pollution abatement program would take care of whatever problem there was. Besides, they argued, the chemicals were present in such low concentrations that the public had nothing to fear.

In point of fact the EPA was then—and still is—doing a poor job of controlling and limiting toxic chemicals, even though the agency received specific authority to act under the Federal Water Pollution Control Act (FWPCA) Amendments passed by Congress in 1972. One of six goals of the FWPCA states, "It is the national policy that the discharge of toxic pollutants in toxic amounts be prohibited."

Section 307 of the 1972 act specifically instructed the EPA administrator to promulgate within one year of passage a list of toxic pollutants for which strict effluent limitations were necessary to protect the environment and public health. At that time nearly thirty thousand industrial chemicals were in use, more than fifteen hundred of them suspected carcinogens. Nevertheless, the EPA's initial list of toxic pollutants requiring stringent regulations consisted of only nine compounds: four pesticides, two heavy metals, and two organic and one inorganic industrial contaminant. Because of the brevity of the list and the apparently arbitrary manner in which the handful of chemicals included were selected, two national environmental organizations filed suit against the EPA, challenging that the list was obviously—and dangerously—inadequate.

While the suit was pending, the EPA held hearings on the effluent standards proposed for the nine compounds. In the end, however, the agency never promulgated the standards in final form, even though the statute required issuance of final effluent standards for toxic pollutants six months after proposal. As a result of this failure the environmentalists sued again, this time asking the court to require the agency to set effluent discharge standards for at least the original nine compounds. Two other lawsuits were filed as well, and the upshot of all the suits was a consent agreement, signed by the agency in 1976, in which it agreed to commit its resources to a broad-scale program aimed at figuring out how best to regulate the discharge of sixty-five priority industrial chemicals or chemical classes by twenty-one major industrial categories on a phased schedule ending in 1983. In addition the EPA agreed to set numerical toxic effluent discharge standards for six of the original nine compounds by 1977.

Now, for the first time, the EPA is systematically canvassing plants all over the country in twenty-one industrial categories in order to find out just what toxic chemicals are in their waste water. Such information is basic, yet it was never before available, except in some cases by accident—usually unfortunate accident. For example, in 1972 the EPA laboratory in Evansville, Indiana, tested the city's drinking water, which is drawn from the Ohio River. The tests showed the presence of numerous industrial chemicals, including relatively high concentrations of the carcinogen bis(2-chloroethyl)ether (BCEE). The EPA traced the pollutant to the Olin Chemical Company, nearly 150 miles upstream, in Ohio. EPA studies showed that BCEE was practically unaffected by the so-called natural assimilative capacity of the river, so that the chemical was passing down the stream to Evansville. The EPA required the company to install treatment devices designed to remove BCEE from its discharge.

In 1975 the EPA discovered the highest concentrations of BCEE ever measured in drinking water, in samples taken in Philadelphia. In this case the BCEE originated at the Rohm and Haas Company, in Bridesburg, Pennsylvania, which discharged its waste water laden with chemicals into the local municipal sewage system. Along with the rest of the sewage the waste water containing BCEE was put through the standard purification treatment, which takes care of bacteria but is largely ineffective for the removal of organic chemicals, and was then discharged from the plant into the Delaware River approximately five miles downstream from the Philadelphia water supply intakes. However, the Delaware is at this point an estuary, and at high tides BCEE was carried back *upstream* over the five-mile distance to the water supply intakes. The regional EPA administrator challenged Rohm and Haas and obtained a compliance schedule for abatement of the offending discharge.

These two cases were exceptional. In both instances the EPA's discovery of the contamination had nothing at all to do with regulation of the culpable industries under the Federal Water Pollution Control Act.

In the summer of 1974 the furor over the quality of the New Orleans water supply erupted anew with the appearance of the first of three articles on drinking water in *Consumer*

Reports. The articles charged that New Orleans officials were ignoring a potentially serious cancer threat. Dr. Robert H. Harris and Edward M. Brecher, who wrote the articles, noted that treatment equipment could easily be installed to reduce the levels of virtually all carcinogens and other toxic chemicals from the drinking water. The process involved installing a bed of activated carbon granules in the municipal water plant.*

But it was the same old story in New Orleans. Again EPA and city officials reacted as they had in 1972. Stuart Brehm, executive director of the New Orleans Sewerage and Water Board, denied that there was any problem. He alleged that a resident would have to drink three hundred thousand gallons of water to produce one tumor. Dr. Doris Thompson, the head of New Orleans' health department, who had previously enjoyed a reputation as an aggressive public health officer, charged Consumers Union with scare tactics and issued pronouncements reassuring the public that the water was perfectly safe to drink. Arthur Bush, administrator of EPA's Region 6 office in Dallas, issued a press release urging the public to stay calm, since there was no threat of an "imminent" hazard. One by one, city, state, and federal officials attacked the *Consumer Reports* articles as irresponsible, alarmist, and self-serving. As public pressure mounted, Stuart Brehm called for a new EPA study, charging that the 1972 report was outdated because pollution had been substantially abated by the industries whose discharges were most egregious. So the EPA complied and began work on a new study.

---

* The purification properties of carbon have been known for centuries. As M. N. Baker notes in *The Quest for Pure Water,* an ancient Indian wrote in Sanskrit around 2000 B.C., "It is good to keep water in copper vessels, to expose it to sunlight, and filter through charcoal." During the eighteenth century sea captains stored water in charred barrels to minimize contamination.

Activated carbon is a porous form of carbon that offers an enormous surface area that can adsorb contaminants. A handful of activated carbon has a surface area totaling about one acre. It has distinctive chemical surface properties, including carboxyl, hydroxyl, and other oxygen-containing chemical groups that help bind chemicals to the carbon. The very chemicals that are most insoluble in water, such as DDT and PCBs, are adsorbed most readily. There is no absolute guarantee that filtration through activated carbon granules will remove *all* pollutants, but it is by far the best water purification technology available.

Accustomed to the political chicanery associated with the drinking water issue in New Orleans, James Moreau, a retired Marine Corps officer who had been elected to the city council, requested that the Environmental Defense Fund prepare a report outlining the nature of the problem and recommendations for remedial action. The EDF began work on its report, drawing upon a study just completed by the National Cancer Institute, *U.S. Cancer Mortality by County: 1950–1969.* With the assistance of Dr. Talbot Page, of Resources for the Future, Inc., a Washington-based research group, the EDF conducted an epidemiological study of Louisiana residents using a statistical technique known as multivariate regression analysis. This technique permits consideration of several factors simultaneously, such as water, diet, and occupation, that may influence cancer rates.

On November 6, 1974, the EDF released its study, which showed a strong and statistically significant association between drinking water from the Mississippi River and cancer mortality rates at certain body sites, particularly of the gastrointestinal and urinary tract organs, in New Orleans residents and other residents in the eleven parishes that received drinking water from the Mississippi. The following day, November 7, the EPA held a press conference at which the results of *its* new analytical study of New Orleans' drinking water were released. To the great chagrin of city officials, not only did the EPA's new analysis confirm the presence of a potpourri of industrial contaminants, but by using improved analytical procedures it identified nearly twice as many chemicals as had been reported in the 1972 study. Despite Regional Administrator Bush's edict that the EPA scientists involved in the press conference reveal no more than the names of the chemicals found, the scientists, Leland McCabe and Dr. Robert Tardiff, discussed the toxicity and carcinogenicity of the chemicals. They also discussed New Orleans' high cancer rates.

With national press coverage of the disclosures in New Orleans the stage was at last set for action in Congress. The Safe Drinking Water Act had been languishing there for four years.

After all, New Orleans was not the only city in the U.S. taking drinking water from a river heavily polluted by upriver municipalities and industry.

Congressman Howard Robison of New York had introduced the act on September 23, 1970. Originally he was motivated not by the presence of carcinogens or other chemicals in the drinking water but by a Public Health Service community water supply study released earlier that year. This study documented widespread deterioration in the ability of state and local water supply agencies to monitor, treat, and deliver water to the public that was free of the threat of infectious disease.

Although Robison's effort was the first in Congress to address the problems of drinking water in this century, the legislation floundered for the next three years, with little support from the Nixon and Ford administrations. Two of its opponents, Representatives James Hastings of New York and David Satterfield of Virginia, based their arguments on states' rights, contending that the protection of citizens against contaminated drinking water had always been the states' concern, and they could see no reason to change things now. Hastings, who spoke only of the costs and not the benefits, put it this way during the House debate: "I can say that what we probably will find is that after the renewal of this legislation three years down the road, every time we open up a water tap in every house in the United States of America, we will find an EPA inspector coming out of that water tap."

On the other side of the issue was one of the most effective advocates for passage of a Safe Drinking Water Act, Ralph Nader. Indeed, it is unlikely that the act would have emerged from Congress in its present form had it not been for Nader. Nader's influence is often subtle, and in this instance he was able to quash a nearly successful effort to gut the bill while it was still in Congressman Paul Rogers's Health Subcommittee of the House Foreign and Interstate Commerce Committee. With most liberal members of the subcommittee absent from a late afternoon meeting, Hastings and Satterfield forced Chairman Rogers to order the subcommittee staff to redraft the bill completely and to strike all federal enforcement responsibility. Nader spent the following morning and early afternoon calling each member of the subcommittee who had previously supported or been sympathetic to the bill. He urged them to attend the afternoon subcommittee meeting and to support Rogers in his effort to thwart Satterfield's and Hastings's efforts. With Nader in attendance "glaring" at the subcommittee, as one observer described it, Rogers confidently called for a vote, and the original bill emerged unscathed from the subcommittee, to be considered by the full Commerce Committee.

By the time the bill found its way out of the Commerce Committee, it was late in the final session of the Ninety-third Congress. Many believe that the Safe Drinking Water Act would never have surfaced from the legislative logjam had it not been for the EPA and EDF revelations in New Orleans. Furthermore, there was some indication that President Ford might veto the bill if it ever arrived at his desk. With the attention that New Orleans was getting, however, coupled with the airing of a CBS-TV special, "Caution: Drinking Water May Be Hazardous to Your Health," Ford quietly signed the Safe Drinking Water Act on December 14, 1974.

Among other things, the Safe Drinking Water Act (SDWA) authorizes the EPA to regulate carcinogens in drinking water. In most other environmental statutes Congress has told the EPA to set numerical standards for individual contaminants based on health criteria, but in the SDWA Congress provided a more careful, thoughtful, and responsive regulatory strategy for carcinogens. This was done by recognizing two important features of the problem of regulating carcinogens that make standard setting difficult. First of all, there is no known way to determine a safe level of exposure to a carcinogen. Second, drinking water treatment plants cannot monitor for most carcinogens because they lack the requisite sophisticated instrumentation. To overcome these problems, Congress gave the EPA both traditional numerical standard-setting authority as well as the additional flexibility to regulate carcinogens by requiring water treatment plants to use the best available treatment technique. As a result the EPA could require a water treatment plant with carcinogens in the source water either to meet a numerical "maximum contaminant level" for the carcinogens or to install or use specified treatment methods if monitoring were not feasible. Congress also requested that the EPA conduct a broad survey on carcinogens in drinking water and that the agency report annually on progress in implementing the statute.

After the EPA and EDF studies on New Orleans drinking water were released, EPA Administrator Russell Train ordered a nationwide study of potentially toxic organic chemicals in drinking water. Known as the National Organic Reconnaissance Survey, the study was to investigate two major areas. First and most obvious was the contribution from municipalities, industries, agricultural runoff, and transportation accidents—all traditional sources of pollution—to the burden of carcinogens in drinking water. The second objective was to determine the extent to which chlorination in drinking water treatment plants contributed to the production of carcinogens in the finished water. During studies at the EPA Cincinnati laboratories, scientists somewhat by accident discovered that several chlorinated organics, notably chloroform, increased dramatically in concentration from the beginning to the end of the drinking water treatment process. Chloroform is a known carcinogen. These observations confirmed studies by scientists in the Netherlands, published a few months earlier, that suggested that chlorination of drinking water produces chloroform and possibly several other chlorinated and brominated organic compounds. Although scientists for decades had studied the interaction between chlorine and naturally occurring organic chemicals, these were the first studies to demonstrate that relatively high concentrations of chloroform and other potentially carcinogenic chemicals were being produced *inside* water treatment plants.

As part of the National Organic Reconnaissance Survey the EPA analyzed the drinking water in eighty cities. These cities represented a diverse sampling. Some drew drinking water from relatively clean sources, while others drew from moderately to heavily polluted supplies. Some cities relied on surface water, others on ground water. There was, in all, a mixture of large, intermediate, and small communities employing various treatment processes, ranging from the barest treatment to the most sophisticated by today's standards. In all eighty cities, the EPA ran tests for six pollutants—three bromine-containing compounds (bromodichloromethane, dibromochloromethane, and bromoform) plus chloroform, carbon tetrachloride, and 1,2-dichloroethane—thought to be produced by the chlorination process.

Chloroform was found in the drinking water of all eighty cities. The three compounds containing bromine—which appeared to be produced by the interaction of chlorine, bromide, and organic chemicals present in the raw water—were found in the tap water of most cities. Although mutagenic, they have yet to be tested for carcinogenicity. Carbon tetrachloride, a common ingredient in cleaning fluid, and 1,2-dichloroethane, used in the manufacture of vinyl chloride, apparently originate mainly from industrial sources and not the chlorination process. Carbon tetrachloride was in the water of ten cities, and 1,2-dichloroethane was in the water of twenty-six.

The EPA also conducted a very comprehensive analysis of the chemical content of the drinking water of ten of the eighty municipalities—Miami; Philadelphia; Cincinnati; New York; Lawrence, Massachusetts; Seattle; Ottumwa, Iowa; Tucson; Grand Forks, North Dakota; and Terrebonne Parish, Louisiana. This analysis identified a total of 129 organic chemicals. At the time fewer than a dozen of these 129 chemicals had been adequately tested for carcinogenicity. More recently a report by the National Academy of Sciences identified 22 of the 129 chemicals as known or suspected carcinogens. These results made it alarmingly clear that the contamination of drinking water by organic carcinogens and other potentially toxic chemicals was widespread and extensive throughout the United States.

In passing the Safe Drinking Water Act, Congress could not have put stronger emphasis on the need to reduce carcinogens in drinking water. Yet the EPA ignored that emphasis. In its first set of standards, published in December 1975, the EPA set maximum contaminant levels for various pollutants, but with the exception of a small number of pesticides and herbicides, no organic chemicals—and no carcinogens—were included on the list. Because of this failure the EDF sued the EPA as soon as the interim standards were published.

Instead of acknowledging the hazards of organic chemicals in drinking water, the EPA in 1975 embarked on yet another nationwide survey, this one including 112 cities. The idea of still another survey by the EPA aroused the ire of Gordon Robeck, director of the EPA's Water Supply Research Division, who voiced his frustration before the National Drinking Water Advisory Council: "I personally am getting a little tired of just constantly analyzing instead of getting on with the changes. Every time that we have done a few samples, somebody says, 'That is statistically weak. You had better do 100 more.' I have yet to find a case where it has really been measurably different from what we predicted in the first place."

It is likely that only about 10 percent of the organic chemicals contaminating drinking water in the U.S. have yet been identified. For instance, several important classes of known potent chemical carcinogens were not identified in the 1974 EPA report on New Orleans or in the National Organic Reconnaissance Survey simply because the analytical techniques required were not developed. Two of these classes are nitrosamines and polynuclear aromatic hydrocarbons. Monitoring for carcinogenic nitrosamines has been the subject of recent research by Dr. David Fine, of Thermo Electron Company in Waltham, Massachusetts, who has developed a sensitive new technique. Fine's studies indicated that drinking water in Philadelphia, Washington, and New Orleans contained concentrations of nitrosamines that may represent a far greater source of contamination than those found in nitrated and nitrited processed meats (see chapter 7).

Similarly, several polynuclear aromatic hydrocarbons (PAHs) were included in the more recent 112-city survey, and their presence appears to be ubiquitous in drinking water obtained from polluted sources. Indeed, studies over the past decade in Western Europe had led to the inclusion of several carcinogenic PAHs in the 1971 international drinking water standards issued by the World Health Organization. PAHs arise from the combustion processes used in fossil-fueled power plants, refineries, and automobiles. Dr. Ronald A. Hites, of the Massachusetts Institute of Technology, who has found PAHs in the Charles River in Boston, writes, "In this case, automobile exhaust condensate which is washed from the streets directly into the river by rainfall is the most likely immediate source." The Canadian Wildlife Service has discovered some thirty different PAHs in the fat of herring gulls from Lake Ontario, with residues measuring from 10 to 150 parts per million, truly elevated levels. In 1977 EPA scientists at the Environmental Research Laboratory in Duluth reported finding "comparatively large concentrations of saturated and unsaturated hydrocarbons" in fish taken from major watersheds in the U.S. The hydrocarbons appeared to be derived from crankcase and fuel oil mixtures. In a note of urgency the EPA scientists wrote that "the highest priority in methodology development will be given to the isolation, identification, and quantitation of the polynuclear aromatic components of these residues."

Levels of PAHs or other chemical carcinogens in fish and birds are usually measured in the parts-per-million range because these animals have the capacity to retain and concentrate them in their body fats. In drinking water, concentrations are usually measured in the parts-per-billion range. Parts-per-billion measurements are often described as "low levels," but carcinogens have been known to cause cancer in extremely low concentrations, in some cases in the parts-per-trillion range. Unfortunately many municipal water officials seem incapable of understanding this. Thus in 1975, when the carcinogen bis(2-chloroethyl)ether was found in Philadelphia drinking water in the 0.4 to 0.5 parts-per-billion range, Carmen F. Guarino, the water commissioner, discounted the risk by saying, "It's like the width of your finger compared to the distance from Philadelphia to San Francisco." Guarino assured Philadelphians, "There is nothing wrong with the water. It's safe. And it meets all the standards that we know of." In the same vein, leaders of the American Water Works Association made light of the threat posed by toxic substances ("The era of Chicken Little appears to be upon us") and ridiculed the credibility of concerned scientists ("our current crop of super-sophisticated hypochondriacs").

Several approaches exist for estimating the level of risk for millions of Americans from exposure to carcinogens in drinking water. Leland McCabe, of the EPA, has had promising results using the Ames test for mutagenicity. McCabe extracted organic chemicals from the drinking water used in seven U.S. cities, tested the extracts by the Ames method, and compared the relative mutagenicity among these cities, as shown in Table 2. Thus, Miami's rating of 80 indicated that there were four

TABLE 2	
City	Relative Mutagenic Activity
Miami	80
Philadelphia	60
New Orleans	16
Cincinnati	20
Ottumwa, Iowa	3
Seattle	22
Tucson	1

times as many mutants per milligram of organic extract as there were for Cincinnati, which rated 20 in the test. These results proved to be consistent with scientific tests done to determine the level of chemical contaminants present in the drinking water of various cities. In other words, the greater the mutagenic activity, the more likely the presence of carcinogenic chemicals. Tucson, with its deep, protected wells, has relatively clean water with few contaminants. Miami, which also has well water, is heavily polluted.

Indeed, Miami's drinking water has the dubious honor of being the most heavily contaminated of any city so far tested by the EPA. In chloroform concentration alone, Miami had

311 parts per billion, the highest concentration found in EPA's eighty-city nationwide survey. Based on this chloroform concentration, an EPA study group concluded, "The level of risk . . . might be extrapolated to account for up to 40 percent of the observed liver cancer incidence rate." In addition, the study group suggested that, in the case of chloroform, other types of chronic diseases (for instance, cirrhosis) might be of equal or greater concern than possible cancer production.

After the EDF released its study on New Orleans drinking water and that city's cancer incidence, other researchers began epidemiological studies. All told, twelve epidemiological studies conducted by independent scientists have found a significant association between pollutants in drinking water and cancer mortality rates. Dr. Ralph Buncher, of the University of Cincinnati, investigated counties in Ohio and Kentucky bordering the Ohio River and found that white females in those counties who drank Ohio River water had significantly more cancers than white females who drank water from other sources. For white males the statistical results were borderline, although the cancer rates were higher in those counties that received water from the Ohio River.

During an international conference in 1976 on the origins of human cancer at the Cold Spring Harbor Laboratory in New York, both Dr. Buncher and Dr. Robert Harris presented the results of further studies in Ohio that confirmed the previously observed patterns of association in Louisiana between elevated cancer mortality rates and drinking water. In both the Ohio and Louisiana studies gastrointestinal and urinary cancers appear prominently. These studies made no effort to identify the chemicals that might be responsible for the cancers, but other scientists have investigated the effect of chlorination and the resultant production of carcinogens on cancer rates. Leland McCabe, of EPA's Cincinnati laboratory, found a statistically significant correlation between the chloroform concentration in drinking water and the age-sex-race-adjusted cancer mortality rate by city in the EPA eighty-city survey for all cancers combined. Another study by Buncher confirmed McCabe's findings.

Buncher found a similar correlation between the chloroform concentration in twenty-three cities with a population of twenty-five thousand or more in 1970 and the total cancer mortality rate for white males. Buncher also reported a statistically significant correlation between chloroform concentration in seventy-seven cities with available data and pancreatic cancer death rates for white males.

Using somewhat more sophisticated epidemiological techniques, Dr. Michael Hogan, at the National Institute of Environmental Health Sciences, and Dr. Kenneth Cantor, of the National Cancer Institute, separately investigated the direct effect of chlorination on cancer rates. The results of both studies suggest that chloroform concentrations of approximately 100 parts per billion would cause about 30 percent more bladder cancers than the expected number and 4 to 6 percent more cancers of the colon and rectum.

Dr. Nancy Reiches, director of the Division of Epidemiology at Ohio State University's Comprehensive Cancer Center, studied cancer mortality and chlorinated water sources in two hundred counties across the United States, including such major cities as Minneapolis, Milwaukee, Chicago, Cleveland, Washington, New York, and Boston. She discovered increased fatality rates for cancers of the bladder and colon, especially in persons over sixty years of age. Reiches also found that among persons using chlorinated water, women suffered from fatal bladder cancer more often than men. Ordinarily men are more exposed to the threat of bladder cancer by carcinogens in the workplace and in cigarette smoke.

In another study Reiches compared cancer mortalities in two populations of Ohioans. One population was composed of the people who get their drinking water predominantly from either the Ohio River or Lake Erie, both heavily polluted. The second population consisted of one million other Ohioans whose water comes from the less polluted Scioto River. The study showed that Ohioans who got their water from the Ohio River and Lake Erie suffered 8 percent higher cancer mortality rates.

Dr. Joyce Salg, of the Department of Epidemiology at the

University of North Carolina, studied National Cancer Institute county mortality data for a population of 18.7 million people in 346 counties in the Ohio River Valley reaching from Pennsylvania to Illinois. Salg found increased rates primarily for cancers of the bladder, colon, rectum, and larynx, and for lymphosarcoma and reticulosarcoma. She also found increased rates, though to a lesser degree, for cancers of the esophagus, trachea, bronchus, and lung.

The EPA commissioned Dr. Michael Alavanja, of the Columbia University School of Public Health, to study cancer mortalities in Allegany, Cattaraugus, Chautauqua, Erie, Rensselaer, Schenectady, and St. Lawrence counties in upstate New York. These seven counties were chosen because they had stable populations and the same water supply systems for fifteen years. All male and female gastrointestinal and urinary tract cancer deaths occurring in the area between 1968 and 1970— some 3,446 cases—were matched with an equal number of non-cancer deaths. For both males and females combined, there were 170 percent more deaths from gastro-intestinal and urinary tract cancer in urban chlorinated areas than there were in urban non-chlorinated areas. Vis-à-vis rural chlorinated areas, the excess was 77 percent. When counties were analyzed separately, the effect of chlorination was not demonstrable in the three largest counties: Erie, Rensselaer, and Schenectady. These results suggest that the chlorination of drinking water may be responsible for more than 300 excess cancer deaths per million population per year in urban areas. The importance of Alavanja's study was that it used "case/control" methods— epidemiological techniques generally considered more precise than the methods used in the previous studies.

Whatever the actual impact carcinogens in drinking water have on cancer rates, it is apparent that most drinking water plants in the United States provide *no* protection against the hazard. No drinking water treatment plant in this country is currently utilizing activated carbon to reduce the level of organic contaminants in drinking water, even though, as the EPA noted in its 1975 report to Congress, "Thus far, the best method for removing environmental contaminants such as carbon tetrachloride, dieldrin and haloethers [all carcinogens] from raw water is the use of beds of granular activated carbon [GAC]." About forty plants do use GAC for taste and odor control. Moreover, the cost is modest. According to a recent estimate the addition of activated carbon granules for treatment plants serving a population of 75,000 to one million would cost a family of three only seven to sixteen dollars a year. It is ironic that in Europe, where American travelers are often told not to drink the water, about twenty communities have already installed activated carbon filters to remove carcinogenic chemicals from polluted river water supplies.

To start to remedy this deficiency and to abate the hazards posed by organic contaminants, the EPA in early 1978 proposed regulations establishing a maximum contaminant level of 100 ppb for trihalomethanes (the products of chlorination) in drinking water. In addition, communities with significant levels of synthetic organics in their source water will be required to install activated carbon filters. Although this represents a 180-degree turnabout by the EPA on the need to control organics in drinking water, the regulations apply only to water systems serving seventy-five thousand customers or more, which covers only 52 percent of the population. Thus half of the population will remain totally unprotected. For those covered by the regulations, the risks of cancer that remain are quite sizable. The EPA estimates that from the 100 ppb of trihalomethanes alone, a lifelong exposure may account for at least two hundred excess cancer fatalities per year nationwide. Other estimates range to over 3,000 cancer fatalities per year.

The EPA's proposal to require municipal drinking-water treatment plants to install activated carbon filters wherever significant concentrations of synthetic organic contaminants have been consistently measured has been bitterly opposed by the water supply industry. Under the leadership of the American Water Works Association (AWWA), an organization of public and private water supply officials and operators who also fought passage of the Safe Drinking Water Act, a campaign of strong opposition to any change in existing water treatment practice has been launched. The AWWA has vocally disparaged the evidence of cancer risk posed by organics in drinking water and has raised questions about the cost, efficacy, and need for activated carbon filters.

By contrast, the EPA's proposal has received wide support from other governmental agencies, including the National Institute of Environmental Health Sciences, the Food and Drug Administration, the Occupational Safety and Health Administration, and the National Cancer Institute. In fact, in a letter to the Administrator of the EPA, Dr. Arthur Upton, director of the NCI, supported EPA's judgment that carcinogens in drinking water "present a potential risk of cancer that should be reduced to the extent feasible."

Whatever the outcome of the controversy, communities affected by the regulations will have at least five years after promulgation to fund and install the necessary treatment technology. Because of this delay, as well as several years' publicity about the dangers of organics in drinking water, millions of Americans have been turning to home water filters and bottled water as alternatives to the questionable drinking water supplied locally. At the present time the combined home-water-filter and bottled-water markets account for several hundred million dollars in annual sales, and growth rates of 50 percent per year or more are predicted for the next decade. The ability of commercially made home filters to remove organic chemicals from tap water is highly questionable, primarily because of the small amount of carbon utilized and the extremely brief time that the water is in contact with the carbon. Similarly, the quality of bottled water varies dramatically and is not monitored vigorously by the FDA. As a result the public is paying an increasingly large amount of money every year for drinking water that may be no safer than the admittedly dubious municipal supply.

CHAPTER 5
AIRBORNE CARCINOGENS

The air in the New-Netherlands is so dry, sweet and healthy, that we need not wish that it were otherwise. In purity, agreeableness, and fineness, it would be folly to seek for an example of it in any other country.
Adriaen Van der Donck,
A Description of the New Netherlands, 1656

Driving north through New Jersey toward Newark on U.S. 1, the change in the air is dramatic. As one leaves the rolling fields of Princeton, the air still smells about as sweet as it did to Van der Donck over three hundred years ago. Although the sod farms are gradually giving way to housing developments, there is still no hint of what lies ahead. As the car approaches New Brunswick, however, one begins to detect a pungent odor, like that of rotting fruit. At first the odor is faint, but as the car swings onto the New Jersey Turnpike, the smell grows stronger. It is unsettling because the fields are still open and there is no visible source.

The miles tick by, and the smell becomes almost overpowering. Closing the windows does no good; the stench pours through the vents. The sky becomes visibly darker, like the twilight or an eclipse of the sun. At last, on the right, almost opposite Newark Airport, the source comes into view. It is perhaps the largest complex of oil refineries and petrochemical plants in existence. Cracking towers mixed with innumerable other processing facilities dominate the skyline. At night the flares atop the refineries produce an eerie light that transforms the scene into something from Dante's *Inferno*. Yet there are no belching smokestacks. The stench seems to come from nowhere in particular. It is simply all-pervasive.

For the auto passenger eventually there is relief. As the car approaches New York, the smell is replaced by that of more familiar pollutants—auto exhaust and sulfur dioxide. But for thousands of people who live in this area, there is no escape. They breathe the air twenty-four hours a day, seven days a week.

Fourteen thousand people die each year from cancer in New Jersey. Twenty-four thousand new cases are discovered each year. Among U.S. males New Jersey has the highest rate of bladder cancer, the second highest rate of cancer of the rectum and large intestine, and the third highest rate of stomach and lung cancers. What percentage of these cases is caused by air pollution? No one knows for sure, but the interim report of the New Jersey State Senate Incidence of Cancer Commission concludes that "despite conflicting testimony . . . air contamination by carcinogens is a primary cause of many types of cancer."

Supporting this conclusion are the results of a number of scientific studies over the past twenty-five years that have established a link between air pollution and cancer. Air pollution is now generally accepted as a source of carcinogenic substances, particularly in densely developed urban-industrial regions. Dr. Michael Greenberg, of Rutgers University, who has studied risk factors responsible for cancer deaths in the New Jersey–New York–Philadelphia metropolitan regions, concludes that the weight of evidence suggests that "a large proportion" of the excess lung cancer deaths in the urban areas and "a smaller proportion of digestive and urinary cancers in the United States" are associated with air quality. As more chemical carcinogens are discovered in urban environments and further epidemiological studies of people living in the vicinity of industrial and mobile sources of air pollution are completed, more and more cancer is likely to be attributed to air pollution.

Dramatic evidence on this point is provided by cancer incidence data from Staten Island, New York. Statistics compiled by the Health Services Administration of New York indicate that although residents of Staten Island show favorable health status patterns in most areas, they have a higher age-adjusted rate of lung cancer than the rest of New York City. Moreover, the incidence of lung cancer is not uniform. On the north end of the island, opposite New Jersey, separated from the Elizabeth–Bayonne industrial complex only by a narrow waterway, mortality from malignant neoplasms of the respiratory system is significantly higher than in the central and southern regions of the island. The fact that this difference is significant for women as well as men strongly supports the premise that polluted air from the neighboring New Jersey industrial complex is in part responsible for the differing respiratory cancer rates observed.

Nationwide, almost twice as many people die from lung cancer in cities as do those in rural areas. City air contains many more carcinogens than the air in rural areas. Within cities themselves the incidence of cancer is greater where more general industrial pollution is present.

Other comparisons can be made. The annual death rate for lung cancer in parts of England and Wales, where industrial concentration is high, is more than twice that of the United States and four times that of Norway. In a recent paper entitled "Chemical Carcinogens" Dietrich Hoffman and Ernst L. Wynder discuss air pollution and note, "Immigrants to the U.S. settle predominantly in cities and have shown striking alterations in their likelihood of developing cancer. The changes were always in the direction of the U.S. incidence rates. For instance, immigrants from England and Wales exhibit a decrease of lung cancer incidence more nearly approximating the lower U.S. level."

None of this *proves* that airborne carcinogens are the cause of elevated cancer rates, but the available evidence, however circumstantial, is so compelling that it is difficult to dismiss the elevated rates as due to random chance.

Under the Clean Air Act Amendments of 1970 the Environmental Protection Agency has the authority to limit or eliminate air pollutants that threaten the public health. But not until six years after the law was passed did the EPA even begin to investigate the contamination of air by carcinogens.

In 1976 the EPA commissioned the Mitre Corporation to study some six hundred potentially hazardous organic compounds emitted into the air by a variety of industrial processes. The Mitre study revealed that there were hundreds of organic compounds entering the atmosphere. Total emissions from all industrial sources probably exceeded 11.35 million tons a year, but no one really had any information on the health hazards posed by these compounds. As a result of the Mitre study the EPA and various state air pollution control agencies began sampling programs to gain further information about emissions, and the findings thus far are startling.

Air samples taken around a Union Carbide plant in South Charleston, West Virginia, revealed the presence of more than one hundred different organic vapors, including such known or suspected carcinogens as benzene, toluene, carbon tetrachloride, and acetaldehyde. Other samples taken from chemical plants in the Kanawha Valley of West Virginia have uncovered a host of other toxic organic vapors, including ammonia, chloroform, formaldehyde, methylene dianiline, morpholine, polyvinyl chloride, propylene oxide, and trichloroethylene. In addition, amine emissions from these plants are suspected of contributing to the formation of carcinogenic nitrosamines.

Similar findings have been made in parts of New Jersey and Texas. In a recent case in northeastern Maryland, Dr. Peter Capurro, a pathologist and hospital laboratory director, found toluene, benzene, carbon tetrachloride, and methyl ethyl ketone, and traced them to a local chemical company whose emissions were contaminating the air of Little Elk Valley. Even though the cancer death rate for valley residents was "about five times higher than it should have been," the EPA did not begin to investigate until five years after Dr. Capurro first sounded the alarm.

Why has it taken so long for the EPA to recognize the hazards of low-level carcinogenic air pollutants? The answer is that the agency simply failed to acknowledge the risk of cancer associated with exposure to "low levels" of carcinogens. Even today, while not disputing the fact that no safe level of exposure to any carcinogen has been demonstrated, the EPA's regulation of such hazardous air pollutants remains woefully inadequate.

Unlike other air pollutants, carcinogens are dangerous at very low levels. As early as the 1950s scientists knew, for example, that asbestos had caused mesothelioma and lung cancer in workers exposed to the dust, and studies of South African miners revealed that even a single exposure could produce cancer twenty or fifty years later. It was also known that asbestos could be released into air from sources other than mining. It can be shredded from automobile brake linings and rise in the dust from demolition activities. Asbestos is to be found nearly everywhere. It has been used in insulation and other building materials, in paints, floor tiles, cement, shingles, spackling compounds, and fabrics. Asbestos is ubiquitous in the urban environment. It is in the lungs of residents of cities everywhere in the country. Nevertheless, the government dismissed the threat of asbestos to the general public because it assumed that levels in the air were simply too low to produce cancer in those who were not also occupationally exposed.

The breakthrough in understanding that this was not true came as a result of research conducted by Muriel Newhouse and Hilda Thompson in the London School of Hygiene and Tropical Medicine in 1965. Rather than look for cases of mesothelioma among those exposed to asbestos, this pair of British researchers started with victims of mesothelioma and worked backward to determine the cause. They were able to obtain good histories for seventy-six of eighty-three cases. Predictably, a large number of the cases could be traced to occupational exposure to asbestos. However—and this is most important—they identified eleven victims of mesothelioma who had apparently had no occupational or domestic exposure. *Each of these victims had lived within half a mile of an asbestos factory.*

The findings of Newhouse and Thompson forced a reexamination of all assumptions regarding airborne emissions of carcinogenic substances. Regulators could no longer dismiss "low level" exposures to carcinogens in the ambient air.

At the same time scientists were discovering that naturally occurring substances such as asbestos could cause cancer at low levels, other researchers were beginning to worry about the threat posed by the "new" synthetic organic chemicals, which had been introduced largely since World War II.

Under the section of the Clean Air Act that enables the EPA to limit or eliminate sources of hazardous air pollutants is the provision that any action not only result in adequate protection of the public but, more stringently, guarantee an "ample margin of safety." Within the EPA no one could define "ample margin of safety" for exposure to a carcinogen. Had it not been for the rapid growth of the organic chemical industry and deaths of more than forty men from exposure to vinyl chloride, the EPA might have been able to avoid resolving the issue.

Vinyl chloride is a colorless gas, the raw material for hundreds of plastic products ranging from credit cards to baby bottle nipples. The gas is polymerized into a resin that is then transformed into final products. In January 1974 the B. F. Goodrich Company announced that three workers at its Louisville, Kentucky, plant had died of angiosarcoma, a rare form of liver cancer. Within a matter of weeks several more cases of angiosarcoma were reported by other manufacturers of vinyl chloride. Public reaction was sharp and swift. To some it appeared that industry had tried to conceal the causes of the deaths. It was discovered that experiments performed much earlier had found that vinyl chloride caused cancer in test animals. Worse, it appeared that the industry had known about the studies and yet had done nothing to protect its employees.

Immediately demands were made for occupational regulations to reduce worker exposure. The Occupational Safety and Health Administration did respond—some felt too slowly —by proposing an emergency temporary standard of 1 part per million in occupational air over an eight-hour period. Industry challenged this standard in court and the permanent one that followed as needlessly strict. In October 1975 the Court of Appeals decided in OSHA's favor.

The EPA found itself under the gun because it knew that the OSHA standard was already being exceeded in the air around some vinyl chloride plants. Still the EPA held back from proposing its own standard to protect the public. Months passed while debate over the format of regulation raged within the agency. Some agency officials argued that the standard should only require industry to install technology that was currently available and "commonly achievable." Others argued that the public could be protected only by a health-based standard (under section 112 of the Clean Air Act) which could require installation of the best available technology or a phased reduction of all emissions to zero.

The industry position on establishing any standard was predictable. When OSHA had earlier proposed its standard, industry claimed it would cause a loss of $65 billion to $90 billion to the economy and from 1.7 million to 2.2 million jobs. One year afterward *no* plants had closed (some were even planing to expand), and the price of vinyl chloride had dropped. But now the Society of the Plastics Industry argued that whatever the occupational hazard might have been, there was no threat to the public. But evidence was growing that vinyl chloride *did* pose a hazard to public health. OSHA uncovered two cases of angiosarcoma in workers in polyvinyl chloride plants who had little or no direct contact with vinyl chloride production. One victim, an accountant, presumably worked well away from the production line. Finally, on December 14, 1975, the EPA announced that it would regulate vinyl chloride and published a proposed emission standard. It acknowledged that no safe level of exposure had been identified for carcinogens such as vinyl chloride but concluded that the law could be satisfied by a standard that required the installation of "best available control technology." This may sound impressive, but it does not mean that the public would be protected by an "ample margin of safety."

The EPA asked for public comment on its proposed regulation, part of the normal process of preparing a standard. Environmentalists objected to the standard as both inadequate and illegal. After almost a year of deliberation, in October 1976, the EPA finally promulgated a vinyl chloride standard. There were few changes from the standard proposed the year previous; in fact most of the changes were minor and were made at the behest of the industry.

But just before the EPA standard went into effect, some startling new animal test data became available. In September 1976 Dr. Cesare Maltoni, an Italian scientist of considerable renown, published the results of inhalation experiments in mice, which showed the induction of tumors from exposure to vinyl chloride at levels much lower than previously reported. Even more important, Maltoni found evidence of mammary tumors at levels of exposure as low as 1 part per million. Up to this point, concern had been limited to the risk of contracting angiosarcoma, not breast cancer too.

Partly because of the new evidence and partly because of continuing dissatisfaction with the regulatory approach, the Environmental Defense Fund sued the EPA over its final standard. In its suit the EDF cited the Maltoni study and alleged that the approach taken by the agency was both illegal and inadequate to protect public health. Within weeks of the filing of the suit, industry joined the EPA in court in an effort to defend the standard.

The EPA chose to settle out of court. The agency agreed to propose amended regulations that would provide for continuing reductions in vinyl chloride levels with the goal of reaching zero, thus finally establishing that an ample margin of safety for exposure to a carcinogen could only be achieved if all exposure was eliminated. Furthermore, the EPA agreed to propose new regulations that would sharply limit increases in vinyl chloride concentrations as a result of the new construction of vinyl chloride plants. The EDF and the agency also agreed not to insist on immediate reductions to near-zero levels because this would have forced the industry to close down, with unacceptable economic consequences. Unfortunately, the EPA has not yet finalized these amended requirements. Further litigation may be necessary.

More than three years have passed since the EPA first initiated action to regulate vinyl chloride as a hazardous air pollutant. What is truly troublesome, however, is that vinyl chloride is only one of a hundred or more airborne chemicals from industrial processes that may pose a carcinogenic risk to the public. Other chemicals of major concern include benzene, arsenic, and cadmium.

Benzene is one of twenty-two "high volume" chemicals studied by the Mitre Corporation and the GCA Corporation, which are under contract to the EPA. Of the twenty-two, benzene presents the most imminent and serious threat to human health. Benzene production amounts to more than 12 billion pounds annually, and a 1977 study indicated that 544.3 million pounds escapes into the environment from a variety of sources.

Benzene is used in many ways—as a component of gasoline to improve octane rating; as a primary raw material, or "feedstock," for the production of other products; as an industrial solvent. To meet demand, benzene production is expected to increase at the rate of 7 percent per year over the next several years.

Vehicle-related emissions account for by far the largest escape of benzene into the environment, approximately 840 million pounds a year, according to GCA (940 million pounds a year according to Mitre). There are two kinds of vehicle-related emissions of benzene. One is by direct combustion of gasoline in a car or truck engine. In recent years the use of catalytic converters and other control devices has reduced these emissions to some extent; however, gasoline combustion still accounts for a significant portion. Second, benzene evaporates into the air at gas pumps during refueling, along with a certain amount of gasoline. At present most domestic gasolines contain between 1 and 2 percent benzene. Studies in the U.S. and England indicate that emissions from refueling can produce air levels as high as 1 to 3 ppm in the air in the vicinity of the pumps. As lead is phased out in gasoline, the amount of benzene in gasoline is expected to increase because benzene and other aromatic hydrocarbons, such as xylene and toluene, must be added to make up for it.

Mitre and GCA differ greatly in their estimates of the loss of benzene during its use as a feedstock in manufacturing processes. GCA estimates annual escape at only 58.1 million pounds, whereas Mitre places the loss at 658 million pounds. Benzene is used to produce more than a dozen organic chemicals, some of which in turn are used to make other products, such as plastics.

Coke ovens are another important source of benzene emissions. They emit a multitude of pollutants, a number of which are known carcinogens. Mitre estimated that coke ovens release 122 million pounds of benzene into the environment each year. Benzene production itself is another significant source of escape, emitting—according to Mitre—89 million pounds annually.

Evidence of the carcinogenicity of benzene has been accumulating for years, and the EPA now has in hand strong evidence demonstrating that occupational exposure has caused leukemia in workers. In June 1977, after months of debate, the EPA agreed to regulate benzene as a hazardous air pollutant. However, the thoroughness of the regulation is already in question. The agency has plans to control gas pump emissions only in locales where it believes hydrocarbons are contributing to severe smog problems. There are eighteen to twenty such locales in the country, but of course these are not the only places where benzene emissions occur. There is no indication that such controls will be extended to other areas to cover the benzene problem.

The alchemist's symbol for arsenic, a menacing serpent, symbolizes its centuries-old reputation as a poison. Yet up until World War II doctors regularly prescribed it in small quantities as a medicine. Since then, evidence of its toxicity at even low concentrations has steadily grown.

Scientists now generally agree that arsenic is both a skin and a lung carcinogen. But this agreement was a long time in coming. In 1963 scientists employed by the American Smelting and Refining Company first studied mortality rates among workers at the Asarco Refinery in Tacoma, Washington, the only one in the United States that refines arsenic-containing ores to produce pure arsenic. They compared the lung cancer mortality rates of employees directly exposed to arsenic within the smelter with the rates of other employees supposedly not exposed to arsenic. They reported no significant difference in lung cancer rates between the two groups and therefore concluded that regular exposure to arsenic did not result in cancer. Because no other studies existed on long-term occupational exposure to arsenic, the federal government relied upon the Asarco report to set several standards.

Six years later, in 1969, scientists at the National Cancer Institute discovered an astonishing deficiency in the Asarco study: Asarco scientists had never compared the incidence rate of cancer for workers with people who did not work inside the Asarco plant. When such a comparison was made, NCI scientists found that lung cancer rates for all smelter workers, whether exposed to arsenic or supposedly unexposed, were three times higher than rates for the general population.

When the NCI study appeared, Asarco officials went back and sampled the air for arsenic and finally admitted that arsenic was present in every area of the plant where air samples had been taken. After reexamining death certificates of workers in its Tacoma plant, Asarco conceded that the death rate from lung cancer was approximately twice that expected.

In 1974 Allied Chemical and Dow Chemical released studies on their own workers who had handled inorganic arsenic. The studies revealed that these workers had been contracting lung and lymphatic cancers at rates three to sixty times higher than workers not exposed to arsenic. The release of these studies prompted researchers to dig back into some of the older studies. Within months reports began to appear that noted that arsenic had been linked to cancer as far back as the turn of the century. This research had been neglected because of the assurances of the Asarco study that arsenic was not a carcinogen.

Copper and zinc smelters account for a large percentage of arsenic emissions. Power plants that burn coal contaminated with arsenic are also potential major sources. Even so, the EPA has refused to regulate arsenic under the Clean Air Act. Congress, however, has decided to force the agency's hand. The Clean Air Act Amendments of 1977 required the agency to decide whether to regulate arsenic by the middle of 1978. When that deadline passed with no decision the EDF sued the agency, and a decision is pending.

Another metal emitted into the air from copper and zinc smelters is cadmium. The EPA estimates that close to 3.5 million pounds of cadmium are emitted into the air each year from smelter operations, and combustion facilities such as power plants and sewage incinerators.

Airborne cadmium can enter the body by several routes. Some is directly inhaled into the lungs, where, as a very fine particulate, it is retained and absorbed. Some particles settle out of the atmosphere and can enter food, drinking water, and tobacco through the soil.

After absorption through the lung or gastrointestinal tract cadmium enters the bloodstream and accumulates principally in the kidneys and to a lesser extent in the liver. Because of its accumulation and persistence in critical organs, cadmium is more toxic at low levels than either lead or mercury. One way in which cadmium does damage is to interfere biologically with the body's use of zinc and certain other essential metals.

Once present in the body, cadmium can lead to a variety

of diseases including anemia, high blood pressure and cardio-vascular disease, liver and kidney damage, pulmonary emphysema—and cancer. Cadmium is a carcinogen in test animals, and studies indicate that it may be one of the most potent metallic carcinogens yet known.

Studies on humans have shown statistically higher concentrations of cadmium in the liver and kidney of patients who died from bronchogenic carcinoma than were found in a control group or a group that died from other forms of cancer. In addition, the high levels of cadmium found in food in Japan have prompted suspicions that these levels may be a cause of the very high incidence of stomach cancer found in that country.

Despite all the evidence of the menace that cadmium offers, the EPA has refused to set an air pollution standard, and this toxic heavy metal is therefore unregulated.

The burning of coal to generate electrical power poses greater risks than simply the release of arsenic and cadmium. As described in chapter 8, certain coal deposits are naturally contaminated with radioactive uranium, which is released into the air during burning. In the next decade the use of coal for electricity production is likely to rise sharply, by perhaps 100 percent, and the magnitude of the cancer risk from this type of pollution will rise with it.

More than 94 percent of all particulate emissions—the minute particles of dust, soot, and grit—come from coal-fired facilities. In 1974 coal-fired power plants spewed 3.2 million tons of particulates into the nation's air. By 1985, assuming no breakthroughs in control technology, coal-fired power plants will release double that amount, 6.4 million tons. This figure could be even larger if large quantities of western coal are used for electric power generation. Because western coal has a lower energy content per ton than Appalachian coal, it releases approximately 38 percent more particulate matter per million BTUs of heat output.

Even more important than the absolute increase in the quantity of particulates generated is the fact that fine particulates, which can enter the lungs, will constitute an increasing proportion of the total. This is attributable to the continued use by most utilities of electrostatic precipitators instead of the more effective devices such as bag house filters for the control of particulate emissions. Electrostatic precipitators do a fairly good job of removing the large particles generated by the burning of coal, but they are able to remove only a tiny fraction of the fine particulates, and this means that amounts of arsenic, cadmium, beryllium, and other trace metals can be expected to increase dramatically. Moreover, researchers at the University of California at Davis have recently established that fly ash and particulates from coal-fired power plants are mutagenic in the Ames test and thus a likely carcinogen. The fine particles used by the researchers in their experiments were found to be covered with cadmium, cobalt, nickel, and other substances that presumably cause the genetic changes in the bacteria. Until this discovery scientists believed that fly ash played an important role in aggravating various pulmonary ailments, but they were reluctant to claim that it was a direct cause of cancer.

Although inorganic particulates constitute the major proportion of particles emitted by coal-fired power plants, another group of particulates, known as polycyclic organic matter, may pose an even greater hazard. Polycyclic organic matter is composed of a huge family of polycyclic aromatic hydrocarbons that condense into particulate matter during the combustion process. There are literally dozens of polycyclic aromatic hydrocarbons, and a number of them—including 7,12-dimethylbenz-(a)anthracene, benzo(c)phenanthrene, 3-methyl-cholanthrene, and benzo(a)pyrene—are highly carcinogenic.

The amount of polycyclic organic matter produced will vary widely. While relatively efficient combustion processes produce little polycyclic organic matter, inefficient burning produces not only extremely high emissions but the particulates formed are generally small, of the right size to be breathed by humans. Refuse burning, coke ovens, and other industrial activities, such as the catalytic cracking of crude oil, also produce significant amounts of polycyclic organic matter.

The Clean Air Act Amendments of 1970 specifically

named polycyclic organic matter as one of the pollutants that the EPA should consider for regulation, but the EPA has persistently refused to set a separate standard for it. The Clean Air Act Amendments of 1977 have finally forced the issue. The EPA must fund studies which will establish by July 1, 1979, whether a separate standard is needed.

Coal-fired power plants may offer still other hazards— the formation of secondary pollutants from the emission of sulfur dioxide and nitrogen dioxide. Nitrogen dioxide is the precursor for nitrates and may play a role in the atmospheric formation of nitrosamines, one of the most potent classes of carcinogens yet uncovered. The EPA currently regulates nitrogen dioxide as a precursor in the formation of photochemical smog, but not as a precursor in the formation of nitrosamines. Dr. David Fine, one of the foremost researchers on nitrosamines, has speculated that nitrogen dioxide produced by coal-fired power plants and other large stationary sources may be an important precursor to the formation of nitrosamines in the atmosphere. Because control technology for nitrogen dioxide emissions is still in its infancy, scientists now predict that nitrogen dioxide levels will skyrocket in the next ten years.

Finally, sulfur dioxide from coal-fired power plants is the primary precursor in the formation of atmospheric sulfate and sulfuric acid. Although sulfates have not been identified as a separate carcinogen, they are suspected of playing a role as cocarcinogens in the presence of particulate matter. The presence of sulfates and sulfur dioxide greatly enhances the carcinogenic potential of certain particulate matter. Large coal-fired power plants put out enormous quantities of sulfur dioxide, and the resulting sulfates can travel for hundreds of miles and thus affect populations far downwind.

CHAPTER 6
PESTICIDES

Despite the public awareness of the dangers of the use of chemical pesticides—an awareness that arose after Rachel Carson sounded the alarm in 1962 with *Silent Spring*—the production of pesticides in the United States has grown enormously. It is true that the federal government banned DDT after a long battle, as well as several other potent and persistent chlorinated hydrocarbons, notably aldrin and dieldrin; yet, between 1962 and 1975, the most recent years for which reliable figures are available, pesticide sales in the U.S. soared from $440 million a year to more than $2 billion. In 1975 the industry produced a record 1.6 billion pounds plus of synthetic organic pesticides, a number of which may be carcinogenic or otherwise harmful.

While the pesticide industry has been going through boom times, the federal government has largely failed to protect the public and the environment. As a 1976 report by the National Academy of Sciences concluded, "The pest control enterprise places a billion pounds of toxic materials into the environment each year, but it is 'normal' for us to have only the vaguest idea of how much of each compound was used and where, and even then only after half a decade's lag."

Despite the publication of *Silent Spring,* there remains a huge gap between government promise and performance. In the uproar that followed the appearance of the book Kenneth M. Birkhead, assistant to the secretary of agriculture, told a Senate committee that the U.S. Department of Agriculture, which then had authority over pesticides under the Federal Insecticide, Fungicide and Rodenticide Act, was trying to find "better methods to control pests." Even though the USDA has always stressed the supposed disaster that would strike agriculture if pesticides were restricted, Birkhead admitted that "Miss Carson presents a lucid description of the real and potential dangers of misusing chemical pesticides." He also emphasized USDA research that would develop biological controls and other techniques to control insects "without the use of chemicals that leave harmful residues."

In 1964 Congress amended the Federal Insecticide, Fungicide and Rodenticide Act (FIFRA) to make the manufacturer of a pesticide prove its safety before registration by the USDA for use. Moreover, under agreement with the USDA the Department of the Interior and the Department of Health, Education and Welfare had the right to review all pesticides submitted for registration for possible adverse effects on humans, fish, and wildlife.

Despite all this a 1969 investigative report by the House Committee on Government Operations showed the USDA to be flagrantly neglectful of its responsibilities. The report disclosed that the USDA granted pesticide registrations as a matter of course. Indeed, the department had hastily—and frequently on the basis of inadequate information—registered 45,000 pesticide products as "safe and effective when used as directed." The report noted that HEW had objected to 1,663 proposed registrations from July 1964 through June 1969, but the USDA paid no attention. Moreover, when HEW requested information on pesticides registered over its objection, Dr. Harry Hays, director of the USDA's Pesticides Registration Division, refused to comply "on the ground that information, if provided, might be used against him."

To assure due process, a manufacturer whose pesticide registration was canceled had the right to request hearings and referral to an advisory committee. But the USDA, perhaps because it granted registrations as a matter of course, never even bothered to promulgate rules of practice for hearings or procedures for advisory committee referrals. In addition to granting registrations routinely, the Pesticide Registration Division "never secured cancellation of a registration in a contested case." Indeed, even in emergency situations, the House report said, the USDA had no procedure whatever to warn the public about specific hazards from particular pesticide products.

The House report concluded with a devastating indictment of the USDA's disregard for the human and environmental risks involved in pesticide use. It found that the USDA had "failed almost completely to carry out its responsibilities to enforce provisions of the FIFRA intended to protect the public from hazardous and ineffective pesticide products being marketed in violation of the Act." It noted that "numerous pesticide products have been approved for registration over objections of the DHEW as to their safety without compliance with required procedures for resolving such safety questions" and that the USDA had "approved pesticide products for uses which it knew or should have known were practically certain to result in illegal adulteration of food." Finally, the report scored the USDA for employing consultants whose ties to the agricultural chemicals industry posed serious conflicts of interest, and for the department's failures both to ensure that label warnings were clear and to cancel many hazardous pesticides. The report deemed it vital to "make certain that pesticide products are not registered or reregistered unless there is adequate assurance that they are safe and effective."

In 1969, the same year as the House report, the Mrak Commission, chaired by Dr. Emil Mrak, chancellor emeritus of the University of California at Davis, made its report called *Pesticides and Their Relationship to Environmental Health* to the secretary of HEW. The Mrak Commission recommended the elimination within two years of all uses of DDT, except those essential to the preservation of human health and welfare, and it called for "corrective action" on such chlorinated hydrocarbons as aldrin/dieldrin, endrin, heptachlor, chlordane, benzene hexachloride (BHC), lindane, and compounds containing inorganic lead, arsenic, or mercury. The Mrak Commission also urged surveillance on toxaphene, then and now one of the most heavily applied pesticides. (In 1975 an estimated 116 million pounds of toxaphene were applied to cotton and a variety of other crops.)

The Mrak Commission recommended that human exposure to a number of other pesticides be minimized as well because of evidence indicating they caused tumors or birth defects in experimental animals. In addition to the pesticides listed above, the list included the herbicides 2,4,5-T and 2,4-D, the fungicides captan and PCNB, and the insecticides carbaryl and chlorobenzilate, to name only a few.

By 1970 the House committee's disclosure that the USDA had not only failed dismally to regulate pesticides but was an active promoter of them led Congress to transfer jurisdiction of the FIFRA to the newly created Environmental Protection Agency. But the change in jurisdiction to the EPA has not produced a solution to the problem, even though Congress passed a revision of the FIFRA in 1972 establishing a comprehensive regulatory plan for pesticides. This plan empowered the EPA to draw up specific regulations to protect human health and the environment, to review all previous registrations of pesticides, and to classify all pesticides by toxicity criteria. Unfortunately, the EPA's attempts to adhere to this plan have been plagued by internal and external difficulties, which have thus far prevented the agency from regulating pesticides to any measurable extent.

Within the EPA, bureaucrats have proposed, discussed, adopted, and argued about reams of regulations and guidelines. Meanwhile pesticide production expands year after year with vast and potentially terrifying implications for human health. Only in a few instances has the EPA acted, and then only in response to petitions from public interest groups.

In response to such petitions, the EPA initiated proceedings to cancel the registration of DDT, aldrin/dieldrin, mirex, 2,4,5-T, and chlordane/heptachlor. After lengthy administrative and legal proceedings the sale and use of DDT, aldrin/dieldrin, and mirex were banned. However, in 1974 the EPA recessed the hearings on 2,4,5-T pending the gathering of further data, so this herbicide remains in common use despite evidence that it contains dioxin impurities that are both carcinogenic and teratogenic. Indeed, dioxin is one of the most toxic substances known to science. The explosion at a plant manufacturing hexachlorophene, from a feedstock of trichlorophenol containing dioxin impurities, in the summer of 1976, contaminated the town of Seveso, Italy, to such an extent that the area may be uninhabitable for fifty years. According to some estimates, scores of people were injured, and more than sixty pregnant women chose abortions because of the birth defects their infants were likely to suffer.

With the exception of the well-publicized demise of DDT, the battles over the pitifully few pesticides that have been banned have been fought without proper press coverage and with a tediousness that would do justice to Dickens's *Bleak House*. No case better exemplifies the labyrinthine procedures involved—procedures that industry and agribusiness and their proponents have attempted to use with one delaying tactic after another—and the reasons why so little has been done to reduce human exposure to pesticides than that of aldrin/dieldrin.

THE BANNING OF ALDRIN/DIELDRIN

In 1974 the EPA finally banned the use of aldrin/dieldrin on the grounds that the substances posed "an unreasonable risk of cancer in man." (The virgule is used between the two chemicals because dieldrin is a metabolite of aldrin.) The litigation took five years. The scientific evidence that caused Russell Train, then administrator of the EPA, to order the ban included data showing that dieldrin in very low doses induced cancer in laboratory animals and that residues of dieldrin were stored in the tissues of virtually the entire U.S. population and were pervasive in the human diet. Herbert L. Perlman, the administrative law judge who presided over the hearing that resulted in the ban, found that,

Surveys conducted by the Food & Drug Administration show that dieldrin is found in as much as 96 percent of all meat, fish, and poultry "composite samples" tested, and 85% of all dairy product "composite samples" tested. In addition EPA surveys indicate that dieldrin is in approximately 90 percent of all air samples taken nationally and residues of dieldrin have been found in virtually *all* of the humans included in the EPA human monitoring survey.

The voluminous hearing record, which exceeded twenty-eight thousand pages, also showed that dieldrin residues circulated in blood, were transferred across the placenta to developing fetuses, and were secreted along with a number of other man-made chemicals in human milk. Clearly, human exposure to dieldrin began even before birth and was continuous throughout life because of widespread contamination of major components of the human diet.

It is not surprising, then, that Judge Perlman concluded,

We are talking of a cancer hazard to man. We must remember, in this regard, the characteristics of a chemical carcinogen such as aldrin/dieldrin, that is, the scientific inability to determine a safe threshold level for man, the fact that the chemicals are carcinogenic at the lowest doses tested, that residues of dieldrin in laboratory species which developed cancer from dieldrin approximate those residues in the American population, the irreversibility of the carcinogenic effect once set in motion by the chemical carcinogen and the long latency period during which the disease has actually set in and is developing but is not yet manifest. Given these characteristics . . . the continued use of aldrin and dieldrin . . . presents a significant potential of an unreasonable risk in the American public.

Aldrin and dieldrin are chlorinated hydrocarbon insecticides. They gained wide acceptance after introduction in 1950 because of their extreme persistence and efficacy against a broad spectrum of insects. Chlorinated hydrocarbons do not break down naturally except over a long period of time, possibly as long as fifteen years. They are readily soluble in fats. They are also highly mobile in the environment and are easily transported following application by vaporization, aerial drift, and runoff of eroding soil particles, to which they readily adhere. As a result aldrin and dieldrin residues have been detected long distances from the site of application and are now widespread in the environment.

Farmers eagerly adopted persistent pesticides such as aldrin and dieldrin because they were inexpensive and easy to apply as well as efficacious. Starting in the early 1950s aldrin and dieldrin were used on several major crops, including cotton, corn, potatoes, peanuts, and sugar beets. For various reasons, including the development of genetic resistance in the insects and concern about the presence of residues in feed crops, after 1964 aldrin and dieldrin were used mainly on corn, citrus, and a number of lesser crops, including grain and rice seed.

Production of corn and other food and feed crops is a highly mechanized, capital-intensive business in the U.S. The record yields harvested over the past twenty-five years are attributable to various factors such as development of disease-resistant plant strains, irrigation, changed cultural practices, improved mechanical devices, generally favorable weather conditions, and greatly increased use of chemical insecticides, herbicides, and fertilizers. In the process of meeting the growing demand for feed grains at home and abroad, while minimizing labor costs, farmers have relied on a chemical technology that involves, among other things, the use of persistent pesticides on a prophylactic or insurance basis. In these applications the pesticides are regularly used prior to planting, on an annual basis, and with no knowledge of whether an insect infestation of economic consequence is likely to occur at all. A trend toward conservation tillage, in which the soil is disturbed only slightly or not at all, has also been developing to combat soil erosion. Inasmuch as the land is not tilled in this practice, vestiges of prior crops are left on the ground and become breeding sites for insects and weeds. Thus large quantities of pesticides and herbicides are applied. Viewed objectively, the common practice of applying millions of pounds of aldrin to corn acreage every year as insurance against insects that might not even be present is nothing less than foolhardy. One study of farmers' pesticide-use decisions concluded that of the almost six million acres of corn in Illinois that have been treated with soil insecticides in recent years for rootworm, only about 40 percent actually needed treatment. The same study estimated that at least half of the corn land in Illinois and Iowa treated with chlorinated hydrocarbons for control of other soil insects did not need such treatment.

In December 1970, following the recommendation of the Mrak Commission, the Environmental Defense Fund (which was already seeking to ban DDT) petitioned the newly formed EPA to suspend and cancel the registrations of all uses of aldrin/dieldrin. At that time approximately nine million pounds of the two pesticides were used in the production of corn alone. The EDF requested action because of the evidence of the carcinogenicity of aldrin/dieldrin in laboratory animals and the presence of widespread residues in the environment and in the diet.

Although the EPA initially declined to remove the two pesticides from the market immediately, the agency issued notice in March 1971 of intent to cancel most uses of aldrin and dieldrin. The EDF's petition had requested both suspension and cancellation, and there is a significant difference between these two statutory procedures. To remove a pesticide from the market, its federal registration must be permanently canceled. Following the issuance of a notice of intent to cancel or to suspend, the manufacturer has an opportunity to challenge the evidence demonstrating risks or else to establish that the benefits of continued use outweigh those risks. Such proceedings are conducted in the form of public hearings, with witnesses, attorneys, and cross-examination. At the conclusion of the cancellation proceeding, the presiding officer recommends a decision to the EPA administrator, whose responsibility it is to make the ultimate decision either to cancel the registration, to restrict that use through label changes, or to permit continued use of the pesticide.

Suspension, on the other hand, involves a more expedited and abbreviated proceeding and, if ordered, has the effect of temporarily revoking the registration (i.e., taking the pesticide off the market) for the duration of the lengthier cancellation proceeding. In a suspension hearing the issue is very narrow: Would continued use of the pesticide during the time required to complete the cancellation hearing pose an imminent hazard to human health or to the environment?

Proponents of continued registration prefer a cancellation proceeding because the pesticide remains on the market during hearings, and so there is incentive to stretch the hearings out as long as possible.

The aldrin/dieldrin cancellation hearings commenced in August 1973, almost two and a half years after issuance of the notice of intent to cancel as the result of legal maneuverings and bureaucratic delay. For the next thirteen months, four days a week, aldrin and dieldrin were literally "on trial." On one side, the manufacturer, Shell Chemical Company, was represented by a team of seven lawyers from the prominent Washington law firm of Arnold and Porter. Ever the pesticide proponent, the USDA intervened on Shell's side with a team of three lawyers. Opposing them and advocating cancellation before Judge Perlman were two attorneys from the EPA's Office of General Counsel and two from the EDF, which had intervened on behalf of itself and the National Audubon Society. In this trial-like setting the adverse health and environmental effects of aldrin/dieldrin, as well as the benefits of continued agricultural and other uses, were explored in minute detail.

More than 250 witnesses testified, and as the evidence of aldrin/dieldrin residues in air, water, food, and humans mounted, studies showing that the pesticides were carcinogenic in laboratory animals appeared increasingly ominous. The most widely used chlorinated hydrocarbon pesticides for control of corn soil insects, aldrin/dieldrin were applied annually to nine million acres of corn land. Researchers found that residues of the two compounds persisted in the soil for as long as thirteen years after application. Root systems took up the residues to the foliage and grain of various food, feed, and forage crops, such as soybeans, barley, oats, and alfalfa, which are commonly rotated with corn. Some contamination of the corn plants themselves also occurred through splash-up of the pesticides from rainfall during and/or as a result of vaporization from the soil.

Testimony from farmers revealed that it is a common practice to permit livestock to forage in harvested fields, where cut plants are often contaminated by contact with treated soil. Other testimony showed that grazing animals absorbed residues of the pesticides directly by lying down on treated soil. The most direct route of contamination came from feeding the animals corn silage, soybeans, and other affected crops. Although the practice of spraying livestock directly to kill insects had been proscribed by label changes and farmers had been cautioned by labels and state recommendations to avoid exposing animals to areas treated with aldrin/dieldrin, it was evident that extensive contamination of meat, poultry, and dairy products was continuing.

Fish, another dietary component, were also shown to be heavily contaminated with aldrin/dieldrin residues. For example, studies conducted by the FDA, the National Fish Monitoring Program, and a number of state agencies disclosed that dieldrin residues were widespread in freshwater fish. The residues found their way into water and ultimately into fish because of runoff from contaminated soil particles, airborne dust particles, discharges into water during the manufacture of the pesticides, and other lesser routes of transport.

As in other organisms, dieldrin accumulated in the adipose tissues of fish. This concentration was intensified by the phenomenon of biomagnification, a process in which the residues accumulated by organisms lower in the food chain are increased manyfold as they move up the chain. Thus, as with PCBs or DDT, residue levels of dieldrin in fish were found to be thousands of times greater than residues in the waters where the fish were caught.

All this did not tell the whole story. Dieldrin residues were so prevalent that the chances of purchasing an uncontaminated chicken, steak, or quart of milk, for example, anywhere in the U.S. were less than 10 percent. There were also measurable residues in drinking water and in the air. Moreover, there were many opportunities for direct exposures around the home because of household insecticides available for use both indoors and on home lawns and gardens. Since dieldrin is absorbed through the skin, home uses appeared to pose additional exposure hazards through inhalation and by walking barefoot on treated lawns. In fact, suburban lawns and gardens receive the heaviest application of pesticides including dieldrin of any land areas in the U.S. According to the National Academy of Sciences, use in and around homes "is of considerable environmental importance because for the average citizen it is the point during which he encounters the highest concentration of pesticides. The characteristics of pesticide use patterns in the home and on the garden play a significant role in incidental human exposures and environmental pesticide pollution in an urban setting." In short, exposure to dieldrin residues was unavoidable. The avenues of exposure covered every aspect of life.

In the aldrin/dieldrin hearing, witnesses testified that the pesticides were in some cases overapplied or carelessly handled and containers improperly discarded. Other examples of misuse included waste-disposal discharges and accidental spills. Perhaps the most widely publicized example of the accidental misuse of aldrin/dieldrin was the discovery, during routine poultry inspection by the USDA in March 1974, that approximately eight million chickens in Mississippi had been contaminated by dieldrin present in their feed. Inasmuch as the residue levels in their tissues exceeded the existing FDA "action" level of 0.3 part per million—the level at which the FDA condemns interstate shipment—the chickens were destroyed, at great cost to the poultry producers involved.

The Mississippi chicken incident was illuminating for a couple of reasons. First, the investigation uncovered numerous cases in which cattle, turkeys, and other livestock had been destroyed as unsafe for human consumption because of pesticide contamination. In other words, the dieldrin contamination of the Mississippi chickens was nothing new; it merely happened to get publicized. Second, the manner in which the decision was made to destroy the chickens gives insight into the politics of pesticide regulation. When word of the problem first reached the EPA, it was feared that as many as 22 million chickens might be involved. Representative Jamie Whitten (D-Miss.), a long-time foe of the EPA's pesticides regulatory actions and then chairman of the appropriations subcommittee that voted on the agency's budget, approached the EPA along with other members of Mississippi's congressional delegation to request that the action level be raised enough to permit the contaminated chickens to be marketed. The pressure was so intense that despite the ongoing aldrin/dieldrin cancellation hearing, EPA officials appeared ready to accede. In desperation, other agency personnel who had worked for years to achieve reduction in exposures of the population to pesticides such as aldrin and dieldrin leaked word to the press in the hope that the publicity would enable the EPA to hold the line. Within minutes, word of the contaminated chickens was on the news wires, and once the media focused on the story, the EPA was able to resist Whitten's pressure.

By definition pesticides are poisonous, and their presence in human tissues and human milk is cause for concern. When residues are also known to cause cancer in laboratory animals, concern heightens into apprehension about the potential consequences of the exposure of virtually every American to these carcinogenic substances every day for the past thirty years. In the case of aldrin/dieldrin, laboratory carcinogenicity experiments were conducted on mice, rats, dogs, and monkeys. Reviewed by expert pathologists, the results of the mouse studies indicated that dieldrin produced cancerous liver tumors in five different strains.

Throughout the hearing, lawyers and witnesses for both Shell Chemical Company and the USDA had argued vehemently that the mouse was not a valid predictor of a cancer hazard for man. The thrust of their argument was that mouse livers are unusually susceptible to cancer, and the extrapolation to man of a carcinogenic effect in mice is inherently speculative. The latter point may be true in a quantitative sense, since attempts to predict the slope of the human dose-response curve and to estimate the number of resulting cancers are necessarily somewhat crude. But as discussed in chapter 2, using mouse data to make *qualitative* predictions of cancer risk in humans is valid.

Judge Perlman agreed, and he recommended that the EPA administrator order a comprehensive ban on the vast majority of uses of aldrin/dieldrin. In his decision, in October 1974, to suspend the registrations of aldrin/dieldrin Administrator Russell Train quoted Dr. Walter E. Heston, chief of the Laboratory of Biology at the National Cancer Institute, who had testified at the aldrin/dieldrin hearing on the basis of thirty-five years' experience in cancer research on experimental animals, that,

knowing the general biological similarity of mice and other mammalian species, including man, we can reasonably expect that in a population of human beings exposed to Aldrin-Dieldrin, cancer of some kind will occur in some individuals, and these individuals will not have been afflicted in the absence of these compounds. . . . The human population is so much more genetically diverse than any laboratory animals, that if a chemical has been shown to be carcinogenic by a significant induction in any laboratory strain of mammal, we can reasonably expect that at least certain human beings would also respond to the chemical by developing some kind of neoplasm [cancer].

Under Train's decision existing stocks of aldrin/dieldrin, produced prior to issuance of the notice of intent to suspend that initiated the hearing, were not included in the ban, apparently to save the EPA the possible cost of indemnification. As a result the following year an additional two and a half million acres of corn were treated with aldrin/dieldrin, despite the suspension of the pesticide's use as an imminent hazard to human health. Both Shell and the USDA appealed the decision to suspend aldrin/dieldrin to the U.S. Court of Appeals. But six months later, in April 1975, the court upheld the ban, finding that the evidence supported the EPA's conclusion that continued exposure to aldrin/dieldrin posed an imminent hazard. Shortly thereafter, six years after the Mrak Commission report, Shell decided to cease all further manufacture of aldrin/dieldrin in the United States, and the registrations of both pesticides were permanently canceled.

Inasmuch as it had taken more than seven years to ban DDT, the fight to cancel the registrations of aldrin/dieldrin might have seemed like a breeze, and it might also have seemed that one could expect a new case to move more swiftly. This has not been so. The EPA's attempt to cancel the registrations for heptachlor and chlordane, two more chlorinated hydrocarbon pesticides that are carcinogenic, took more than three years and was concluded with a settlement agreement phasing out all uses of the two pesticides involved in the case over the next five years.

It would be repetitious to an extreme to recite the details of this case, because heptachlor and chlordane not only had the same administrative law judge as aldrin/dieldrin but the same kinds of witnesses, the same kinds of testimony. This case also cost millions of dollars and tied up the efforts of environmentalists and personnel at the EPA for thousands of hours. Except that a suspension hearing was also involved and that there were different manufacturers (Velsicol instead of Shell), the heptachlor and chlordane case is practically an identical twin to the aldrin/dieldrin case.

Even with EPA's success in withdrawing chlordane and heptachlor from the market and thereby beginning to eliminate human exposure to their residues, only six of the original nineteen pesticides identified by the Mrak Commission as posing a potential health hazard to man have been dealt with by the agency. In terms of the universe of pesticides currently registered for use and known or suspected of being carcinogenic or otherwise severely hazardous to humans, however, much energy and effort will have been expended to accomplish relatively little. Other pesticides cited by the Mrak Commission, such as endrin and toxaphene, remain in heavy use. Both are in the same chemical family as DDT, aldrin/dieldrin, chlordane, and heptachlor and are currently under review by the EPA. Both, according to the most recent scientific studies available, cause cancer in laboratory animals.

It is apparent that a case-by-case approach, in which each compound becomes the subject of extremely lengthy and detailed hearings, will not suffice to ensure that pesticides do not cause "unreasonable adverse effects" upon man and the environment. Yet the regulatory mechanisms enacted by Congress ostensibly to protect the public and the environment from potentially harmful exposures to pesticides move only at a snail's pace, because the cumbersome statutory procedures provide a chemical with the full panoply of due process rights accorded to any individual in our constitutional system.

Another reason why the hearings are so lengthy is the extensive support enjoyed by many widely used compounds in the agricultural community and, of course, in the chemical company–agricultural college complex. Each specific use of the pesticide at issue in the hearings—and there can be hundreds—is ordinarily defended by the company, by the Department of Agriculture and corresponding state-level entities, and by user groups such as nurserymen or pineapple growers or pest control operators. Each of these interest groups, either alone or in conjunction with the others, presents testimony and exhibits favoring continued registration of the pesticide for their particular use.

For years the chemical industry has promoted and fostered continuing reliance on pesticide control strategies. Studies have shown that farmers rely most often upon local agricultural chemical dealers for information about pest control methods. Other lesser sources of information include the product labels, other farmers, university and local extension agents, and extension publications. Although the university, local, and county extension personnel are apparently regarded by farmers as very useful information sources, one study of farmers' pesticide-use decisions characterized these sources as "outnumbered by pesticide industry representatives and sellers by such wide margins that their messages reach a much smaller percentage of growers directly." Reviewing the problem, the National Academy of Sciences (NAS) concluded,

Practically no information is available to growers on the possible side effects from the use of pesticides over the long term, or on interactions between various insect, weed, and disease control measures; crop rotation, tillage, cultivation and other agronomic practices; soil erosion; profits; and (a newly added concern) farm fuel requirements. Tackling these problems would require systematic interdisciplinary studies which, at least up to the present, universities and other agricultural agencies have not mounted.

So long as farmers continue to believe that heavy reliance on chemical pesticides is the only viable technology for pest control, the problems of regulating exposures to pesticides, and ensuring that only compounds proved to be safe will be marketed, are probably insurmountable.

THE BACKLOG

The 1972 amendments to FIFRA provided for premarket screening of pesticides, through promulgation of new requirements for manufacturers and other registrants to prove the safety of their products as a prerequisite to registration; classification of all hazardous pesticides into a "restricted" category for use only by applicators certified as competent to handle them; and automatic cancellation of all registrations at the end of five years, unless an affirmative decision to reregister is made after review of the sufficiency of the data supporting such reregistration. The goal—adequate regulation of pesticide use— seemed in sight. Yet seven years later the goal remains unrealized. There are several reasons. One is the magnitude of the physical task of reviewing more than one million scientific studies supporting an estimated fifty thousand separate registrations. Another is a serious shortage of competent and available personnel. There have been lengthy delays in establishing criteria to govern the registration process, as well as a number of lesser problems such as intra-agency squabbles and the general bureaucratic inertia that plagues all federal agencies because of their size and distance from the subject area of regulation.

Revised registration regulations published in July 1975 set forth both the data required to be submitted in support of registration of a pesticide and the criteria by which that data would be evaluated. Thus a company applying for a new registration had to submit the results of animal tests conducted to discover whether the pesticide caused tumors or birth defects, interfered with reproductive capacity, or produced any other long-term adverse effects. Data showing the pesticide's effects on fish, mammals, and birds were also required. In addition, submission of information on environmental persistence, residues, and efficacy was included among the requirements for registration.

The trouble is that such data may take years to develop. Moreover, the energies of the EPA's Office of Pesticide Programs have been focused almost entirely upon attempting to review existing registrations rather than upon expediting the registration of new pesticides. Thus the pace of new pesticide registrations has slowed to barely a trickle in the past several years. One consequence has been that potential substitutes for some of the persistent chlorinated hydrocarbons the EPA has withdrawn from the market are still not available. In response to this situation farmer opposition to further regulation of the remaining chlorinated hydrocarbon pesticides has stiffened considerably. One recent example was the eleventh-hour intervention in the chlordane/heptachlor cancellation hearings by the states of Iowa and Missouri, literally demanding that heptachlor and chlordane—suspended in December 1975—be reinstated for use against cutworm on corn. Despite a record corn crop in 1977 there had been an extensive outbreak of cutworm, which caused a large number of farmers to lose some of their crop. Only a few effective substitute materials are available to control this insect. Although another substitute promising excellent control is in the registration "pipeline," approval could take years.

A recent change in the pesticide law is likely to expedite the registration of new pesticides, but at a serious cost to the goal of preventing exposure to compounds that may cause "unreasonable adverse effects on the environment." To break the registration logjam, Congress, at the EPA's urging, has provided for "conditional" registration whereby compounds that have not fulfilled all of the mandatory requirements can be marketed. The EPA has discretion to deny conditional registration status where studies demonstrating the health and safety effects of the compound have not been submitted, but Congress and the EPA have created a loophole through which manufacturers can place untested pesticides on the market. The magnitude of the task facing the EPA is enormous. The agency must review fifty thousand federal and state registrations representing numerous different formulations of approximately fifteen hundred different active ingredients. For example, while there are hundreds of registrations of chlordane, they all contain only one active ingredient.

A House committee investigating the EPA's pesticides program found that in May 1976 the agency had reviewed 889 of the 1,500 active ingredients to determine if its files contained enough information to assess safety. The committee reported that

only 419 of the 889 active ingredients review[ed] had sufficient information to make a determination, and of those 419 ingredients, 238 met or exceeded the risk criteria. More than 80% of those 238 active ingredients meeting or exceeding the risk criteria are suspect carcinogens. Moreover, by the number of registered products and by production volume, the 238 suspect active ingredients represent approximately one-third of all pesticides currently on the market.

The preceding figures indicate that as of May 1976 almost 200 of the 1,500 active pesticide ingredients registered were suspected carcinogens, and the data in the registration files were insufficient to permit any conclusions about the possible carcinogenicity of the other 470 active pesticide ingredients that had been reviewed by then. In addition, the EPA has not yet reviewed the files on more than 600 other active pesticide ingredients.

To complicate the problem further, Congress and other investigatory bodies have raised serious questions about the adequacy and propriety of safety testing of pesticides and drugs done by private laboratories under contract to the manufacturers. A group of agency and outside scientists, asked to review testing reports submitted by manufacturers on the forty-three pesticide active ingredients for which tolerances permitted residues on the greatest number of food and feed commodities, reported the existence of serious deficiencies in both the conduct and the reporting of the safety tests. Not only were certain procedures incorrectly or inadequately performed, but the data were often so poorly tabulated and summarized that a conclusion as to carcinogenicity could not be made. Other problems were created by methodological shortcomings—an inadequate number of animals, failure to report findings on all tissues studied, and lack of data on statistical differences in effects on treated as compared with control animals.

In testimony before a Senate committee, then EPA Deputy Administrator John Quarles admitted that the investigation showed that "serious problems may exist." He also acknowledged that valid results could be deliberately withheld because "a lab might be so dependent upon a pesticide producer for contract work that its independent scientific judgment could be impaired by the close economic relationship." Moreover, "a lab might intentionally misrepresent results at the request of the manufacturer." A vivid illustration of what Quarles meant was the recent indictment in Chicago, by a federal grand jury, of six corporate officers of Velsicol Chemical Corporation for allegedly withholding studies indicating the carcinogenicity of heptachlor and chlordane from the Environmental Protection Agency. (The indictments were subsequently dismissed because of improprieties in the conduct of the grand jury's investigation.)

At present, pesticide sales continue to skyrocket at the same time that the EPA and the other regulatory authorities are permitting human exposure on a grand scale. As noted earlier, pesticide salesmen have succeeded in expanding sales dramatically over the past decade, particularly through the printed media. Yet the Federal Trade Commission, the one federal agency that could require that pesticide advertising contain affirmative disclaimers about known or unresolved safety questions, recently decided not to regulate the pesticide industry. Only the most flagrantly misleading or deceptive advertising will be dealt with on a case-by-case basis. The public will continue to serve as the innocent victim of a regulatory breakdown of mammoth proportions. Pesticides either known to be harmful or not shown to be safe will continue to be marketed and used; residues of these compounds in food and feed, if detected at all, will be approved as safe because they do not exceed questionable tolerance levels; and advertisers will continue to stimulate pesticide sales on the unfounded premise that they may be used "safely." And all of this will occur against a backdrop of federal regulatory agencies presumably serving the public interest.

CHAPTER 7
DIET

Epidemiological evidence suggests that nutrition, as used in the broadest sense, affects the incidence of a large portion of human cancers, perhaps relating to as much as 50 per cent of all cancers in women and one-third of all cancers in men.

Dr. Ernst Wynder,
Cancer Research, 1975

You are what you eat, the adage goes, and the high rates of colon and breast cancer in the United States have been attributed in good part to diet. What you eat is not confined to food alone. Thanks to present-day marketing procedures, "food" often contains additives used to prolong shelf life or to "improve" the taste or color. Food may also contain residues of pesticides applied to crops under cultivation or residues of other contaminants such as PCBs, aflatoxin, vinyl chloride, lead, and asbestos—substances that have entered the food in nature or during processing, packaging, or storage. Meats and poultry may harbor residues of hormones, antibiotics, or other drugs given to animals to promote weight gain and protect them from disease. So what you eat is—unfortunately—composed of everything that you ingest: essential elements and nutrients, color additives, preservatives, antioxidants, hormones, fiber, fats, proteins, carbohydrates, naturally occurring carcinogens, and residues of industrial chemicals, pesticides, and other environmental contaminants.

The ways in which some of these components act as carcinogenic agents remain largely unknown and speculative. Independent associations between dietary fat and fiber content, the presence or absence of carcinogenic residues, the makeup of the bacteria that live in the intestine, and the nature of bile salts and acids also present there have all been correlated with cancer incidence. None has a clearly proven cause-and-effect relationship. But all are highly plausible and suggest that it makes sense to follow a diet that minimizes their potential harms.

According to Dr. Joseph J. Vitale, of Boston University School of Medicine, diet can play a role in cancer causation in several ways. Diet can

—carry carcinogens or their precursors
—promote change in the intestinal bacteria so that carcinogenesis is made easier
—increase the levels and reactivity of carcinogens
—influence absorptive properties or the morphology of tissues
—modify the host defense mechanism that would ordinarily help defend the body against cancer.

For example, for several years epidemiologists have noted a strong correlation between the rates of colon and breast cancer and the amount of fat that people in certain countries consume. Fats (also called lipids) are organic compounds that provide necessary energy for cells. In fact, fats provide more calories (or energy value) than any other food source. Fats yield nine calories per gram whereas proteins and carbohydrates each yield only four calories per gram. Fats are vital to the storage of energy reserves, and also act as the medium in which vitamins A and D are dispersed throughout the body.

The U.S., England, Canada, and Australia all have both high levels of dietary fat intake and high rates of breast and colon cancers, whereas several non-Western cultures show low rates of these cancers and have less fat in the diet.

DIETARY FAT IN RELATION TO TUMOR DEVELOPMENT

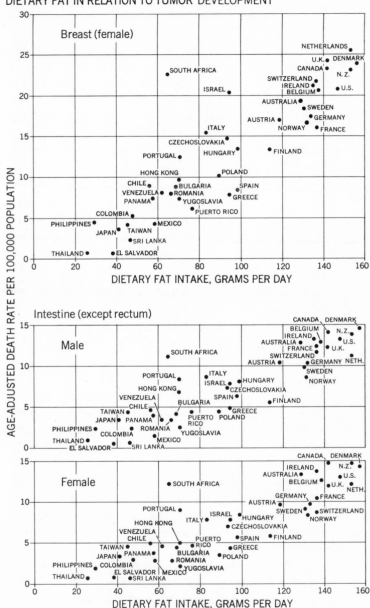

This has led many researchers to postulate that the amount of fat in the diet is a good index of the colon or breast cancer rate in the population.

There is other evidence that fat consumption has a bearing on cancer rates. Colon cancer is rarely found among Seventh-Day Adventists in California, who, because of religious beliefs, avoid meat (a prime source of dietary fat), coffee, tea, alcohol, spicy condiments, and tobacco. By contrast, American Jews of Eastern European ancestry have traditionally consumed a diet rich in fats, and this population shows a higher-than-average death rate from cancer of the colon.

Fat is probably not a direct-acting carcinogen itself. Although it may be a solvent for residues of carcinogenic chemicals, such as pesticides, large amounts of uncontaminated fat may make it easier for carcinogens or cocarcinogens in the digestive tract to do their work. Animal evidence supports this theory because dietary fat seems to encourage the growth of skin and breast tumors in rodents. In one experiment mice fed a diet high in Crisco, lard, butter, wheat germ oil, or coconut oil developed tumors in a significantly shorter time than did their fellow mice not so fed, when both groups were deliberately treated with carcinogenic agents.

Another distinction between Western (often termed "affluent") and traditional African diets is the extent of food refinement. Western processing techniques greatly decrease the amount of fiber by removing, for example, the germ and bran from grain. The word *fiber* is a general term used to describe plant products that pass through the digestive tract without being digested and without contributing any nutritive content. Fiber in the diet does serve a very important digestive purpose, however. It absorbs water from the stomach and intestinal tract, adding bulk to the fecal material and hastening its elimination.

The high-fiber diet has been touted lately as a panacea for prevention of colon cancer, diverticular disease of the colon, high levels of serum cholesterol, hemorrhoids, varicose veins, and gall bladder disease. This diet owes some of its popularity to Dr. Denis Burkitt, a British medical missionary who some time ago observed that colon cancer incidence is low among African populations that consume large quantities of raw fruits and vegetables and unrefined grain products. The high-fiber theory has it that the rapid fecal transit time through the gastro-intestinal tract prevents any carcinogens in the food from staying for long in contact with the intestinal walls. As logical as this might seem, other studies have failed to show increased colon cancer rates in the chronically constipated. Burkitt also believes that dietary fiber promotes the growth of intestinal bacteria, which are unlikely to form carcinogenic metabolites.

The rate at which waste passes through the system may also influence another potential carcinogenic factor: bile salts. Some authorities have suggested that degraded bile salts may be carcinogenic precursors, and slow transit of wastes increases contact with resultant carcinogens. Bile is a digestive chemical produced by the liver and stored in the gall bladder. It is composed of bile acids, pigment, neutral fats, cholesterol, inorganic salts, nucleoproteins, and other compounds, and it acts to emulsify fats during digestion. One theory holds that the large amounts of bile required to emulsify excessive dietary fat may change the type or number of intestinal bacteria. These altered bacterial populations may then metabolize bile acids into carcinogens or cocarcinogens.

The American diet is very complex, varying widely from person to person and place to place but containing perhaps too much fat and probably too little fiber. Even the sheer *amount* of food consumed seems to bear a relationship to the risk of cancer. Obesity is associated with increased cancer incidence, especially in women. Numerous studies have established a relationship between obesity and endometrial (uterine lining) cancer. Dr. Ernst Wynder, of the American Health Foundation, believes that overnutrition contributes not only to endometrial cancer rates but also to other endocrine-related cancers, including those of the breast, ovary, and prostate. Studies of overfeeding in animals have shown enhancement of carcinogenesis. In one experiment a low-calorie diet completely prevented spontaneous breast cancer occurrence in female mice, while 71 percent of the mice on normal control diets developed mammary tumors. Obesity caused by overeating may cause stimulation and hyperfunction of certain organs.

Similarly nutritional deficiencies are also associated with cancer. A weak, poorly nourished body may be far less prepared to cope with or defend itself against carcinogenic agents. Deficiencies of specific nutrients also show specific relationships to cancer. What is known as the Plummer-Vinson iron deficiency in northern Scandinavia is associated with high risks of cancer in the pharynx and esophagus. Molybdenum deficiencies in both the U.S. and Africa correlate with high rates of esophageal cancer.

It is clear that the nature of the diet undoubtedly influences the likelihood of cancer. It is less clear how each precise element of the diet fits into the puzzle alone or in conjunction with everything else consumed. But although the nature of the food we eat is important, the presence of naturally occurring chemicals and the use of man-made chemicals to increase or change the food supply are additional risk factors that cannot be discounted.

Nitrosamines are a case in point. Nitrosamines are potent carcinogens that are formed naturally from nitrites and amines, both found in the diet. The nitrites may come from food additives used as colors or preservatives in bologna, bacon, or other processed meats, or they may come from natural constituents of foods such as lettuce and spinach. The amines may come from a natural component of food, such as trimethylamine oxide in fish, or they may come from common drugs such as Darvon or antihistamines taken for allergy, or they may come from cigarette smoke. By avoiding foods to which nitrates and nitrites have been added a person can minimize the chance of exposure to nitrosamines.

Another naturally occurring carcinogen is safrole, an ingredient of sassafras leaves. Safrole was long used to flavor root beer. The Food and Drug Administration banned safrole in 1960 after it was shown to cause cancer in test animals. Old-timers sometimes remark that modern root beer doesn't taste as good as the old-fashioned kind. Unfortunately, that good old taste was safrole.

Oil of calamus, structurally similar to safrole, was banned for the same reason in 1968. This natural chemical was used to flavor vermouth and bitters.

Yet another natural carcinogen is aflatoxin, a toxin produced by a mold that grows only under conditions of sustained high humidity on peanuts and other agricultural products such as rice and corn. Aflatoxin does harm immediately—it can cause liver damage and suppression of growth—in animals at levels as low as 220 parts per billion in food. Aflatoxin in lower levels is not immediately poisonous but is among the strongest known carcinogens, causing cancer in laboratory experiments with rats at 1 part per billion of the daily diet.

Apart from whatever carcinogens may occur naturally, the American diet is replete with man-made chemicals, a number of them known or suspected carcinogens. In 1952, after two years of public hearings, the House of Representatives Select Committee on Food Chemicals concluded that the increased use of chemicals in food had already created "a serious public health problem."

This committee, colloquially referred to as the Delaney Committee after its chairman, Representative James J. Delaney of New York, heard testimony from the Food and Drug Administration that of about 700 chemicals employed in food production, 276 lacked any evidence of safety.

The surgeon general, the American Cancer Society, and the medical witnesses were virtually unanimous in the opinion that the public needed more protection from food chemicals with harmful long-range effects. The American Medical Association stated that unless food additives could be shown harmless beyond reasonable doubt, "they should not be employed in basic foods."

As a result of the work of the Delaney Committee, Congress finally passed two laws designed to meet the food chemical problem, the Food Additives Amendment to the Food, Drug and Cosmetic Act of 1958 and the Color Additives Amendment of 1960. These new laws gave the Food and Drug Administration authority to require testing of chemicals and to scrutinize additives prior to marketing. In addition the FDA was given power to set "tolerances," or upper limits, on pesticide residues on fresh produce and residues of chemicals in meat. The law required manufacturers to shoulder the burden of proof that their additives were safe. Contained in these laws is this special anticancer provision, called—after the congressman—the Delaney Clause: "No additive shall be deemed to be safe if it is found to induce cancer when ingested by man or animal, or if it is found, after tests which are appropriate for the evaluation of the safety of food additives, to induce cancer in man or animal."

The Delaney Clause prohibits the use of *any* amount of food additive that causes cancer. If an additive causes other kinds of harm, such as birth defects, liver damage, and so on, the FDA may allow small amounts, or "tolerances," of the additive if it determines that only high amounts cause such damage. The law prohibits the FDA from determining that any amount of a carcinogenic additive is "safe." It prohibits the FDA from permitting acknowledged hazards on the basis of "overriding benefits." In sum, the Delaney Clause embodies the scientific knowledge that no safe level of exposure to a carcinogen has been shown to exist. Its explicit prohibition on carcinogen exposure is unique in regulatory law.

The Food Additives Amendment, especially the Delaney Clause, has given the FDA full opportunity to ensure a wholesome food supply. It has not done the job. Twenty-five years after the Delaney Committee report, the bulk of food additives are still improperly tested for safety. "Lack of scientific data concerning harmlessness," as that committee put it, is still the rule. The issues raised in 1952 are fresh today.

One reason is that the FDA has taken advantage of a loophole in the food additives law to exempt from testing the large majority of food chemicals. The Food Additives Amendment of 1958 defines *food additive* as a substance "not generally recognized among experts . . . to be safe." In order for a substance to win approval for use in food, the manufacturer had to demonstrate that it was safe. The FDA skirted this regulatory responsibility by creating the new classification of chemicals called "Generally Recognized As Safe," or GRAS. Such chemicals by definition did not—and still do not—require testing for safety.

Initially the FDA compiled a tentative list of 198 substances that might be considered GRAS. At best the list was based on educated hunches. The agency conducted neither laboratory tests nor searches of the scientific literature and it made no explicit estimates of consumer exposure to each of the 198 substances. The FDA sent the list to 900 scientists asking if the substances were safe. Only 324 scientists replied. Of these, only 69 commented on specific substances. The FDA records show that the agency summarily dismissed the 69 comments, with such written notations as "critic not qualified" and "safety established." Even in rejecting views critical of the proposed GRAS substances, the FDA made no tests, literature searches, or calculations of consumer exposure.

As use of these GRAS substances soared in the 1960s with the boom in processed foods, the safety of some of them was called into question. The FDA banned safrole after evidence was found of its carcinogenicity. Other substances banned were oil of calamus, also for carcinogenicity; nordihydrogualaretic acid (NDGA) for causing abdominal cysts and kidney lesions; and the artificial sweetener cyclamate for causing birth defects and cancer. Understandably GRAS additives became a matter of public concern. The presidential consumer address to Congress in 1969 called for a review of the GRAS list. At present the FDA is reviewing this list, which now numbers more than seven hundred additives, with the aid of an outside advisory committee. But the agency is not solving the problem of untested additives and is again reaffirming the GRAS status of many substances whose toxicological properties are simply not well known. The majority of substances the FDA proposes to continue on the GRAS list have not been tested at all for long-term safety. Some substances even lack studies on their short-term safety. The outside advisory committee has commented on the lack of data. The committee termed data on oil of rue, for example, "meager" and asked that more studies be done on gum arabic, which was reported to be toxic to pregnant animals. The FDA is ready to keep substances on the GRAS list not because they are, in fact, safe, but because nothing in the scientific literature proves that they are hazardous. The case of saccharin shows how the FDA, in practice, ignored the law that says that the manufacturer must carry the burden of proof of safety.

As early as 1948 animal studies associated saccharin with cancer. Nevertheless, the FDA determined that saccharin was GRAS in 1959, and it remained so until 1972. Then the FDA classified saccharin as a suspect carcinogen and terminated its GRAS status. Ordinarily an additive that is not GRAS cannot be marketed unless there are studies to prove its safety. But rather than remove saccharin from the market the FDA used a legal category it had invented called "interim food additive regulations," which was designed to allow the marketing of additives for which positive but not conclusive evidence of harmfulness existed. The FDA argued that although the available animal studies on saccharin were alarming, the tests were conducted with commercial saccharin rather than pure saccharin and that contaminants could have caused the animal cancers. (Consumers were, of course, drinking diet soda that contained commercial saccharin, not the pure chemical.) In addition, the FDA challenged the experiments, stating that in one a set of animals might have had parasites of the bladder and that this could have influenced the test results. In another, the agency claimed, the significance of the results was questionable because a higher incidence of cancer was seen in the test animals given a low dose of saccharin than in those given a high dose.

Saccharin remained in its unusual interim status until March 1977. In that month the Canadian government published the results of a two-year rat study that showed an increased incidence of bladder cancer in the test group. The saccharin used was chemically pure. The FDA then banned saccharin as a proven hazard.

Public opposition to the belated ban was strong because saccharin was the last artificial sweetener remaining on the market. Inflamed by an industry-financed public relations campaign, many people wrote to their congressmen, ignorantly belittling the value of animal studies and suggesting that saccharin remain in use because its benefits exceed the risks. The American Diabetes Association urged that saccharin remain in use because of alleged psychological benefits. Deluged with letters, Congress passed an eighteen-month moratorium on the ban.

The weight control claims made for this carcinogen are unsupported. The law requires proof of a food additive's function and the fact that saccharin imparts a sweet taste meets this requirement, but proof of saccharin's ability to help control weight is not required and does not exist. Dr. Jesse Roth, chief of the diabetes branch at the U.S. National Institutes of Health, has stated: "Artificial sweetener has no special place in the diabetic's regime. The saccharin ban is of no consequence." This view is shared by other diabetologists. The way to control diabetes is to control the intake of calories and carbohydrates. Those who want soda must reckon the calories of soda in their daily consumption.

There is no evidence that artificial sweeteners generally help in dieting, and tests show that those animals fed artificially sweetened drinks make up for the fewer calories in the drink by eating more solid food. For saccharin in particular, studies have shown that saccharin lowers blood sugar. This is significant because lowered blood sugar levels trigger hunger. Very fat animals, in particular, ate *more* when fed saccharin. Stimulation of the appetite was also seen in rats fed very low doses of saccharin comparable with human daily exposure in soft drinks. These rats experienced greater increases in weight than rats not fed saccharin. In sum, no important health benefits have so far been demonstrated, and the continued use of saccharin is clearly inappropriate.*

---

* Congress, in its eighteen-month moratorium on the saccharin ban, had the FDA commission the National Academy of Sciences to write a report on saccharin. The NAS panel released its fifth report on saccharin (since 1955) in November 1978. The NAS concluded that this sweetener does pose a potential carcinogenic risk to humans, and that, while a weak carcinogen by itself, saccharin promotes the development of cancer initiated by other substances. The report also called attention to the increased consumption of saccharin-containing soft drinks by children under age ten.

Dietary exposure to coal tar dyes is another serious problem that, like saccharin, reflects the FDA's failure to require that safety be established prior to use. Approximately four million American children will have consumed more than one pound of coal tar dyes in food by the time they are twelve years old. Some will have consumed as much as three pounds.

Coal tar dyes belong to a suspect chemical family. A number of them, including butter yellow, an additive singled out by the Delaney Committee as a particular hazard, have been banned for causing cancer. Other banned coal tar dyes include red 1, red 32, green 1, red 2, and red 4. Others, such as blue 1, blue 2, and green 3, are banned in Europe but permitted by the FDA.

The FDA has complete legal authority to prevent carcinogenic coal tar dyes from being added to food. According to the law, permanent approvals for dyes may be granted only upon presentation by the manufacturer of scientific evidence proving safety. The success of the law, however, depends on the thoroughness of the scientific data required by the FDA to be submitted by the manufacturers and on the degree to which the FDA examines the data critically.

Since 1974 the FDA has permitted public inspection of the scientific data submitted in petitions for food additive approvals. Up until that time the only parties with access to the studies were the manufacturer and the FDA. Inspection by the Center for Science in the Public Interest and Ralph Nader's Health Research Group revealed that two of the six permanently approved food dyes cause cancer in animals. One of these is the omnipresent red dye 40, added to ice cream, candy, baked goods, and other processed foods.

Although the other permanently approved coal tar colors are not proven carcinogens, the long-term studies on these dyes in FDA files are substandard by any toxicological measure of the last twenty-five years and, moreover, provide suggestive evidence of cancer causation.

These studies have been in FDA files for some time, but there is little indication that officials have taken them seriously.

To the contrary, the FDA approved the dyes in a perfunctory manner. When safety concerns were raised within the agency, they were dismissed. Moreover, the FDA has permitted other coal tar food dyes to be used on the basis of temporary licenses, even though the agency admits that adequate safety studies on them are not available. The 1960 Color Additives Amendments permitted the FDA to give temporary licenses to food dyes then on the market, but these licenses were to last two and a half years, with a provision for extension "with the objective of carrying to completion in good faith, as soon as reasonably practical, the scientific investigations necessary for making a determination as to listing such additive." Eighteen years later four out of five of these temporary licenses remain in effect. There is still no definitive evidence that the dyes are harmful, but neither is there evidence that they are safe. In 1976 the FDA banned red 2, the most widely used food dye, after years of pleas by consumer groups that it was a suspect —though not a proven—carcinogen.

Little toxicological information of any kind exists on any of the non-coal-tar dyes approved by the FDA. Most of the twenty-three non-coal-tar dyes, such as titanium dioxide, carrot oil, caramel, azanth, and ultramarine blue, have been approved on the basis of poorly conducted studies or no studies at all. Only four of these twenty-three dyes were studied for long-term effects, and the results are difficult to assess because the data in the FDA files are so sparse. The FDA approved thirteen of the dyes permanently without tests of any kind.

Dyes and artificial sweeteners may be intentionally added to food, but some synthetic chemicals, such as animal feed additives and pesticides, wind up contaminating food as a result of their use in food production. The FDA has the power to regulate the use of animal feed additives that can become part of the human diet. For at least thirty years cattle farmers have used commercial feed containing a wide variety of chemicals, including the sex hormone diethylstilbestrol (DES) to promote weight gain in cattle. The residues of DES—or any other chemical—that end up in meat or poultry after slaughter are legally classified as "food additives" and, as such, need food additive approval from the FDA.

DES is a powerful carcinogen. It has caused cancer in at least six species of laboratory animals and at eight different organ sites. DES has caused cancer at virtually all dose levels. In one study the low dose of 6.25 parts per billion in feed induced cancer in mice. There is also evidence (detailed in chapter 10 of this book) that DES causes cancer in humans.

The FDA approved DES as a feed additive in 1954 upon assurances that residues would not occur in table meat if cattle producers stopped using the hormone in feed two days before slaughter. The 1958 Delaney Clause permits addition of carcinogens to animal feed if an FDA-approved "practicable" detection method shows that residues in meat for human consumption do not occur. As DES use continued, neither the FDA nor any other government agency searched for residues. The U.S. Department of Agriculture finally, in 1971, inspected meat samples and found DES residues. However, DES was not banned. Instead the FDA determined that residues would not be expected to occur if farmers stopped using DES feed seven days before slaughter. There was no way of knowing if this was true. Moreover, a seven-day grace period was unrealistic because farmers do not always know that far in advance when they will ship their animals to slaughter. Slaughter depends not only on the age of the animal but also on market price and the availability of transportation. The charade of the seven-day withdrawal period continued for two more years, until the FDA conducted another survey and conceded that DES used in feed could be expected to reside in table meat. The FDA then banned DES, but the manufacturers promptly took the agency to court and obtained a ruling that the ban was improper because it was not preceded by a hearing. In 1977 the agency again moved to ban DES, but proceedings have not been completed. To this day DES residues are detected in 1 to 2 percent of table meat.

DES is only one of fifteen sex hormones that the FDA permits in animal feed. Ten of these, such as melengestrol acetate, chlormadinone acetate, estradiol benzoate, and dienestrol diacetate, are proven or potential carcinogens. Like DES, dienestrol diacetate is associated with human vaginal cancer in the daughters of women who received it during pregnancy, and it has been the subject of an official FDA warning against its use as a drug in pregnancy. Yet no one can say the extent to which this feed additive appears in food. Since DES ends up in the human food supply, it is quite possible that other hormones do too. However, we do not know for sure. No one is monitoring for these drugs. As in the case of DES, there are no test methods that can be employed effectively in a regulatory program.

Other known carcinogens are used in animal feed. Nitrofuran drugs are added to prevent growth of parasites, as are the 5-nitroimidazole drugs. These drugs are added not to treat the occasional diagnosed parasite infestation but for daily, lifelong use in animal feed. Other antibiotics are also added to animal feed for the same reason. Drugs such as penicillin and tetracycline are added to promote growth and egg production. Essentially all turkey feed, an estimated 80 percent of the food for swine and veal calves, 60 percent of feed for cattle, and 30 percent of feed for chickens raised for food in the U.S. contain antibiotics. In volume this rivals all the antibiotics used in treating human disease in this country. In many cases residues of these antibiotics remain in the flesh of animals sold in the marketplace. For example, antibiotic residues in calves have been a continuing problem. Between 5 and 10 percent of the samples tested showed illegal residues. In swine, violations have averaged close to 9 percent.

Routine use of antibiotics in feed, as opposed to treatment of actual animal infections, is thought to pose two possible hazards to the public. Even minute residues of antibiotics in meat and poultry can sensitize people and cause allergic reactions, such as rashes and shock, when one of these antibiotics is medically administered. The continuous use of antibiotics can promote the growth of antibiotic-resistant bacteria responsible for antibiotic-immune infections in humans, as witness the recent emergence of typhoid, meningitis, gonorrhea, and pneumonia caused by antibiotic-resistant bacteria. It is not known whether this is the result of overuse of antibiotics in medicine or in animal feed. One study has revealed that the intestinal bacteria of some farm personnel were antibiotic-resistant when feed containing antibiotics was used on the farm. Because of these dangers, in 1970 Great Britain prohibited the routine use in feed of antibiotics commonly used to treat illness of people or animals. Only recently has the FDA proposed restrictions on penicillin and tetracycline in feed, but enactment of these restrictions is still a long time away.

Pesticides are another man-made contaminant found in food as the result of food production practices. Congress has charged three different regulatory agencies with the mission of controlling pesticide residues in food. The Environmental Protection Agency is responsible for establishing tolerance levels for pesticide residues on raw agricultural commodities and in processed foods. The United States Department of Agriculture is supposed to monitor beef and poultry products to assure that the EPA tolerances are not exceeded. And the FDA is supposed to monitor for residues in agricultural products and take enforcement action when foods with residues higher than the tolerance levels enter the market.

However, this elaborate approach has failed to protect the public. The EPA has set many tolerance levels without adequate evidence of safety. Inasmuch as it is impossible to establish any safe level of exposure to a carcinogen, the EPA has generally not set tolerances for pesticides known or suspected of being carcinogenic. This has not prevented carcinogenic pesticides from being used and contaminating food. In place of a tolerance level, a new term, *action level,* was adopted. An action level is the maximum amount of a residue that will be tolerated in food. Higher levels are prohibited. Lower levels are accepted. Action levels currently exist for several carcinogenic pesticides, including DDT, chlordane, heptachlor, aldrin, and dieldrin. Yet an "action level" bears little if any relationship to "safe level"; it is merely an arbitrary figure, based mainly on customary usage. It may or may not be safe. This circuitous regulatory tactic was adopted because if the sale of foods contaminated with carcinogenic pesticide residues were prohibited, a major portion of the U.S. food supply would be lost. As a combined result of agricultural practices and regulatory failure, contamination is general and pervasive.

Approximately four hundred pesticides are used on food crops, and the EPA has issued about six thousand tolerances or tolerance exemptions covering various products that are likely to be contaminated with residues. In 1975 the General Accounting office (GAO), the investigative arm of Congress, took a close look at the FDA's ability to monitor for 233 permanent tolerances in effect. The GAO found that the FDA was absolutely incapable of detecting 62 percent of the insecticides, 87.5 percent of the herbicides, 85 percent of the fungicides, and 86 percent of the other pesticides known to leave residues on food. Although the number of permanent tolerances has increased since 1975, the FDA's detection capabilities remain woefully deficient.

Because of the FDA's inability to detect the presence of most pesticide residues in the food supply and the unreliability of the data supporting existing tolerances, the GAO concluded that we have "little assurance that human health and the environment are being adequately protected from possible pesticide hazards."

The GAO recommended that the Environmental Protection Agency review all the supporting scientific data used to establish tolerances, evaluate human exposure to determine the actual level of dietary intake of residues, establish a procedure for routinely reassessing and revising existing tolerances, and develop a program with the FDA to test all residues for established tolerances. The head of the EPA's Office of Pesticide Programs accepted these recommendations, but to date nothing has been done. The problems of pesticide residues in food loom as large as they have in the past—or larger.

CHAPTER 8
RADIATION

There are two kinds of radiation—ionizing and nonionizing. Ionizing radiation is so named because it is able to strip electrons from atoms, leaving ions, which are electrically charged particles. Since atoms are the components of molecules, and molecules make up a cell, ionizing radiation is able to disrupt the most basic building blocks of life.

Although ionizing radiation and chemical carcinogens are obviously different from one another, they share some of the same characteristics in their ability to induce cancer. Both pose undisputed risks of cancer at high levels of exposure. Further, scientists have not been able to demonstrate a threshold for the activity of either chemical carcinogens or ionizing radiation, and consequently in neither case is a safe level of exposure known to exist. Therefore, as with chemical carcinogens, each exposure to ionizing radiation is believed to increase one's risk of cancer.

Like some chemical carcinogens, some ionizing radiation occurs naturally. Indeed, life on earth evolved in an atmosphere of what is known as natural background radiation. Each year the average American receives 130 millirems of ionizing radiation from natural background sources. (One millirem equals one-thousandth of a rem, a standard unit of measurement used to quantify dosage of radiation received.) Of the 130 millirems received by the average person, 26 come from radioactive elements, mainly potassium, within the body. The other 104 millirems come from external sources, cosmic rays in space, and radionuclides in the terrestrial environment. Exposure to cosmic radiation increases with altitude. For instance, the average annual dose of cosmic radiation received by people living in Colorado or Wyoming is 115 millirems as compared with 45 millirems for people living in Kentucky or Indiana. Terrestrial radiation, which averages about 60 millirems a year for each American, comes from exposure to radioactive elements, chiefly uranium, thorium, and potassium, in the crust of the earth.

In addition to natural sources of ionizing radiation there are man-made sources. The Office of Radiation Programs in the Environmental Protection Agency estimates that the average American receives between 100 and 190 millirems of ionizing radiation a year from man-made sources. This means that the man-made dosage is often equal to or greater than the 130 millirems the average American receives from all sources of natural background radiation.

X rays and radiopharmaceuticals—radioactive drugs used in the diagnosis or treatment of disease—account for 90 percent of the man-made dosage. The use of radiopharmaceuticals is limited to a restricted portion of the population, but X rays are not. A survey by the U.S. Public Health Service revealed that in 1970 a total of 129 million Americans underwent 210 million medical and dental X-ray examinations, during which 650 million pictures were taken. These figures do not include the sizable number of X rays taken in the armed forces, prisons, and other institutions.

Exposure to man-made ionizing radiation is a relatively recent development in the history of mankind. The use of X rays began in 1895, when Wilhelm Roentgen, a German physicist, discovered that emissions from a high-voltage cathode ray tube would cause a phosphorescent screen to glow and that the rays that caused this could be blocked by objects of sufficient density. Roentgen had his wife place her hand between the cathode ray tube and a photographic plate, and then he turned on the tube. When he developed the plate, he could see her hand and the bones within it. The medical profession was quick to adopt Roentgen's invention of the X ray. Within a few years nearly fifty books and a thousand articles had appeared on X-ray diagnosis and treatment.

By as early as 1906 some researchers suspected that ionizing radiation from X rays could pose a serious health hazard; however, the first documentation of this did not come until 1944, when Dr. Herman C. March, who had spent fifteen years studying the obituaries in the *Journal of the American Medical Association,* reported that radiologists who worked with X-ray machines on a regular basis were ten times more likely to die from leukemia than other physicians. That same year Drs. Paul S. Henshaw and James W. Hawkins, of the National Cancer Institute, also reported that the incidence of leukemia in physicians as a profession was nearly double that in the population at large, and they attributed the high incidence to X-ray exposure.

But the curious fact is that few physicians read research journals, and X-ray abuse persisted for decades. After World War I medical irradiation was deemed highly beneficial for large segments of the population. X rays and, to a lesser extent, radium and other radionuclide treatments were directed at the head and neck to alleviate any of a dozen maladies. These treatments were believed to cure enlarged or inflamed tonsils and adenoids and to eradicate ringworm, acne, and other skin disorders. It was said that X rays would alleviate asthma, whooping cough, enlargement of the lymph nodes of the neck, and deafness caused by enlarged lymphoid tissue around the eustachian tubes. It was also believed that X rays could effectively atrophy the thymus, a gland in the neck that may become enlarged in youngsters, affecting growth, development, and metabolic rate. All told, a million people, including hundreds of

thousands of infants and children—who are especially susceptible to cancer from radiation—received these dangerous treatments between 1920 and 1955.

In the early fifties, articles in medical journals began to report a significantly increased incidence of thyroid nodules and
cancers in persons who had received radiation treatment five
to thirty-five years previously. In the case of former acne suf-
ferers, cancer sometimes appeared as long as forty-five years
after treatment. Not until the late 1960s did radiation of the
thymus gland in infants and children cease as a common practice, but by then the results were appalling.

Between the National Cancer Institute's second and third
national cancer surveys, in 1947 and 1969–71, the age-adjusted
incidence rate for thyroid cancer in the overall population
jumped from 2.4 to 3.9 per 100,000. This was an abnormally
large increase, but the NCI did not make a large-scale effort
to inform the public of the potential dangers until 1977, when
it made press releases and information available to the public
and to physicians. Hospitals and doctors were encouraged to
try to identify former patients who may have had the X-ray
treatments. Those who had been irradiated were urged to have
a check-up of the condition of their thyroid gland.

Other instances of excessive exposures have come to light.
One study of childhood malignancies indicated that children
irradiated *in utero* during maternal diagnostic X ray had twice
as great a risk of death from leukemia or other malignancy by
the age of sixteen. Subsequent studies lowered this risk to one
and a half times, but even that figure demonstrates that pregnant women should carefully weigh the need for X-ray diagnosis or treatment that may cause irreparable damage to the
fetus.

In 1975 epidemiologists W. M. Court Brown and Sir Richard Doll conducted a study of fourteen thousand British youngsters who had been irradiated for an arthritic disease of the
spine known as ankylosing spondylitis. Their study revealed
that leukemia accounted for ten times the expected number of
deaths.

Prior to the 1950s there were no laws to regulate the manufacture, sale, and use of X-ray devices. The machines themselves often had defective collimators, which are supposed to adjust the beam to match the size of the film with reference to the exact part of the body being X-rayed. To make matters worse, operators often had only a rudimentary understanding of the machine. Some operators even removed the collimators, allowing the X rays to scatter. In 1963 more than half of the inspected medical X-ray units registered with state health departments did not meet minimal safety standards.

A 1972 report by the National Academy of Sciences estimated that the number of diagnostic X rays could be cut by 30 percent, either through improved technology or through elimination of unnecessary or repetitive examinations. There could also be significant reduction in patient exposure by proper adjustment of X-ray field size, correct collimation, and the use of shielding for the gonads. In 1973 the United States Public Health Service promulgated a series of standards for X-ray devices, but compliance is largely voluntary.

Considerable controversy has surrounded the use of X rays to detect breast cancer, the leading cancer killer of American women, with 33,000 deaths a year at last report. In 1963 the National Cancer Institute supported a study undertaken by the Health Insurance Plan of Greater New York in which 62,000 women, ages forty to sixty-four, were split into two groups. Of these, 31,000 women were offered yearly X-ray breast examinations, and 20,000 accepted. The second group of 31,000 women did not receive mammographic X-ray exams. After five years the women who had been X-rayed experienced a one-third reduction in deaths from breast cancer because of cases diagnosed early enough for treatment, and many persons were led to believe mammography was highly useful in combating the disease. But there was a catch here: The lower rate of breast cancer death was observed only in participants age fifty and over. For women under fifty, breast cancer death was as frequent in the study group as in the control. Moreover, in light of current knowledge the X-ray examinations may have significantly increased the risk of breast cancer for women in the under-fifty age group, but this will not be known for at least ten to twenty years.

In 1973 the NCI and the American Cancer Society jointly organized a nationwide Breast Cancer Detection Demonstration Project at twenty-seven medical centers in hopes of recruiting, screening, and following 270,000 women for early detection of breast cancer. Mammography was one of the screening techniques. The program came under attack after Ralph Nader's Health Research Group learned that seventeen X-ray machines at some of the centers were delivering unnecessarily high levels of radiation. In fact, one machine at Georgetown University in Washington, D.C., was giving three times the prescribed dosage. In late 1975 the NCI requested expert reports on the use of mammography in women under fifty. Dr. Arthur Upton, who has since become the director of the NCI but who was then at the State University of New York at Stony Brook, noted in his report, "We cannot recommend the routine use of mammography in screening asymptomatic women ages 35 to 49 years in the NCI/ACS [program] at this time. Although the presumptive risk to a single individual may be small, the total risk to a large population of healthy women might not be justified unless outweighed by the expectation of a commensurate benefit."

As a result the NCI has ended routine screening by X-ray mammography for women under fifty, except in cases where the benefits are believed to outweigh the risks. Such cases would involve women with histories of breast cancer either in themselves or in their mothers or sisters.

Few would argue against the benefits of X-ray diagnosis where the need is real, but far too many Americans get far too many X rays for their own good. Dr. Karl Z. Morgan, professor of health physics at the Georgia Institute of Technology and a pioneer in the study of the health effects of radiation, estimates that as a result of exposure to radiation from medical sources, up to 13,500 Americans are seriously disabled and 7,500 die each year from cancer.

Despite the obvious hazards, only five states—New York,

Arizona, New Jersey, Kentucky, and California—and Puerto Rico require that X-ray technicians be licensed, and no states call for periodic reviews of competence in the field. As Dr. Samuel Epstein, then of Case Western Reserve University, and Richard Grundy, of the Senate Committee on Public Works, have written, "Serious policy questions can be raised regarding the efficacy and validity of current radiologic practices that, in effect, allow all physicians to prescribe virtually any radiologic service even though they may not have demonstrated their knowledge of proper procedures or of radiation protection."

Although exposures to ionizing radiation from sources other than medical devices are currently of a far lesser magnitude, they are no less real and important. Exposure to strontium-90 and other radioactive elements released as fallout from nuclear weapons testing account for approximately 2.5 percent of the man-made radiation received yearly by the average American. Contamination from testing is so pervasive that all of us carry residues in our bodies. Indeed, the entire planet has been affected.

It is probably too early to say what effect nuclear testing has had on the incidence of cancer. Sufficient time may not yet have elapsed to overcome the characteristic latency periods for cancer induction. In any case it would be difficult to ascribe specific cancers to fallout because it is so widespread, and cancers induced by radiation are indistinguishable from cancers caused by other agents.

Even so, there is concern. Studies of Japanese by the Atomic Bomb Casualty Commission showed that without question single exposures to high doses of radiation increase the rate of incidence for leukemia and for breast, lung, and thyroid cancers. In 1977 the cancer branch of the Center for Disease Control in Atlanta began investigating cases of leukemia after two army veterans—Paul Cooper, of Elk City, Idaho, and Donald Coe, of Tompkinsville, Kentucky—came down with the disease. Cooper and Coe and some 3,000 others participated in a 1957 atomic test in the Nevada desert staged by the army to determine how troops would react to nuclear warfare. In

1976, after Cooper came down with leukemia, which he attributed to his participation in the test, the Veterans Administration rejected his application for disability benefits. The VA eventually approved the application, although the government has yet to admit a connection between the leukemia and the atomic test. However, when Coe's leukemia came to light amid the publicity given the Cooper case, the Center for Disease Control asked the army for a list of personnel who might have been in the area at the time of the test. The search for all these men still continues, and the center has so far identified six more leukemia victims. The expected number of leukemias in an average group of 3,000 Americans is little more than three.

Additional concern about fallout comes from the experience surrounding the detonation of a hydrogen bomb near Bikini Atoll in the Pacific in 1954. Prior to the test the U.S. evacuated all residents of Bikini to another island four hundred miles distant. In 1968 President Lyndon B. Johnson announced that Bikini would be rehabilitated and the natives returned. In 1969 the Atomic Energy Commission (AEC) surveyed the island, and an AEC official reported, "There is virtually no radiation left, and we can find no discernible effect on either plant or animal life." The U.S. spent $3 million planting fifty thousand coconut trees and building forty houses. One hundred islanders returned, and when some sought to move to the interior of the island, a radiological survey disclosed that the interior was too contaminated for safe occupancy. Moreover, two staples raised on the island, pandanus and breadfruit, contained excessive radioactivity. The Bikinians asked for more studies, and these showed that the level of strontium-90 in the well water exceeded standards and that the radiation levels in coconuts were so high that the natives were warned to eat no more than one coconut a day. In 1978 the Interior Department asked Congress for $15 million to move the Bikinians to still another island, stating, "It is now clear that for the foreseeable future the island of Bikini in the Atoll should not be used for agricultural purposes, particularly for local consumption, and should not be considered a residential area."

Other exposures to man-made, or, more properly, "technologically enhanced," sources of ionizing radiation include radon in natural gas, radon in drinking water, radiation emitted by coal-fired power plants, and radioactive emissions associated with the nuclear fuel cycle.

The public has not generally associated the use of natural gas in the home with risk of exposure to radioactive elements, but unvented kitchen ranges and space heaters can serve as sources of radioactive radon-222, a potentially considerable risk to health. The EPA has calculated that in 1970 almost 141 million Americans were at risk from radon in natural gas. Radon is sometimes found in the same geological strata as natural gas, and there it can diffuse and mix with the gas. When a well is drilled and the gas is tapped, distributed, and burned in unvented systems, exposure to radon occurs. The EPA figures that 125 million Americans are exposed to an average of 15 millirems per year from radon in unvented ranges, and nearly 16 million people are exposed to an average of 54 millirems annually from radon coming from unvented space heaters. The EPA estimated that in the course of a year anywhere from 15 to 109 persons die from lung cancer as a result of this radon exposure.

Potable water supplies may also contain radon. Neither the size of the risk nor the extent of contamination is known, but recent EPA research indicates that many groundwater supplies may exceed the established safe level. In fact more than a fourth of 507 groundwater samples taken throughout the country exceeded the safe level. Contamination was highest in Maine and New Hampshire, where close to 80 percent of the samples exceeded the safe level, in some cases by at least fifty times. A person drinking a glass of contaminated water ingests any radon remaining in solution, but the potential for trouble does not end there. When water containing radon is heated, as in cooking; aerated, as in a shower or dishwasher; or agitated, as in washing by hand or machine, radon can escape rapidly and enter the home atmosphere, where it can be inhaled by all members of the family. The dangers from radon in water have yet to be defined, but action to limit exposure is obviously imperative.

The expected emphasis on coal to meet energy demands is likely to increase exposure to radioactive elements. Some coal deposits contain uranium, and when coal containing uranium is burned, the uranium is released into the air. Concentrations of uranium in coal vary. Higher concentrations are generally found in coal from western states—North and South Dakota, Montana, Wyoming, New Mexico, Idaho, and Nevada—whereas lower concentrations occur in coal from the Appalachian region. Exposure to ionizing radiation from coal depends on what coal is burned and where one lives. At present, average exposure from coal burning is believed to range from between 0.5 to 15 millirems per year.

The use of enriched uranium as a fuel in nuclear power plants has caused great public controversy, even though government estimates minimize the nuclear fuel cycle as a source of exposure to ionizing radiation. The EPA's Office of Radiation Programs lists "nuclear fuel cycle, jet travel, consumer products, etc." under the catch-all heading of "other sources" and calculates that they constitute less than 1 percent of exposure to man-made ionizing radiation.

Still, proliferation of nuclear power plants throughout the United States and other parts of the world is a source of increasing anxiety. At present, sixty-five nuclear plants are operable in this country, and some two hundred are expected to be on line by 1990. Concern ranges from the disposal of mill tailings to plant operation and the storage of radioactive wastes.

The mining of ores containing uranium actually began in this country at the turn of the century, but milling, the extraction of uranium from the ore by mechanical crushing, did not begin until the 1940s. Ore is mined both underground and on the surface by stripping. Strip mining produces the largest amounts of waste. For instance, in 1974 stripping for uranium ore in Wyoming produced a very high volume of wastes: 103,531,000 tons of overburden, 515,000 tons of waste rock, and close to 3,000,000 tons of mill tailings.

The proper disposal of these radioactive tailings has been and continues to be a serious problem. Only since the 1960s have licensing requirements provided for site neutralization, and even then to varying degrees. As a result there are twenty-two sites where tailing piles have been abandoned. The largest is in downtown Salt Lake City, Utah. As of 1970 more than 80 million tons of tailings covered 21,000 acres of western land. Casual regulation of abandoned mills used during the Manhattan project has led to the use of uranium tailings in the construction of more than 6,000 structures around Grand Junction, Colorado, not including streets and sidewalks. Steps have been taken to correct this situation, but this thoughtless and careless construction exposed the public to an unnecessary radiation hazard, and it takes only one incident like this to prompt concern about future disposal.

Processed uranium fuel powers nuclear reactors, which generate electricity. Radiation from plant reactors reaches the environment either as direct radiation, which may be of significance within the reactor boundary, or through discharges of low-level radioactive gaseous and liquid wastes. The extent of the risk posed by these sources of ionizing radiation remains unclear, though several studies suggest that the hazards may be sizable. For instance in 1974 Dr. Samuel Milham, of the University of Washington, after studying the deaths of 310,000 workers of various occupations in the state who died between 1960 and 1971, reported that there appeared to be more cancer deaths than expected among atomic workers. Two years later, in 1976, Dr. Thomas Mancuso, of the University of Pittsburgh; Dr. Alice Stewart, a well-known British epidemiologist; and George Kneale, a statistician, reported on the deaths of 3,883 atomic workers at the U.S. nuclear facility at Hanford, Washington, who died between 1944 and 1972. They found that these workers suffered an increased risk of at least two types of cancer—cancer of the pancreas and bone marrow. The Mancuso study created considerable stir because the average total dose received by the workers during their years of employment was well below exposure levels permitted. If correct, the findings strongly suggest an increased cancer risk at low levels of occupational exposure. According to Karl Morgan, of Georgia Tech, the Energy Research and Development Administration, now the Department of Energy, has made a serious effort to find fault with the Mancuso study, but so far it has been unable to uncover substantial reason to doubt the conclusions.

The National Institute for Occupational Safety and Health is investigating reports of a high incidence of cancer among workers on nuclear submarines at the Portsmouth Naval Shipyard in New Hampshire. The investigation came about after the Boston *Globe* reported that Dr. Thomas Najarian, of the Veterans Administration Hospital in Boston, had found that workers exposed to radiation while performing maintenance on nuclear submarine reactors at the shipyard suffered cancer at twice the rate of the general population. After the *Globe*'s story appeared, the navy, which had refused to release information on radiation exposures to shipyard employees, announced it was asking the Department of Energy to oversee a study of possible links between radiation and cancer at Portsmouth.

Dr. Ernest Sternglass, of the University of Pittsburgh, and Dr. Morris de Groot, of Carnegie-Mellon University, have generated considerable furor with studies on the rates of infant mortality in relation to the location of nuclear power plants. In 1977 de Groot stated that he had confirmed Sternglass's earlier finding of significant increase in infant mortality in areas adjacent to three nuclear power plants. No such correlation with infant mortality was observed around a fourth plant.

While controversial and certainly not universally accepted, the studies of Milham, Mancuso, Sternglass, and de Groot raise serious questions about the safety of normally functioning nuclear power plants both for those who work in them and those who live near them. The evidence is not conclusive, and many questions remain unanswered, but doubt has been raised in the minds of some about the safety of the daily operation of nuclear power plants.

The disposal of nuclear wastes from power plants and other

sources is a problem that has yet to be solved satisfactorily. How does one dispose of plutonium 239, with a half-life of 24,400 years? Thus far, the nuclear power industry has accumulated an inventory of 2,500 metric tons of wastes, and temporary storage areas are already becoming difficult to find. By the year 2000 the inventory will amount to almost 200,000 metric tons, and no one knows where this radioactive waste can be stored permanently and safely. This does not count the high-level wastes accumulated by the production of plutonium for weapons. The threat to public health or the environment from nuclear wastes would be minimized if satisfactory disposal procedures were easily at hand, but they are not, and unfortunately experience to date gives reason for concern. For instance, there are 600,000 gallons of highly radioactive liquid wastes and two million cubic feet of radioactive trash buried at the Nuclear Fuel Services reprocessing plant in West Valley, New York, 30 miles southeast of Buffalo. On occasion, water has leaked from this trash, carrying radioactivity into Cattaraugus Creek, a tributary of Lake Erie. The $32.5 million plant was the first of its kind in the country. It opened in 1966 and ceased operations in 1972 because it was losing money and state officials opposed expansion. The state attorney general at the time complained of "an operation record which raises serious questions about risks to those who work there."

In the course of an investigation for the *New York Times Magazine* in 1977, reporter Richard Severo uncovered some 400 "incidents" at West Valley. Among them:

—In 1968, a malfunctioning ventilator backfired and spewed radioactivity into the lunchroom, into the lobbies, and onto the front lawn. Radioactivity was found on vending machines and lunch tables. Some plant personnel inhaled radioactive particles. The lunchroom was "decontaminated the next day," but the grass and soil of the front lawn had to be dug up and interred in a radioactive burial site.

—In 1969, company representatives visited the home of a worker and confiscated a pair of boots, workshoes, socks and pants, a footrest cover, two throw rugs, a mattress cover pad, and a baby blanket. Some of this was decontaminated and returned, while the rest was buried. Severo wrote, "It remains unclear how long the baby blanket and other items contaminated by something the worker brought home from the plant had been in the home before the confiscation."

—Because a worker failed to turn on a valve, radioactive water went through regular drainage pipes.

Inasmuch as federal law does not require the company to do follow-up studies on workers, there are no data showing the effect employment at the plant may have had either on workers or on their families. Even so, a local physician, Dr. Reza Ghaffari, of Springville, told Severo, "I have practiced in this area for seven years, and my impression is that the number of congenital abnormalities is high for the number of people who live around here. We have had lots of cancer, lots of hydrocephalics, lots of cleft palates. But this is just my impression based on what I know of the area. It is not possible to make any broader statements; the statistical information is simply not there."

Estimates are that it will cost between $500 million and $1 billion to decommission the plant and dispose of the wastes. This cost will be borne not by Nuclear Fuel Services but by the taxpayers of New York state. The company had leased the land from the state, then governed by Nelson Rockefeller, an ardent proponent of nuclear power, and according to an agreement with the state Atomic Research and Development Authority, "Upon any cancellation or termination of the leases . . . the Authority will assume full responsibility for perpetual operation, surveillance, maintenance, replacement and insurance of the then high level storage facilities."

"There is no information on potential doses to individuals or the general population from low-level waste burial practices," the EPA Office of Radiation Programs reported in 1977. "However, two of the commercial burial sites, the West Valley and

Maxey Flats disposal facilities, have failed to perform as planned. Authorization to operate the burial facilities was based on analyses of the site hydrology, meteorology, etc., which, it was believed, demonstrated that the buried radioactive wastes would not migrate from the site. That is, they would be retained on the site for hundreds of years. In 10 years or less, radioactivity has been detected off-site."

Ionizing radiation leaves its debris in the form of radioactive material, which continues to emit energy long after its usefulness. By contrast, nonionizing radiation leaves no wastes to be buried but may cause irreversible biological harm. Unlike ionizing radiation, nonionizing radiation does not strip electrons from atoms but heats by causing molecular vibrations within cells. The jury is still out on the risks inherent in exposure to low-level sources of nonionizing radiation. However, one source of nonionizing radiation—ultraviolet waves from the sun—is known to cause skin cancer.

Even though physicians have known since the 1890s that ultraviolet waves can cause skin cancer, overexposure to the sun is a growing problem in the United States. In the last twenty-five years the rate of incidence of skin cancer has doubled, and with upward of 300,000 cases a year it is the most common cancer in the country. The increase is largely attributable to the popularity of sunbathing and possibly to the adoption of more revealing clothes. The effect of all this has been particularly noticeable on women, who have in recent decades begun to suffer increased incidence of skin cancer on their legs.

The highest rate of skin cancer incidence occurs among whites living in the southern and western states, the so-called Sun Belt. Genetic predisposition also appears to play a role inasmuch as fair- or ruddy-complexioned persons of northern European stock are most vulnerable. This is borne out by data from abroad. South African whites have the world's highest mortalities from skin cancer. Australians are next, and the Irish are third, even though Ireland receives only half the ultraviolet radiation of the other two countries.

If treated early, the majority of skin cancers are curable, but about seven thousand deaths a year occur in the U.S. from malignant melanoma, a virulent type of skin cancer, which can spread rapidly to other parts of the body. Fortunately, people can protect themselves by limiting exposure to the sun, using sunblock ointments, and wearing protective clothing.

As with ionizing radiation, man-made or technology-enhanced forms of nonionizing radiation exist. At high levels of exposure some forms of nonionizing radiation are proven health hazards. At low exposure levels our knowledge is inconclusive. It is fair to say that exposure to low doses of nonionizing radiation has yet to be proven safe. Further, as in many other cases, suggestive evidence is emerging which indicates that heretofore unrecognized risks really do exist.

Man-made forms of nonionizing radiation include ultrasonic radiation, radio frequency waves, and microwaves. Almost nothing is known about possible harm from low-level exposure to ultrasonic radiation, yet hundreds of thousands of patients are being examined and treated medically by the use of ultrasonography. A number of scientists believe that because of the low power level of this medical equipment, diagnostic use is relatively harmless to the patient. However, this is something we should know with a greater degree of certainty than we now have before ultrasonics are used without hesitation or used very extensively to examine fetuses, women's breasts, and other body tissues. We should not forget that during the first years of medical use of X rays thousands of patients received X-ray doses capable of inducing carcinogenic effects not seen until many years later.

It is well known that at high power levels ultrasonic radiation can produce serious harmful effects, including enzyme inactivation, chromosome aberration and breakage, nerve blockage, paralysis, cataracts, liver necrosis, brain damage, and fetal anomalies. Whether or not any such effects can occur at the extremely low levels of diagnostic exposure is unknown. But what we know about the hazards of low-level ionizing radiation should prompt caution.

In recent years radio frequency waves and microwaves

have become so pervasive that the U.S. is now blanketed in "electronic smog." Before World War II there were about fifty thousand radio-frequency transmitting devices in the country, but now there are more than seven million, not counting those used by the military. At the end of World War II television was in its infancy with less than ten stations, but now there are almost a thousand, each transmitting at very high or ultrahigh frequency. Microwaves are emitted by radar, orbiting satellites, TV transmitters, telephone relay systems, burglar alarms, CB radios, and diathermy units used to treat arthritis, bursitis, congested sinuses, and muscle and joint ailments. Microwave ovens are literally the hottest home appliance on the market. In 1975 the sales of microwave ovens exceeded those for gas ranges, and by 1980 sales will be second only to color TV sets among all appliances.

As Paul Brodeur made evident in *The Zapping of America,* there is considerable controversy regarding the magnitude and types of risk from exposure to microwaves and radio frequency waves. For a long time most scientists in the United States believed that the only harm that could result from those long-wavelength radiations was from excessive heating of critical body tissues. Scientists in the Soviet Union, however, strongly disagreed. In fact, starting in the 1930s, Soviet scientists pioneered a study on the effects of low-level microwave radiation on the human central nervous system, and as a result the Soviet Union, Poland, and Czechoslovakia have set occupational microwave standards one thousand times stricter than the occupational standards in the U.S. The Soviets have reported that workers in prolonged or repeated contact with microwaves or radio frequency waves suffered eye pain, headache, malaise, dizziness, irritability, emotional instability, depression, diminished intellectual capacity, partial loss of memory, loss of hair, hypochondria, and loss of appetite. In 1975 the president's Office of Telecommunications Policy noted that after years of denigrating Eastern European studies, U.S. researchers were beginning to confirm some findings that showed that low-level exposure to microwaves was indeed injurious to biological systems.

Until recently there was no reason to suspect that exposure to microwaves could result in an increased risk of cancer. But several cases have now been reported where the incidence of cancer is higher than expected in those persons occupationally exposed to microwaves. The data are not conclusive. They are, at best, circumstantial. But they do include the following:

—Two cases of leukemia and one case of skin cancer were found among seventeen men, aged thirty to fifty, who had been conducting electromagnetic pulse tests at U.S. missile sites between 1968 and 1972.

—Two brain tumors were diagnosed among twenty-three technicians testing microwave equipment for an army project in the late 1960s. Both men, who were in their thirties, died, but when their deaths became known in 1970, the contracting company, Philco-Ford, refused to divulge any information on the grounds of security. In March 1971 *Medical World News* quoted Philco-Ford officials as dismissing the two brain tumors as a "statistical curiosity."

—Three out of eight civilian employees at a naval air station in Rhode Island who were repairing equipment similar to radar that emitted both microwaves and X rays developed cancer. One man died of lung cancer in 1970, one died of pancreatic, lung, and liver cancer in 1973, and the third has also been found to have cancers of the pancreas, lung, and liver. Pancreatic cancers are very rare in people under the age of forty, and both victims were in their thirties.

While most people do not believe that microwave radiation will turn out to have the same potent biological effects as X rays and other forms of ionizing radiation, the fact is that we still do not know what the long-term effects of exposure to low levels of microwaves will be. If microwave radiation does turn out to have irreversible biological effects, it will be too late for many to do anything about it.

CHAPTER 9
CONSUMER
PRODUCTS

Led by Ralph Nader in the early 1960s, consumers began to organize to demand performance and safety in all kinds of products. From automobiles that were "unsafe at any speed" to unnecessary additives in baby food, consumers started to force changes upon once-unquestioned industries. But for all the advances of the consumer movement, manufacturers still offer many items for sale that pose a carcinogenic risk. Just go to your friendly neighborhood hardware store, drugstore, or supermarket for spot cleaners, solvents, lacquers, hair dyes, children's sleepwear, and birth control pills. Among them, one or another of these products may contain chlorinated petroleum products, benzene, 4-methoxy-m-phenylenediamine, Tris, or estrogen—all chemicals that have caused cancer in test animals or man.

Literally hundreds of products may contain cancer-causing ingredients and, through normal use, pose risks to the consumer. They present a health threat of unknown magnitude, pointing again to the need for the premarket testing of chemicals. We will examine five major products: cigarettes, alcohol, synthetic hormone drugs, hair dyes, and flame retardants. The history of their wide public use and the voluntary nature of exposure to them make each of them important in any consideration of environmental carcinogenesis.

CIGARETTE SMOKING

Americans know that cigarette smoking is a prime factor in this country's high incidence of lung cancer. Or do they? As the Tobacco Institute, a trade association, puts it, "For many adults, cigarette smoking is one of life's pleasures. Does it cause illness—even death? No one knows." At stake is a fifteen-billion-dollar industry. Despite a 1971 ban on radio and television advertising of cigarettes and a mandatory warning label on the pack and in print advertising, sales are still climbing. After the surgeon general's 1964 report on the health consequences of smoking, cigarette sales dropped from 516 billion to 505 billion per year. In 1969 sales dropped again, this time by 12 billion, in part attributable to antismoking Public Service announcements. When these announcements were virtually gone from the air, in 1971, sales increased by 13 billion and had risen to 620 billion cigarettes in 1976. The cigarette sales continue to increase by 1 to 2 percent yearly, despite a smaller number of smokers. Women, for example, smoke an estimated two more cigarettes per day than they did in 1970.

From the earliest days smoking has been a subject of controversy, though not necessarily concern. In 1859 a French physician named M. Bouisson documented adverse health effects from smoking. Bouisson described sixty-eight patients with oral cavity cancer at a Montpellier hospital. Of these, he noted, sixty-six smoked pipes, one chewed tobacco, and one used tobacco in some form. Lip cancer, he observed, developed most frequently in the men who smoked short-stemmed clay pipes called mouth burners. Those who smoked pipes with longer and cooler stems were not observed to have lip and mouth cancers with such high frequency. Bouisson suggested that these cancers were caused by the irritation of oral tissue by the joint action of the heat and the tobacco.

At the turn of the century cigarette smoking came into vogue, and after World War I cigarettes surpassed pipes, cigars, snuff, and chewing tobacco in popularity. In 1936 Dr. Alton Ochsner, of New Orleans, an internationally known surgeon, reported that *every one* of his lung cancer patients was a heavy smoker of cigarettes, and he predicted a lung cancer epidemic unless people stopped smoking. In 1939 A. H. Roffo, of Argentina, reported that tarlike tobacco extracts induced cancers when painted on rabbits' skin.

After World War II the push to study smoking and its effects on the body intensified. Among others, Dr. Richard Doll, in Great Britain, and Drs. Daniel Horn and E. Cuyler Hammond, in this country, found remarkable consistency in their studies despite cultural and age differences among the participants. The studies showed that lung cancer was on the rise and that cigarette smoking was to blame. Between the early 1920s and 1960 cigarette sales zoomed. During that time the per capita yearly cigarette consumption by U.S. adults jumped from 750 to 3,900. The number of people who smoked also grew significantly. Given the latency period for lung cancer, the mortality rates reflect this increased consumption and increased popularity of the smoking habit. In 1935 deaths from lung cancer in the U.S. totaled 4,000. In 1945 deaths from lung cancer rose to 11,000. By 1960 there were 36,000 lung cancer deaths, and in 1971 an estimated 60,000. This is a fifteenfold jump in only thirty-six years, and the population did not even double in that time.

The link between cigarette smoking and lung cancer is one of the few readily observable cause-and-effect situations outside the workplace. In the first report to the surgeon general in 1964 a committee of ten physicians and scientists noted that

—Animal studies identified seven carcinogenic polycyclic aromatic hydrocarbons, a number of cancer promoters, and other toxic and irritating gases and particulates in smoke.
—Clinical and autopsy studies of smokers described damage to a variety of cells, tissues, organs, and body functions.

—Retrospective and prospective population studies found increased incidence of cancer and circulorespiratory illness in smokers as compared with nonsmokers.

—A 70 percent increase in the age-specific death rate for males (and lesser, but still increased, death rate for females) was associated with cigarette smoking.

Cigarette smoke and subsequent cancer causation show remarkable dose-response relationships. For example, lung cancer death rates increase with the depth of inhalation of smoke. The death rate also tends to be higher in people who began smoking at younger ages. Lung cancer rates increase proportionally with the number of cigarettes smoked per day. It has often been said that after ten years, lung cancer death rates of ex-smokers approach those of people who never smoked. British epidemiologist Richard Peto has reexamined the data on which these conclusions were based and has come up with a different conclusion. He says, "The truth seems to be that when smokers quit, their extra lung cancer incidence rate remains remarkably constant for at least 15 years thereafter, and probably for longer."

Of course, there are other causes of lung cancer. Various chemicals, ionizing radiation, air pollutants, industrial hazards, and viruses have all been named. Conversely, lung cancer is not the sole malady associated with smoking. Cancers of the urinary bladder and pancreas have elevated rates in smokers. Coronary artery disease is 70 percent more prevalent in smokers than in nonsmokers.

In the last decade the case against cigarettes has become even stronger. In a 1977 paper Dr. Bruce Ames, of the University of California at Berkeley, reported that smokers have substantially more mutagenic substances in their urine, and since mutagenicity in the Ames bacterial test is highly correlated with carcinogenicity, an association between cancer at various sites and smoking may be supported. Ames tested both morning and evening urine samples. The morning samples were either nonmutagenic or less mutagenic than the evening samples. The evening samples were all mutagenic. Indeed, the urine became more mutagenic as the day—and the smoking—went on. Two of the smokers in the study did not inhale, and the mutagenicity of their urine was similar to that of non-smokers. With two smokers who smoked low-tar cigarettes, defined by the American Cancer Society as having 15 milligrams or less of tar, one had mutagenic urine and the other did not. Samples of urine from a control group of nonsmokers were not mutagenic.

Tobacco apologists sometimes claim that lung cancer is not caused by smoking but by genetic susceptibility—in other words, that some people are inherently susceptible, since many non-smokers develop cancer and many smokers do not. A new theory does link genetic susceptibility and cigarette smoking, and it attempts to explain why some smokers develop cancer and others do not. The theory involves an enzyme called aryl hydrocarbon hydroxylase (AHH). AHH is known to metabolize polycyclic aromatic hydrocarbons (PAHs) found in cigarette smoke. Some of the metabolitic products of PAH that result are carcinogenic. The theory has it that some persons have higher levels of AHH in their bodies and thus may have increased risk from exposure to PAHs in smoke. This has yet to be confirmed because no one has found a marked familial occurrence of lung cancer, but AHH activity is known to increase during smoking and to recede when smoking stops. There is genetic susceptibility to all types of cancers—but smokers do not have a genetic component that causes cancer. Cigarettes cause cancer. Genetic factors may just influence the severity or likelihood of an individual's response to a carcinogen like cigarettes.

There are some who maintain that the carcinogenic agent in cigarette smoke has never been identified. In a strict sense they are correct, because no single component isolated from tobacco smoke has been shown to be the sole causative agent in human lung cancer. But there is a wealth of information on the toxic and carcinogenic chemicals contained in tobacco smoke—and there are many—that may play independent or synergistic roles in the initiation or promotion of carcinogenesis. More than three thousand components have been identified in the particulate and gas fractions of cigarette smoke. The gases include water vapor, ammonia, carbon dioxide, carbon monoxide, hydrogen cyanide, and various phenols, aldehydes, organic acids, and oxides of nitrogen. Particulates include tar, nicotine, cadmium, benzo(a)pyrene, nitrosamines, some pesticide residues, and several radioactive elements such as polonium-210 and thorium isotopes.

Given the overwhelming evidence, it is surprising that smoking continues. In 1964 the Department of Health, Education and Welfare began surveying the public attitudes on smoking. The most recent survey, on the adult use of tobacco, in 1975, began, "Cigarette smoking continues to pose a major public health problem in the United States, in spite of more than ten years of efforts on the part of concerned organizations and individuals to counteract it." The survey found that 39.3 percent of males and 28.9 percent of females smoked, which was down from the 1970 figures of 42.2 percent of males and 30.5 percent of females. Divorced or separated persons had the highest smoking rates. Sixty percent of divorced or separated men smoked, whereas 50 percent of the women in the same categories smoked. By contrast only 33 percent of the married men and women smoked. Of college graduates who did smoke, half have quit.

Of those interviewed, 90 percent agreed that smoking is harmful to health, and 84 percent thought it represented enough of a health hazard to warrant doing something about it. About two out of every three smokers and three out of four in the general population felt that teachers, doctors, and health professionals should set an example by not smoking. In 1964 little more than half of those interviewed believed that smoking should be allowed in fewer places than it was then. In 1970 that attitude was shared by 57 percent of the public, and by 1975 70 percent believed in such limitation. In fact 40 percent of *smokers* favored stricter federal regulations on cigarette smoking.

Many nonsmokers object to smoking because they contend it violates their right to clean air in offices, restaurants, planes, buses, and other enclosures. Much current research deals with the adverse effects suffered by persons exposed to "sidestream smoke," the smoke coming from a burning cigarette when it is not being smoked.

In an increasing number of instances the "right" to smoke is being curtailed. In 1976 a New Jersey court banned smoking in an office after an employee sued on the grounds that tobacco smoke made her sick. The Civil Aeronautics Board (CAB) rules guarantee every air traveler the right to a seat in the nonsmoking section of an airplane. The CAB has also banned the smoking of cigars and pipes on airlines.

Cigarette smoke, like pollen or dust or animal dander, can be an active allergen for many nonsmokers. The range of reactions is wide, and it varies from eye irritation and breathing difficulty to nausea and headache. No one knows whether or not sidestream smoke can have chronic effects, such as cancer, on bystanders. It is exceedingly difficult to separate the effects of sidestream smoke from that of polluted air. How would one know that a nonsmoking bystander got lung cancer by living with a cigarette-smoking spouse and not by exposure to a smog inversion?

Half the tobacco burned in a cigarette becomes sidestream smoke, and this half releases about two-thirds of all the aerosol particles. Sidestream smoke also contains an overwhelmingly high nitrosamine content, far higher indeed than that in mainstream smoke. Nitrosamines are among the most potent carcinogens. For example, dimethylnitrosamine (DMN) was found at levels of 1.7 to 97 nanograms (billionths of a gram) in mainstream smoke, but in sidestream smoke, the DMN levels were 680 to 1,770 nanograms. A smoker can partially block intake of nitrosamines in the mainstream smoke by using a cellulose acetate filter, but there isn't a thing a nonsmoker can do to avoid an overwhelmingly high dose.

The clearest insight on the effects of smoking on non-smokers comes from studies of carbon monoxide (CO) levels in the blood. The blood has specially constructed molecules—hemoglobins—that carry oxygen to all cells. Carbon monoxide does not cause cancer. The problem with CO is that it preferentially binds to the hemoglobin, forming carboxyhemoglobin, so that the heart must work harder than usual and cells, and in severe cases the entire body, suffocate. In one study volunteer smokers and nonsmokers were put in an unventilated room. The nonsmokers suffered a mean increase of 1 percent in blood carboxyhemoglobin levels. The investigators in this study suggested that nonsmokers absorbed an amount of CO equivalent to that of smokers of one cigarette. Some researchers have suggested that the concentration of tobacco smoke in crowded rooms can exceed the federal air quality standard for particulate matter (260 nanograms per cubic meter for not more than one day per year). Dr. Nicholas T. Iverson, of the U.S. Public Health Service Hospital in Staten Island, New York, wrote recently in the *New England Journal of Medicine,* "It is nearly inconceivable that when enough studies have been done, there will be no long-term ill-effects from passive smoking."

ALCOHOL

People who smoke increase their risk of cancer. People who both smoke and drink alcoholic beverages, including beer and wine, increase their risk even more. Studies indicate that alcohol and cigarette smoking act synergistically to enhance the carcinogenic potential, particularly in the mouth and throat. Indeed, the combination of alcohol and cigarettes accounts for about 75 percent of the oral cancers in American men.

It is possible that alcohol itself is a carcinogen, but at present it is generally accepted that alcohol is a cofactor in cancer causation, although no one knows the exact biochemical processes involved. Contaminants in alcoholic beverages may also play a part in the development of cancer. Nitrosamines, alkaloids, PAHs, asbestos, and as-yet-unidentified compounds in alcoholic beverages may act as promoters, initiators, or cocarcinogens.

Strong correlation exists between alcohol consumption and cancer of certain oral sites. Some recent studies have attempted to remove confounding factors such as cigarette smoking in order to obtain a more accurate estimate of the cancer risk attributable to alcohol alone. A 1972 study by Kenneth Rothman and Andrew Keller showed that heavy drinkers who did not smoke were more than twice as likely to develop oral cancer than nondrinkers who were also nonsmokers. A heavy drinker was defined as one who consumed one and one-half ounces of absolute alcohol a day, the amount contained, for example, in three twelve-ounce beers. Smokers who smoked more than two packs per day but who did not drink ran about the same rate of risk as the heavy drinkers. But persons who were both heavy drinkers and heavy smokers were fifteen times more likely to get oral cancer than the nondrinkers-nonsmokers.

In a French study published in 1962, D. Schwartz and his colleagues reported that "alcoholism was also significantly more common among patients with cancers of the [mouth, hypopharynx, larynx, and esophagus], and also among those with cancer of the tongue, even after adjusting for tobacco use and age." Dr. Ernst Wynder and his colleagues at the American Health Foundation have studied cancer rates for drinkers and found that even with smoking and other confounding factors removed a heavy drinker might expect almost a tenfold increase in oral cancer risk over a person who consumes only a little alcohol.

In discussing the role of alcohol in producing esophageal cancer, Dr. John W. Berg, a former editor of *Cancer* and now a professor at the University of Colorado School of Medicine, recently stated that alcohol "is strongly associated with esophageal cancer in this country. [Studies] have explained this by showing the alcohol dissolves the normal barrier in the esophagus that keeps food in and keeps chemicals in the food away from those cells of the esophagus that are capable of becoming cancerous."

Alcohol is also believed to be in part responsible for some of the observed incidence of liver cancer. Of all liver cell cancers, 60 to 90 percent are found in cirrhotic organs. Dr. Albert Lowenfels, of the New York Medical College, writes, "The incidence of hepatoma [primary liver cancer] varies markedly throughout the world, but when it does occur in Europe or

North America, the patient is most likely a chronic alcoholic with cirrhosis of the liver."

HORMONES

About thirteen million women in the U.S. routinely use estrogens. Eight million take them in oral contraceptives for birth control, while another five million use them during or after menopause. But drugs containing estrogens or other hormones present a serious problem. First of all they are, in a great number of cases, taken by healthy women, not from medical necessity but because of personal convenience or treatment of minor ailments, and they are often taken over a period of many years. Now the efficacy of estrogens in treating some symptoms of menopause is being questioned, and new evidence on the hazards of birth control pills has come to light. In short, women who take oral contraceptives or use hormones to get through menopause are increasing their risk of cancer. Indeed, the risk of uterine cancer for some women who took menopausal estrogen supplements for more than a year was five to ten times greater than for a woman who had never used them.

In 1977 the Food and Drug Administration began requiring drug manufacturers to insert special notices warning consumers about the use of menopausal estrogens. The FDA did this despite opposition by the drug industry and the American College of Obstetrics and Gynecology. The agency's concern was based on the idea not that estrogen drugs should never be used—there are times when they may be of valid medical assistance—but that they are often used too frequently and for too long a time. Commissioner Donald Kennedy of the FDA has remarked, "It is entirely possible for a woman to take estrogens during her entire adult life." This is not in the least farfetched. A young woman might take oral contraceptives in her teens to clear up acne, alleviate menstrual cramps, or regulate the menstrual flow. She might then take oral contraceptives for birth control or use estrogen drugs to relieve postpartum breast engorgement, which can occur if a mother does not nurse an infant. In her forties and fifties a woman might take estrogens to alleviate the nervousness, hot flashes, and depression of menopause. Some women continue to take estrogens after menopause in the hope that they will retain a soft, supple skin and feel "younger." But in fact current scientific opinion holds that not only are estrogen drugs ineffective in treating menopause nervousness, depression, or making the user feel youthful, but they are likely to promote cancer.

The data support this. Since the 1930s estrogens have initiated cancers of the uterine lining, breast, cervix, ovary, pituitary, testicle, kidney, and bone marrow in laboratory tests on mice, rats, hamsters, rabbits, and dogs. In humans epidemiological studies show a significant rise in endometrial (uterine lining) cancer. In the U.S. the death rate for endometrial cancer rose from 18.7 per 100,000 in 1970 to 23.8 per 100,000 in 1976. According to a recent review, endometrial cancer is becoming the predominant uterine cancer in industrialized countries. In point of fact the ratio of endometrial cancer to invasive cervical cancer, the other common uterine cancer, is now 5.5 to 1. Although it is clear that the Pap smear screen for cervical cancer has significantly lowered the incidence of cervical cancer, there is little doubt that the rising incidence of endometrial cancer has been caused by the increased use of estrogen drugs in the last twenty years.

Other studies stress the danger. A dose-response relationship for estrogens shows that in women who use them for one to five years the risk ratio is 5.6 to 1. In everyday terms a woman who uses estrogens is more than five and one-half times as likely to develop endometrial cancer than a woman who does not. For five- to seven-year users the risk ratio is 7.2 to 1, and for women who use estrogens for more than seven years the risk ratio jumps to 13.9 to 1.

A gynecological tumor service in the Kaiser Permanente Medical Center in Los Angeles observed the following:

—Postmenopausal women who received estrogen developed endometrial carcinoma, on the average, five years earlier than did those who did not take estrogen.

—In premenopausal women 31 percent of the cancer patients had received estrogen as compared with only 4 percent of the controls.

—In postmenopausal women 70 percent of the cancer patients had taken estrogen, whereas only 23 percent of the controls did so. In this regard it is worth noting that endometrial cancer has shown the most marked increase in white women over the age of fifty, probably because women who are more affluent are the most likely to receive estrogen therapy for postmenopausal symptoms.

As Dr. Marvin Schneiderman of the NCI says, "We've got to decide whether hot flashes are more important than cancer of the endometrium."

Many of the estrogen products are simulated versions of naturally occurring sex hormones. The body uses estrogens and progesterone (female hormones) as well as testosterone (a male hormone) to send chemical messages that control reproduction, growth, and other functions. Medical science has derived a number of synthetic hormones for similar purposes. Diethylstilbestrol, or DES, is an example. No molecule in the body looks like DES, but this synthetic hormone has the capability to perform a number of hormone-related functions. It is widely used to promote weight gain in animals, and has been used in a number of human drugs.

In the late 1940s and early 1950s DES was thought to help prevent miscarriages. It is now known that DES was not effective in this regard. Nonetheless, some of the women who took it did bear children. In 1971 Dr. Arthur Herbst and his colleagues at Massachusetts General Hospital shocked the medical world with a report describing seven cases of a very rare genital tract cancer—clear-cell adenocarcinoma of the vagina—in young women between the ages of fourteen and twenty-two in Boston. Ordinarily this tumor is found only in much older women. The mothers of six of the seven girls had taken a DES drug during pregnancy years before.

At present more than 200 cases of adenocarcinoma have been diagnosed in "DES daughters," who ranged in age from seven to twenty-eight. Inasmuch as 500,000 to 2 million women took synthetic nonsteroid estrogens during pregnancy, it would seem that the cancer has occurred in only a very small number of the daughters exposed. It is also possible that other cases have yet to be discovered. Besides adenocarcinoma other abnormalities of vaginal cells have been observed in 70 percent of DES daughters.

Abnormalities have been found in male offspring, but so far as is known, DES has not caused genital cancers in males. Herbst suggests that prostate disorders may be discovered in these men fifteen or twenty years from now. In animal experiments male DES offspring have very high rates of sterility and suffer various abnormalities of the reproductive tract. In 1977 the Occupational Safety and Health Administration fined a pharmaceutical house in Illinois more than fifty thousand dollars after male workers in DES production suffered from breast enlargement and impotency.

The use of DES to prevent miscarriage ended in the late 1950s, after it was found to be ineffective. But DES is still prescribed—to healthy, young adult females. It is popularly called the morning-after pill, and it is used as a postcoital contraceptive on many college campuses across the country. The dose is large (25 milligrams) and is often taken twice a day for five days to protect a woman who had intercourse while possibly ovulating.

Birth control pills are a daily source of exposure to hormones for users. Since 1976 the FDA has required that the following notice be included in each package of birth control pills:

Women who have or have had clotting disorders, cancer of the breast or sex organs, unexplained vaginal bleeding, a stroke, heart attack, angina pectoris, or who suspect they may be pregnant should not use oral contraceptives. Birth control pills are not recommended for women past the age of 40 because they increase the risk of heart attacks. . . . However, proper use of oral contraceptives requires that they be taken under your doctor's continuous supervision, because they can be associated with serious side effects which may be fatal. Fortunately, these occur very infrequently. The serious side effects are:

1. Blood clots in the legs, lungs, brain, heart or other organs.
2. Liver tumors, which may rupture and cause severe bleeding.
3. Birth defects if the pill is taken while you are pregnant.
4. High blood pressure.
5. Gall bladder disease.

Notify your doctor if you notice any unusual physical disturbance while taking the pill.

Although the estrogen in oral contraceptives causes breast cancer and other cancers in certain animals, it is not known whether or not oral contraceptives can cause cancer in humans. At this time there is no definite evidence that they do.

The term *the pill* is actually a misnomer, since there are more than 150 brands of oral contraceptives on the market. Each manufacturer controls the type and amount of the active and inert ingredients. Most of the preparations contain from 5 to 10 percent of an estrogenic compound. Mestranol and ethinylestradiol are the most widely used, and a small amount of a progestagen is employed to even out the menstrual cycle. Brands differ widely in the type of progestagen employed. The best-known progestagen is progesterone, which, like estrogen, is a hormone produced by the body. Put into very simplified terms, oral contraceptives work by tricking the body into believing it is pregnant. No eggs are released, and menstruation does not occur unless the hormone stimulation is removed. Thus, most pill preparations are taken daily for twenty-one days, then stopped for seven days so that the menstrual cycle can be completed.

A relatively new concept is the "minipill." Estrogen has been removed from these oral contraceptives, leaving only a progestagen. Doses of 500 micrograms or less of progestagens can inhibit pregnancy, probably by making the uterine lining unreceptive to the implantation of the embryo.

Oral contraceptives can cause temporary side effects, which are essentially the same as the body changes seen in pregnancy. Nausea; vomiting; cramps; edema; breast tenderness, enlargement, and secretion; changes in weight; and mental depression are common symptoms. Other side effects are "breakthrough" bleeding, changes in menstrual flow, changes in cervical erosion and secretion, cholestatic jaundice, lowered milk production when given immediately after childbirth, migraine and headache, allergic rash, changes in the curvature of the cornea, cataracts, nervousness, dizziness, hirsutism, loss of scalp hair, and changes in appetite and libido. Pill users also run an excess risk of developing blood clots or strokes.

There is no clear evidence that suggests that oral contraceptives cause or inhibit breast cancer in the general population. However, it appears that they may increase the risk of breast cancer in certain subgroups of the population, including young women, women with benign breast neoplasia, and women using oral contraceptives before the birth of their first child, according to a World Health Organization study group's 1978 report. The long-term effects of oral contraceptives on breast cancer are poorly defined because the pill has been in use for less than twenty years.

The cervix is the mouth of the uterus. Cervical cancer detection and prevention are among the triumphs of preventive medicine, thanks to a simple, painless, and effective test that can be used routinely in the doctor's office. Called the Pap smear, after the late Dr. George N. Papanicolaou, who devised the cellular smear, it has drastically reduced the incidence of cervical cancer.

There are many unanswered questions regarding the effects of steroidal estrogens on cancer of the cervix. To date, there have been equivocal results in studies that compared cervical cancer rates in pill users with rates in women using other birth control methods. There is difficulty in evaluating these studies because of the many "personal habit" factors that correlate well with cervical cancer incidence. These include age at first experience of sexual intercourse, number of sexual partners throughout life, and personal and partner hygiene. Many researchers believe that a sexually transmitted virus will eventually be implicated in this phenomenon. Because cervical cancer when treated in its earliest stages can be stopped, women on the pill who have regular Pap smears may show lower cervical cancer rates because a physician annually evaluates the cervical cells.

The cells of the cervical surface are known to change under the influence of hormones, whether or not the hormones come from internal sources, such as with increased estrogen levels during pregnancy, or from external sources, such as the pill. For a time, it was believed that these cellular ("atypical hyperplasia") changes did not always lead to cervical cancer. In 1977, however, Dr. Elizabeth Stern and her colleagues at the University of California reported that in a prospective study of women with cervical dysplasia the severity of the dysplasia and its conversion to cancer were heightened in pill users as compared with women using other contraceptive methods. Stern reports, "A clinical implication of the study is that women with dysplasia who take the pill are at increased risk for developing cancer in sites of the cervix."

Some of the strongest evidence against the use of artificial hormones is showing up not in the genital organs but in the liver. Benign hepatomas (liver lesions), a relatively rare malady, are appearing with increased frequency in users of oral contraceptives. J. K. Baum first reported this in the British medical weekly *The Lancet* in 1973, and by March 1976, 107 cases of the rare liver lesions had been reported, with 90 percent of the patients confirmed oral contraceptive users.

In 1977 the Center for Disease Control in Atlanta released its study on the development of nonmalignant liver tumors in oral contraceptive users. The center reported that about five hundred cases of such tumors have been seen in this country, primarily in the last decade. Although "benign," the tumor can kill by sudden rupture and hemorrhage. Longtime users of oral contraceptives ran the most serious risk. Compared with women who had used oral contraceptives for a year or less, women who had taken the pill for seven years or more were found to be 500 times more likely to develop hepatocellular adenoma, and women who had taken birth control pills for four to seven years were found to have a 120-time risk factor.

Many factors compound the connections between hormones and cancer. Diet, smoking, sexual activity, and child-bearing can have an effect. The International Agency for Research on Cancer suggests that hormones may act in any of the following ways to induce cancer:

—They may be direct-acting carcinogens.
—They may stimulate the production of other hormones that when present in excess are carcinogenic.
—They may act together with other factors to promote neoplastic growth in tissues that have been affected by a physical, chemical, or viral carcinogen.
—It is possible that hormones are able to modify the metabolism of otherwise harmless chemical agents, changing them into carcinogens.
—Hormones may modify the body's immune-response system, which would in other cases protect against carcinogens.

HAIR DYES

I'd rather get cancer than stop dyeing my hair.
> Diana Newton,
> Washington *Post,* December 27, 1977

Many women agree with Diana Newton. But thousands of others do not and have sought alternatives to the hair-dyeing procedures they have traditionally used for years.

Hair dyes have been used in the U.S. for more than fifty years, a fact often cited as establishing their safety. However, neither this length of time nor the evidence from scientific testing that has been done has established the safety of hair dyes. To the contrary, recent research indicates that several chemicals commonly used in semipermanent and permanent hair dyes are absorbed through the skin and cause cancer in laboratory animals.

The hair dye industry is a $300-million-a-year business, supplying an estimated more than 30 million Americans each year. But hair dyes are only a small part of the enormous cosmetics industry with yearly sales of $7 billion. There are more than twenty-four thousand different cosmetic formulations on the market, and they contain any one or a combination of approximately eight thousand different ingredients. Because of inadequacies in laws governing the sale of cosmetics, the public is exposed to thousands of ingredients about which there is little, if any, health effects information. We simply don't know what these chemicals can do to people. Nor, given the present statutory and regulatory situation, are we likely to find out.

The FDA is responsible for regulating cosmetics, but it has no authority to require that manufacturers test their products *before* they enter the marketplace. A cosmetics producer does not violate the law even if he fails to conduct a single safety test either before or after introducing a new product. Moreover, the FDA has no authority to require the cosmetics manufacturers to provide the necessary information that would enable the agency to conduct its own premarket evaluation. Manufacturers cannot be legally compelled to submit ingredient lists, consumer complaints, or test data to the FDA. Consumer products such as hair dyes sold for use in beauty salons do not have to be labeled with the ingredients they contain. Cosmetics manufacturers are not even required to inform the FDA that they or their products exist.

In the case of hair dyes the situation is even worse. Unlike other cosmetics, which can be removed from the market if they are shown to contain "poisonous or deleterious" substances, hair dyes cannot. They are specifically exempted from regulation as "adulterated cosmetics," and therefore, even if they contain hazardous ingredients, they cannot be removed from the marketplace by the FDA. There is no scientific or legal basis for this exemption. Its continuance is a reflection of the political muscle wielded by the cosmetics industry.

The vast majority of hair dyes are known as coal tar dyes, because the chemicals contained within these products were once derived from tar obtained through the distillation of bituminous coal. (They are now synthesized in the chemistry laboratory.) Approximately 75 percent of hair dye products currently sold are permanent hair dyes, which when applied to the hair penetrate into the hair shaft and form a permanent color. Only when new hair grows does the coloring have to be reapplied. The average woman using these dyes applies them every four to six weeks, thus exposing herself to a wide variety of chemicals initially present or formed during the dyeing process.

The fact that hair dyes can be absorbed through the skin is most vividly demonstrated by a report in the *Journal of the American Medical Association* entitled "Dark Urine after Hair Coloring." The authors, S. Marshall and W. S. Palmer, reported that a woman had noted discolored urine, suggesting the presence of dye chemicals, after dyeing her hair with commercially available products. Many similar cases had been reported in the scientific literature. Even more recently it was reported that one hair dye manufacturer had reformulated his product for men because male users were getting hysterical when they noticed their urine turning dark brown or black. Previously the same formulations had been manufactured for both men and women. The company, however, did not change the women's dye because women don't ordinarily bother to notice the color of their urine.*

Once absorbed, hair dye can circulate through the bloodstream, entering organs such as the liver, where they can be metabolized and then circulated further to affect specific target organs. In studies performed at the National Cancer Institute on mice and rats, hair dye chemicals that entered the bloodstream following ingestion had multiple adverse effects on organs throughout the body. Rats fed 4-methoxy-m-phenylenediamine (4-MMPD), used in about 80 percent of the permanent hair dyes, developed tumors of the skin, preputial gland, clitoral gland, and thyroid in statistically higher numbers than in control animals. Likewise, mice developed tumors of the skin, thyroid, and ear canal. The NCI staff and its advisory group, the Clearinghouse on Environmental Carcinogens, both concluded that 4-MMPD was carcinogenic to mice and rats and

* As an NCI spokesman noted, "It's a matter of anatomy."

therefore posed a potential carcinogenic risk to humans. Fortunately, on products sold for home use the contents are usually listed. Therefore, consumers can avoid products containing this hazardous chemical. However, the problem is not limited to 4-MMPD. Other hair dye chemicals, such as 2-nitro-m-phenylenediamine, 4-amino-2-nitrophenol, direct black 38, and direct blue 6, have also been shown to be carcinogenic.

Safe alternatives must be developed, but the hair dye industry is in no rush to produce safe formulations.

Unlike the NCI, the FDA, the Clearinghouse on Environmental Carcinogens, and the EDF, the cosmetics industry does not agree that 4-MMPD, or any other hair dye chemical or product, poses a risk. They argue that other animal tests and human experience itself support the safety of hair dyes. This argument is totally incorrect.

Animal studies performed by the hair dye industry have been scientifically inadequate. They were skin-painting studies, which may appear more appropriate than the NCI feeding studies, but which have several very significant scientific limitations. Too few animals were used in most experiments, and this alone was likely to preclude the detection of any carcinogenic risk. Moreover, the frequency of application had to be severely limited because of the irritating properties of hair dyes themselves. Further, given the small size of the test animals to which the dyes were applied, the dose received was in many cases less than that comparable to human exposure. Even in the instances where the number of animals and the frequency of application were increased, the tests were inadequate because of the low dose actually absorbed through the skin. As noted previously, it is essential, when using small numbers of animals, to maximize their exposure to the chemical in question in order to see any possible effects. This procedure is widely accepted as scientifically necessary and proper. Otherwise, important findings can be missed. Only after a hair dye enters the bloodstream can it exert harmful effect. Therefore, the route of entry into the blood, whether it is by absorption through the skin or absorption through the intestine following ingestion, is not likely to affect the conclusions on the carcinogenicity of these products.

The cosmetics industry also cites studies on cosmetologists —hairdressers, beauticians, and barbers—that show that they have no higher incidence of cancer than the general population. Therefore, the industry argues that their exposure to hair dyes has not caused any problems and is indicative of what can be expected for hair dye users. The story is not that simple. Although some studies on cosmetologists indicate no increased risk of cancer, others do. The latest study, done by Ph.D. candidate Judy Walrath at Yale University, shows cosmetologists had a significantly higher rate of acute leukemia than did a control population of teachers. Even if cosmetologists have a higher incidence of a particular type of cancer than either the general population or a specific subgroup, this does not necessarily tell us that hair dyes are unsafe. Cosmetologists are exposed to a variety of chemicals in their work, and clearly any increased risk of cancer cannot be attributed solely to one exposure. On the other hand, a failure to find any difference in cancer patterns does not establish the safety of hair dyes. Most cosmetologists wear gloves when applying hair dyes to their clients, thus minimizing their own risk. Unfortunately, studies on hair dye users have for the most part been scientifically inadequate. Those studies that have shown an increased incidence of cancer among hair dye users have not been controlled for other hazardous exposures such as cigarette smoking. However, a recently published study by Dr. Roy Shore and his colleagues at the New York University Medical School shows that when such factors have been taken into account, hair dye users experience an increased risk of breast cancer.

Although evidence keeps mounting on the carcinogenic and teratogenic dangers of hair dyes, their sale and use continue because of inadequate regulatory authority. In August 1978 Clairol, the largest American manufacturer of hair dye products, announced that it had removed several carcinogenic ingredients from its products. The company stated that it still did not believe that such chemicals posed a risk to users, but it would nonetheless formulate the products without them. Other manufacturers have made similar efforts.

TRIS

Tris was a chemical flame retardant applied to children's sleepwear. It also happens to be an extremely potent carcinogen. The Tris case is the classic example of what can happen when we try to right a wrong with an untested chemical.

The facts are these. In 1953, as a result of public protest against so-called torch sweaters that could ignite instantly, Congress passed the Flammable Fabrics Act. It was a weak act, as first measures often are, and physicians, concerned about youngsters who were still being badly burned, became vigorous proponents of strict flammability standards for children's sleepwear. As a result, in 1967 Congress enacted the Flammable Fabrics Act Amendments, and under the law, the National Bureau of Standards in the Department of Commerce was designated to develop a test for flammability of children's sleepwear. The test that was developed called for a strip of fabric to be suspended vertically from a frame and exposed to a flame for three seconds. Any flaming droplets were supposed to self-extinguish within ten seconds, and the vertical char length of the fabric could not exceed seven inches. Some members of the textile industry regarded the test as unrealistic, and while they argued with the bureau, consumer groups began to pressure the Department of Commerce to propose regulations.

Bolstered by congressional hearings, a CBS documentary, and more news reports of burn victims, Commerce finally decided to ignore objections and in 1971 promulgated sleepwear standards for sizes 0 to 6X to take effect in July 1972. In 1975 the Consumer Product Safety Commission issued similar standards for sleepwear sizes 7 to 14. These standards required, in effect, that all sleepwear sold for children under the age of about thirteen meet minimum federal flammability standards. The only significant difference between the 0 to 6X and 7 to 14 standards was that the 0 to 6X standard had the "melt-drip" requirement, and the 7 to 14 standard did not. This distinction may seem trivial but, as will become evident, is central to the Tris story.

Industry had no choice, and soon various textile companies began to announce new products that would meet the standards. The big breakthrough came in the fall of 1972, when the William Carter Company, which dominates the children's sleepwear industry and which had been field-testing an all-polyester garment treated with Tris, announced it would begin marketing its new line of flame-retardant sleepwear. "It looks like a winner," a Carter spokesman exulted. "The mothers who took part in the test liked the ease of care properties, washability, and comfort." The spokesman added, "We are offering value in addition to flammability protection. The shrinkage properties are very good."

Michigan Chemical Corporation was the major producer of Tris, chemically known as Tris(2,3-dibromopropyl)phosphate. Tris derives its flame-retardant properties from bromine and phosphorus, which are, as was to become well known later, a toxic combination.

Tris is largely insoluble in water. It is applied to fabrics from an emulsion, and the fabrics then undergo heat treatment, which allows the compound to penetrate the outer layer of the fiber and become physically "embedded" without actually reacting chemically or significantly altering the basic fiber. Polyester fabrics are the easiest to treat and, as such, soon dominated the children's sleepwear market. It is a substantial market, and Tris became the major flame retardant used. By 1975 total sales of flame-retardant textiles amounted to almost $394 million, and by 1980 sales were expected to reach more than $817 million. In 1976 about three million pounds of Tris was used to flame-retard children's sleepwear, and the quantities used on polyester, acetate, and triacetate blends were exceptionally large, generally varying from 5 to 10 percent of the total weight of a treated garment.

It is worth noting that during the controversy that ensued prior to Commerce's promulgation of standards in 1971, officials of the William Carter Company had argued that the standards might require the use of chemicals that would be a health hazard. Although Carter's concerns were mainly addressed to allergic skin reactions, no one took them seriously, and their concern appeared to be diversionary and designed only to forestall stringent flammability standards. If Carter's concern was indeed serious, it is surprising that neither Carter nor the sleepwear industry conducted toxicity tests on Tris.

Tris is a brominated organophosphate, and organophosphate chemicals similar in molecular structure were developed for chemical warfare during World War II. This alone should have warranted thorough testing. After the war organophosphates, such as parathion and malathion, were widely used as pesticides by farmers and gardeners. As is true of organophosphate pesticides, Tris is readily absorbed through the skin and poisons the nervous system by interfering with the enzyme cholinesterase, a vital component of nerve transmission. Moreover, Tris contains two atoms of bromine, which might be expected to heighten its toxicity. Most brominated organics tested cause cancer in laboratory animals. Shortly after Carter's announcement that it would begin marketing Tris-treated sleepwear, Dr. Benjamin Van Duuren, of New York University, mentioned his interest in brominated organics like Tris to Dr. Elizabeth Weisburger, of the National Cancer Institute, and in 1973 she decided to place Tris on the NCI's bioassay monitoring program.

Another scientist, Dr. Farley Fisher, was also interested in Tris and other flame retardants. Fisher, who had recently joined the new Office of Toxic Substances at the EPA, was appointed to a National Science Foundation panel convened to develop a priority list of chemicals that might affect the environment or human health. Fisher suggested that Tris be studied, and the panel eventually listed it as a critically important chemical of environmental and health concern.

Still another scientist in the Office of Toxic Substances, Dr. Michael Prival, was concerned about Tris, and he arranged to have Dr. Herbert Rosenkranz, of Columbia University, conduct the Ames test for mutagenicity on Tris and about eighty other flame retardants. Rosenkranz found Tris strongly mutagenic, and Prival sent the findings to industry and the Consumer Product Safety Commission in October 1975. Neither the apparel manufacturers nor the public were apprised of these findings.

Bruce Ames himself tested Tris, and in January 1976, after obtaining results similar to Rosenkranz's, Ames spent the rest of the year using every forum available to question the wisdom of treating sleepwear with a mutagenic chemical that is absorbed through the skin. Through washing, Tris can enter waterways, and Dr. Donald Lisk, of Cornell University, demonstrated its toxicity to fish by immersing Tris-treated pajamas in a goldfish bowl. All the fish died within twenty-four hours.

All this was discussed in detail at a meeting of the National Academy of Sciences attended by members of the Consumer Product Safety Commission (CPSC) and the EPA in 1976, but not a word of warning went to the public. The CPSC did not even make an effort to conduct further tests or prod the industry. Shortly afterward EPA Administrator Russell Train cited Tris as an example of what could happen when an untested chemical was allowed into public circulation. Train made his remarks before the National Press Club while Congress was debating the Toxic Substances Control Act, but no reporter wrote a story about Tris. For all the notoriety that Tris was attracting in scientific circles, the public did not learn that it was a potential hazard until March 24, 1976, when the EDF petitioned the CPSC for regulatory action.

The petition requested that the CPSC order Tris-treated sleepwear to be labeled with a warning that the garment contained Tris and should be washed at least three times before wearing. It further asked that the CPSC develop a series of protocols that manufacturers could use to test chemical flame retardants before putting them on the market. The petition was based on the preliminary data that indicated that Tris might be a carcinogen and that it might also represent a mutagenic hazard to children and possibly an environmental hazard to fish. The petition also noted that one of the major metabolites of Tris, dibromopropanol (DBP), was structurally similar to ethylene dibromide, a known potent mutagen and carcinogen. Overall, the evidence was frightening. Unwittingly an estimated forty-five million children were wearing sleepwear treated with from 5 to 10 percent of a chemical that indirect evidence suggested passed readily through human skin; that was mutagenic and probably carcinogenic; that interfered with nerve transmissions; and that was present in wash water at concentrations sufficient to kill fish.

The CPSC met the petition with hostility. Two weeks after the petition arrived at the commission Richard Simpson, CPSC chairman, urged the industry not to panic. As if to assure companies involved that he was as much under attack as they, he told a meeting of the American Apparel Manufacturers Association, "If you expect regulators to have courage, show some yourself." Along with other members of the commission and the technical staff, Simpson felt threatened by the petition because it undercut years of effort, however misguided, to develop, promulgate, and enforce flammability standards on the children's sleepwear industry.

At the time of the petition the textile and apparel industries were deeply committed to Tris for the treatment of polyester and polyester blended with acetate or triacetate for children's sleepwear. In April 1976 the American Apparel Manufacturers Association estimated that 50 to 60 percent of all children's sleepwear was treated with Tris. About 240 million Tris-treated garments were on retail shelves or in warehouses. Although the industry responded publicly to the petition with guarded skepticism, there was fear within corporate boardrooms. If the ongoing National Cancer Institute tests confirmed that Tris was indeed a carcinogen, then the CPSC would probably have to ban its use and stop further sales of Tris-treated sleepwear. Even if the NCI tests were not positive, enough suspicion about Tris had already been raised to cause worried consumers to look for sleepwear that was not Tris-treated. Lawyers were also warning their companies that the question of liability could not be ignored, since the industry was now forewarned of the potential health threats posed by further use of this chemical.

But the children's sleepwear industry could not just drop

Tris. For one thing, there was no acceptable alternative for polyester and blends with acetate and triacetate. Tris had worked so well at a reasonable cost and with such excellent consumer acceptance that practically no research had been undertaken to investigate substitutes. Flame-retarding cotton, once the leading fabric, wouldn't do. It was relatively difficult to manufacture, it was expensive, and it was not altogether acceptable to the consumer. Polyester had largely replaced cotton's dominance in the children's sleepwear market since the 0-to-6X-size standards were promulgated in 1971. In that year cotton accounted for 80 percent of the sleepwear market, but by 1976 its share had plummeted to only about 10 percent.

Almost everyone in the industry started looking for alternatives to be used on polyester fabric. Two were Antiblaze 19, a cyclic phosphonate ester, manufactured by Mobil Chemical Corporation, and Fyrol FR-2, a chlorinated organophosphate very similar in structure to Tris, manufactured by Stauffer Chemical Company. Neither of these two alternatives had been tested for its carcinogenic, mutagenic, or teratogenic potential. However, both Mobil and Stauffer quickly ran the Ames test on Antiblaze 19 and Fyrol FR-2 and proclaimed them nonmutagenic. Many in the industry made the decision to switch to these.

Despite the evidence, however circumstantial, that Tris was a potent carcinogen, the CPSC continued to ignore the EDF petition. In private some members of the CPSC's technical staff actually laughed at it, and one wisecracked, "These guys want us to ban Tris because a few fish fell over dead." Other CPSC staff regarded the potential implications more seriously, and they undertook additional testing of Tris on rats and rabbits. By late 1976 preliminary results indicated that when Tris was painted on the skin of rabbits, it caused testicular atrophy and sterility in males, suggesting that Tris might cause mutations that could be passed from one generation to the next. Despite this, the CPSC wrote a letter to the EDF in December 1976 (in what was, by the way, the commission's first official correspondence on the matter) saying that it would await the results of the National Cancer Institute's tests before taking any regulatory steps.

By the beginning of 1977 the apparel industry had largely made commitments to abandon Tris and was announcing that no more Tris-treated sleepwear would be on the retail shelves beginning with the fall/winter 1977 season. The industry thought that it was home free. The Tris-treated sleepwear that was currently on retail shelves or in warehouses would be sold by the time the NCI results were made public and the CPSC had a chance to act. It came as a shock when the NCI results were released on February 4, 1977, and the EDF scientists made public evaluation of the data that showed that the cancer risk to children was exceptionally high. The NCI studies demonstrated that Tris was carcinogenic at both high and low dose levels in rats and mice. With 50 parts per million of Tris in the feed, tumors were induced in 7 and 26 percent of the female and male rats, respectively. With 100 ppm of Tris in the feed, Tris induced kidney tumors in 19 and 29 percent of the female and male rats, respectively. Tris also induced stomach and lung tumors in both male and female mice, liver tumors in female mice, and kidney tumors in male mice. In sum, Tris met the requirements that established it unequivocally as a potential human carcinogen: it induced a statistically significant excess of tumors in both mice and rats, with the incidence increasing with dose, and at multiple sites. Rarely have bioassay results been as unambiguous and as clearly indicative of a cancer threat to humans.

On February 7, 1977, the EDF repetitioned the CPSC to ban further use and sale of Tris-treated sleepwear, and on April 7 the CPSC unanimously voted to grant the petition and ban from further manufacture and sale any children's sleepwear treated with Tris. The commission's technical staff was quick to agree with the EDF's analysis of the NCI data. The only question that remained was how significant a cancer threat Tris posed to children wearing treated sleepwear.

The CPSC asked Dr. Marvin A. Schneiderman, head of Field Studies and Statistics at the NCI, and Dr. Bruce Ames to arrive at a cancer risk estimate by evaluating the NCI data and the likely exposure resulting from skin absorption and ingestion of Tris from mouthing sleepwear.

Schneiderman estimated that the risk might be as high as six thousand cancer deaths per year per million children exposed. Ames, following the recommendations of the National Academy of Sciences report on estimating the risk of human carcinogens, used slightly different methods. He calculated that as many as 1.7 percent of the children exposed for only one year to Tris-treated sleepwear might develop cancer. That comes to more than fifty thousand cancer deaths per year. Ames also compared the NCI carcinogenicity data on Tris and its mutagenicity data with other known human carcinogens. Ames found that Tris was a "strong" carcinogen. It was more potent than several known human carcinogens, including benzidine, beta-naphthylamine, and cigarette smoke. If Ames is correct, then Tris-treated sleepwear, brought on the market to save children from burns, may eventually cause as much cancer in one year—among children—as cigarette smoking does among adults.

At this writing, the Tris ban of April 7, 1977, has been legally stayed following a procedural challenge of the CPSC ban by Springs Mills in the Federal District Court in South Carolina. Although some retailers have tried to continue selling Tris-treated sleepwear, the CPSC has taken seizure action under the Federal Hazardous Substances Act to stop such sales.

Although some of the sleepwear has been exported, prompting congressional questions as to the moral and legal implications, the fate of most of the estimated twenty million Tris-treated garments now in storage is in doubt.

The Tris fiasco took an ironic twist on February 6, 1978, when the CPSC voted to amend the 0 to 6X children's sleepwear standard by dropping the "melt-drip" requirement. The industry had argued, as early as 1971, that the "melt-drip" requirement served no useful purpose since children could be adequately protected against burn injury without it. Furthermore, it was the "melt-drip" requirement that forced textile manufacturers to use Tris in polyester sleepwear. So by dropping the "melt-drip" requirement, the CPSC finally agreed that adequate protection from burn injury could be had without the use of add-on chemicals like Tris. A bizarre ending to a government effort to protect our nation's children against one risk, only to substitute another.

CHAPTER 10
CHILDREN
AND CANCER

In March 1976, when Mrs. Betsy Van Winkle, of Rutherford, New Jersey, took her son, Wesley, who was suffering from leukemia, to a specialist in New York City, she learned that another mother from Rutherford, Mrs. Vivian Cleffi, was seeing the same specialist for the treatment of her son, James, who was also suffering from leukemia. The Van Winkles and the Cleffis lived only two blocks from each other, and both boys attended the Pierrepont Elementary School.

James Cleffi, age nine, died six months later, and Wesley Van Winkle, age twelve, died in January 1977. At Mrs. Cleffi's suggestion the two mothers began their own investigation. "People in town knew I had lost a son to leukemia," says Mrs. Cleffi. "From time to time, they would tell me of other cases." Mrs. Van Winkle recalls, "I'd check out one name, and she'd check out another. She wrote down the list of names, and we realized there were a lot of names."

In March 1978 Mrs. Cleffi presented a list of eleven names of cancer victims to Dr. Luke Sarsfield, the superintendent of the Rutherford schools, and he phoned local and state health authorities. Rumors began to sweep through town, and on March 31, Dr. Sarsfield made public disclosure of the mothers' findings.

Skeptical state health officials dispatched researchers to examine local records. Two weeks later Dr. Ronald Altman, the state epidemiologist, informed a town meeting in Rutherford that the number of cancer cases involving both children and adults was even higher. Instead of eleven cases there were thirty-two—thirteen of leukemia, eleven of Hodgkin's disease, and the remaining eight were cases of the less common blood cancers of reticulo cell carcinoma, lymphoma, and myeloma.

Thirteen leukemia cases were about what a town of twenty thousand, the population of Rutherford, could expect statistically. However, six of those thirteen cases involved youngsters between the ages of five and nineteen, and Rutherford's rate of incidence for this age group was about six times higher than the national average. Moreover, all six of these leukemia victims had attended the Pierrepont Elementary School.

At this writing, technicians from the Division of Environmental Cancer in the state's Department of Environmental Protection are testing air, soil, and water samples (including those from the drinking fountains in the school) for possible contaminants. As Mrs. Van Winkle says, "What we've done is to make people aware. It isn't just Rutherford."

Indeed, it is not just Rutherford. Although the rates of cancer incidence and mortality for children under fifteen are lower than those for adults in the United States, cancer is second only to accidents as a cause of death in youngsters. In 1976 seven thousand cases of cancer were diagnosed in children, and in that same year four thousand children died of the disease, about two thousand of them, including James Cleffi, from leukemia.

Some childhood cancers show genetic predisposition by occurrence in siblings or twins or in families for more than one generation. Some other cancers are believed to be caused by viruses. Circumstantial evidence indicates that Burkitt's lymphoma, often seen in African children and constituting more than half of all childhood cancers in Nigeria, is attributable to what is known as the Epstein-Barr virus.

In all likelihood environmental agents play a critical role in causing cancer in children. Trouble can begin after a mother conceives and agents make contact with the fetus. Interference with fetal development can cause birth defects, cancer, or both. Until the early 1960s it was widely believed that the placenta, the organ that allows oxygen and nutrients to be transferred from the mother to the fetus and that also removes wastes from the fetal bloodstream, served as a barrier to protect the developing embryo from chemical damage. However, the tragedy involving the sedative thalidomide alerted the world to the fact that the placental barrier could be pierced by chemical agents. Thalidomide proved to be a teratogen, a substance capable of causing birth defects. Besides thalidomide a number of agents are now known to be teratogenic in humans. They include organic mercury, polychlorinated biphenyls (PCBs), rubella virus, syphilis, androgenic hormones, and ionizing radiation. Ionizing radiation has been shown to act transplacentally as a carcinogen as well, increasing the risk of childhood leukemia. DES, the synthetic hormone, is a proven transplacental carcinogen affecting both those in late childhood and those in early adulthood.

Medical experience with teratogenesis is much greater than with transplacental carcinogenesis, but what is known should serve as a grave warning. Most authorities believe that the fetus is especially vulnerable to these two effects because alteration of the genetic message controlling development of the fetus can destroy its rapid and precisely regulated growth. The timing of the interference appears to be the critical factor. Dr. Robert P. Bolande, of the Montreal Children's Hospital and McGill University, who has studied the relationship between teratogenesis and transplacental carcinogenesis in experimental animals, says, "It seems clear that carcinogenesis tends to be maximal in the latter stages of gestation, occurring only after organogenesis [formation of body organs] is complete. Prior to this time, teratogenesis is the prevalent response."

Dr. Bolande based his conclusions on a number of experiments in which chemicals including urethane, alkylnitrosureas, and estrogens could induce either birth defects or cancer, depending on when they were administered during pregnancy. Drs. Joseph M. DiPaolo and Paul Kotin, of the NCI, in 1966 observed that many of the substances teratogenic to the fetus are carcinogenic if applied later in life. They investigated twenty-six chemicals that had been tested for either their carcinogenic or their teratogenic activity in animals. Of twenty carcinogens, nineteen were also teratogens.

Cancer in children is often linked with a number of malformations, and this does not occur by chance. For instance, Wilm's tumor of the kidney occurs in about one out of ten thousand live births and is usually diagnosed between the ages of three and four. A most curious aspect of Wilm's tumor is its association with aniridia, a birth defect in which one or both eyes lack an iris. In the general population aniridia, a dominantly inherited trait, is seen no more than once in fifty thousand live births. However, a child born with aniridia is more prone to develop Wilm's tumor than a normal child, and about one-third of aniridic children eventually do develop it. The risk of developing Wilm's tumor is also increased when aniridia is accompanied by malformations of the genitourinary tract or by mental retardation.

Clearly childhood cancers can reflect the effects of exposure to a variety of causative agents, including viruses, radiation, and chemicals, and no one has identified any one factor that is singularly responsible. However, the continually increasing exposure of the fetus and newborn infant to carcinogenic chemicals may pose serious consequences in the future. These consequences should not be seen as factors only in childhood cancer; they may also increase the incidence of cancer in adult life. DES, the synthetic hormone administered to as many as two million pregnant women in the late 1940s and the 1950s, induced a rare form of vaginal cancer in some of their daughters. The cancer was initiated during fetal development but was not manifest until the victims had entered or passed puberty.

Unfortunately during early pregnancy, when the fetus seems to be most susceptible to environmental insults, a woman may not even know that she is pregnant, and thus she can unwittingly expose the fetus to potential damage by her exposure to drugs, occupational toxins, X rays, contaminated drinking water or food, or polluted air. In addition to chemicals that find their way into the body during gestation, the pregnant mother already has stored a number of chemicals in her adipose tissue through the course of her life. Pregnancy mobilizes the residues of these chemicals, such as PCBs, DDT, DDE, aldrin, dieldrin, and others, and allows them to migrate to the fetus. Several studies have shown that the umbilical cord of newborn infants can contain chemical residue. It is safe to say that all newborns in the U.S. harbor residues of halogenated hydrocarbon contaminants at birth, but, incredibly, the ramifications of having entire generations born with carcinogens in their body tissues are largely unknown.

Exposure does not stop or diminish with birth. The mother who chooses to breast-feed her baby continues to pass on halogenated hydrocarbons to the child via her milk. Her body's fat stores are used to make the milk fat, and in the process the chemical contaminants in the fat are mobilized and become incorporated into the milk. For the first few months of life at least, a nursing infant has no food other than milk. Although the level of pollutants in the adult body is highly variable, the nursing infant, which is very small in size, is assured of a very large dose on a body weight basis. In 1976 the Environmental Protection Agency conducted a study of breast milk from 1,400 nursing women across the country to check on the spread of contamination. The EPA found that essentially all women had some level of DDT and its metabolite DDE in their breast milk, more than 75 percent of the women had significant levels of dieldrin and benzene hexachloride, and more than half had oxychlordane and heptachlor epoxide at detectable levels. PCBs were found in over 90 percent of the preliminary samples, and dioxin, mirex, and kepone have been seen in milk in some regions of the country. Calculations based on these preliminary data reveal that the "average" nursing infant in the U.S. ingests daily about one-sixth the quantity of PCBs that caused adverse effects on health in rhesus monkeys studied by Dr. James Allen at the University of Wisconsin Medical School.

More astonishingly, the same average human infant exceeds by ten times the maximum daily PCB intake level set by the Food and Drug Administration. Indeed, if human milk were marketed in interstate commerce, much of it would be seized and condemned by the FDA. Because an infant is so small as compared with an adult, and because an infant derives all its nourishment from milk or formula, the average baby receives a dietary dose of PCBs almost one hundred times greater than that of an adult on a body weight basis. This also holds true for certain pesticides. The 1976 EPA study revealed that the average infant's daily intake of dieldrin exceeded the FDA standards by nine times. In one case the level of dieldrin ingestion was greater than seven hundred times in excess.

Cow's-milk formulas, on the other hand, rarely have high levels of agricultural and industrial contaminants; the animal fat is removed from the milk during processing and is replaced by vegetable fats. Moreover, cow's milk has little in the way of stored contaminants because of cows' daily lifelong lactation.

But formulas are by no means the panacea for optimal infant nutrition, nor do they supply a source of food safe from chemical contamination. Although progress has been made since the days when "formula" meant diluted cow's milk with sugar added, many modern powdered and liquid products do not duplicate the exact ratios of fat, protein, and carbohydrates found in human milk. For example, many commercial formulas have more protein and more vitamin D than mother's milk. Moreover, lead, a toxic contaminant, has been known to exist in some formulas, primarily those packaged in cans but also in formulas packaged in glass bottles. Its source is unknown, although the FDA has made efforts to identify the mode of contamination. A number of toxic chemicals have been discovered in the drinking-water supplies in much of the country. Consequently, if powdered formulas prepared at home and prediluted commercial formulas are made using tap water, the formulas are likely to be contaminated. For example, a glucose-water solution for newborn infants manufactured by the Mead-Johnson Company, of Evansville, Indiana, was found to contain many chemicals that contaminate the Evansville drinking supply. These include chloroform, methylene chloride, and bromodichloromethane—known or suspected carcinogens.

By choosing a formula that closely simulates human milk and by filtering tap water through activated carbon (as described in chapter 11), parents can be more confident that they are providing a nutritious and, one would hope, uncontaminated food for their infant. A mother who prefers breast feeding can also exercise some control over the quality of her infant's first food and take steps to significantly lower the store of toxic pollutants in her body by adopting the personal practices also suggested in chapter 11.

As children grow, they are exposed to more carcinogenic agents from various sources, as witness the Tris case discussed in chapter 9. New studies on this flame-retardant chemical used in children's sleepwear show that youngsters who have worn Tris-treated sleepwear regularly washed over a six-month period have measurable amounts of the Tris metabolite dibromopropanol in their urine. The average level was 0.5 part per billion. Children wearing unwashed Tris-treated pajamas have had as much as 20 ppb of dibromopropanol in their urine, vivid demonstration of how the skin can absorb a carcinogen that eventually enters the bloodstream.

Then again, there may be exposure to hazardous occupational chemicals brought home. Dr. Irving J. Selikoff, of the Mount Sinai School of Medicine, says, "The spread of occupational illness [specifically pleural mesothelioma, a tumor of the pleura] to families of workers [primarily in asbestos factories] is a general rule. It's not a curiosity." A research group headed by Jacqueline Fabia and Truong Dam Thuy at Laval University Medical School in Quebec City, Quebec, investigated the cancer incidence among children whose fathers worked in occupations where they were exposed to hydrocarbons from gasoline, oil, and solvents. The research group compared statistics on almost four hundred children who died of cancer before age five with statistics on nearly eight hundred other children drawn from the general population. Twice as many of the cancer victims had fathers who worked at jobs where they were exposed to hydrocarbons. Pondering this, Fabia and Thuy asked, "Could it be because the child is himself exposed to the repeated or continued presence of certain items in the household or prolonged contact with his father? Could it be the result of a direct effect of some hydrocarbon contained in petrol and oil on spermatogenesis—the carcinogenic defect would then be transmitted to the child?"

In addition a study made by the National Institute of Occupational Safety and Health, the Center for Disease Control, and the University of North Carolina School of Public Health shows that the wives of men working in vinyl chloride monomer plants suffer twice the rate of miscarriages and stillbirths as do the wives of men working in polyvinyl chloride resin and rubber plants, where concentrations of the carcinogenic monomer are much lower. The likely cause is sperm cell damage in the father by direct exposure to vinyl chloride monomer.

Environmental pollutants may be proportionately more dangerous for children than adults because children are growing. As a result they have higher metabolic rates than adults. For instance, given the same rate of exposure to an air pollutant, children will inhale two to three times as much as adults per unit of body weight. Furthermore, children often engage in intense physical activity, and as their activity level increases, so does their rate of respiration. It is no coincidence that illnesses of the respiratory tract account for 50 to 70 percent of all acute childhood illnesses and for about 30 percent of all deaths in children under the age of fifteen. Many children play near roads or parking lots where auto exhaust concentrations are high. As they run and play, they kick up the dust on which many pollutants have settled, and because of their short stature they may come in contact with more of the heavy pollutants that remain suspended near the ground. In some parts of the U.S., for example, some roads and even playgrounds have been resurfaced with crushed rock containing asbestos. When cars drive over the roads or children stir up the playground, they can release asbestos fibers into the air.

Exposure to asbestos is also a serious problem in many of

the nation's schools. Between 1940 and 1973 thousands of ceilings in schools and other municipal buildings were routinely sprayed with asbestos-containing material for both decorative and fireproofing purposes. The normal wear of these materials releases asbestos into air, and measurements have shown up to 100 times more asbestos indoors than in the ambient outdoor air.

Writing in the November 1976 issue of *Environment,* Dorothy Noyes Kane notes that there have been a number of studies in Europe and Japan (but none in the U.S.) on the effects of air pollution on the growth and development of children, and, in brief, "the investigations indicate that air pollution from sulfur dioxide, nitrogen oxide, dust, arsenic, ammonia, fluorides, and other materials is responsible for an adverse effect on children's growth and development as manifested by retarded bone maturity, certain abnormalities in blood chemistry, and an excess of larger than normal tonsils and lymph nodes." In recent years, Kane points out, clues have begun to surface showing a relationship between certain pollutants (asbestos, for example) and cancer in children.

In the past, protecting the health of children meant immunizing them against the ravages of polio, smallpox, diphtheria, measles, and other infectious diseases. There is no vaccine for cancer, and there may never be. The answer to cancer in children is the same as that for adults—the elimination or reduction of exposure to carcinogenic agents.

CHAPTER 11
THE SOLUTION TO THE PROBLEM

When it becomes impossible to avoid the cancer-causing agents, we react by avoiding the reports of scientists that tell us about them. . . . There's no choice, really, for what the scientists are telling us is that life is carcinogenic.

Columnist William Raspberry,
Washington *Post*, May 19, 1978

Mr. Raspberry is wrong. "Life" is not carcinogenic. But his sentiments reflect those of a growing number of Americans who feel helpless in the face of the seeming inevitability of cancer. His is an understandable but mistaken attitude. We have been a long time realizing that cancer is largely an environmental disease. Newly developed analytical techniques are just now "discovering" carcinogens that have been present for some time or that entered the environment in the last ten, twenty, or thirty years. Yet make no mistake about it: Even though the list of cancer-causing agents is likely to grow with announcements of new findings in the years ahead, when all is said and done and the last carcinogen has been the subject of headlines and a fresh source of despair for columnists and numbed readers, the total number of agents capable of causing cancer will be low compared with the number of substances in common use. In a National Cancer Institute study of 120 compounds that *looked* carcinogenic because of their chemical structure, only 11 of them—less than 10 percent—caused cancer in test animals. The percentage is likely to be even lower for other chemicals, since the 120 studied by the NCI were all suspect from the start. Instead of despair, we need determination—determination to use our intelligence in order to *deal* with the environmental causes of cancer, coolly, practically, and realistically.

Many of our present difficulties stem from the fact that we have let our priorities get out of kilter. Instead of seeking to prevent diseases, including cancer, we have sought to cure them. In 1978 the nation's soaring medical bill approached $200 billion, and more than $180 billion of this was spent on attempts to cure and control sickness. By contrast less than $6 billion was spent on preventive measures and only about $1 billion on health education. Our failure to use preventive medicine has become part of the structure of our health programs, so much so that health insurance has really become disease insurance. There is no economic incentive for good health programs. The slogan seems to be, "You catch it; we'll try to cure it—if we can." Every year the federal government spends $1 billion treating coal miners for black lung disease. Black lung has no cure, but a small fraction of the annual sum spent on treating the afflicted might well have prevented occurrence of the disease thirty years ago. Our failure to use the many benefits of preventive medicine has been extraordinarily costly in health and money and other ways most of us can't even imagine. "It isn't so that an ounce of prevention is worth a pound of cure," says Dr. Henry Blackburn, director of the Laboratory of Physiological Hygiene at the University of Minnesota. "It isn't so because there is no cure for the major maladies of modern man. Prevention is the only answer."

Until recently cancer was not thought of as a preventable disease, but we know now that we can take measures to help prevent its occurrence. Cancer is by no means inevitable, not even as a process of aging. It is true that we will never be able to state that we can prevent cancer completely, but we can move to reduce the rate of risk significantly. Success in the prevention of cardiovascular disease illustrates this point.

Before 1950 persons at high risk of cardiovascular disease, primarily men, could be identified only on the basis of their disease history, that is, whether or not they had had a heart attack. In other words the symptoms were the disease. Since then medical science has found a number of risk factors for potential victims, and although cardiovascular disease is still the leading cause of death, mortalities are decreasing. According to Dr. Robert Levy, director of the National Heart, Lung and Blood Institute, the risk factors for cardiovascular disease are age and sex (factors over which the individual has no control), high blood pressure, cigarette smoking, diet, serum cholesterol, diabetes, sedentary life-style, obesity, and stress. Levy estimates that by eliminating cigarette smoking within this identifiable population 150,000 cardiovascular deaths could be prevented each year. Moreover, reduction would be observed in oral and lung cancer rates.

In the opinion of Dr. Marvin Schneiderman, director of Science Policy at the National Cancer Institute, one-third of the cancer deaths of known cause could be prevented each year if persons at risk changed their habits and behavior. This is not to dismiss the impact of pervasive environmental contamination as a causative factor in carcinogenesis but to emphasize that the individual stands to benefit greatly by adopting sound health practices. "People do change their bad habits," says Dr. John Knowles, president of the Rockefeller Foundation. "We have plenty of evidence to encourage us to do more in this direction. Changing human behavior involves sustaining and repeating an intelligible message, reinforcing it through peer pressure and approval and establishing clearly perceived rewards which materialize in as short a time as possible. Advertising agencies know this, but it is easier to sell deodorants, pantyhose and automobiles than health."

Starting with yourself, you can eliminate a number of carcinogens from your life and reduce exposure to many more by examining the following.

Smoking. Cigarette smoking has a huge impact on cancer rates in the United States. Are you likely to end up as one of the statistics? The following table shows the number of cancer deaths in 1974 caused by smoking.

Type of Cancer	Deaths in 1974	Excess Deaths due to Smoking	
Bronchogenic [a]	78,873	63,966	81.1%
Laryngeal	3,262	2,150	65.9%
Oral [b]	7,968	4,494	56.4%
Esophageal	6,652	3,998	60.4%
Bladder	9,397	2,819	30.0%
Pancreatic	17,376	5,213	30.0%
Renal	7,073	2,122	30.0%
Total	130,601	84,762	64.9%
All types of neoplasms [c]	360,472	84,762	23.5%

[a] Includes carcinoma of trachea, bronchus, and lung
[b] Includes malignant neoplasms of buccal cavity and pharynx
[c] Includes benign neoplasms and lymphatic and hematopoietic malignant neoplasms

Smoking increases your risk of lung cancer by ten times. Smokers who work with asbestos are ninety-two times as likely to get lung cancer as nonsmokers. The American Cancer Society estimates that smoking is responsible for one out of every five cancer deaths. But you can stop smoking now.

Between 1964 and 1975, 29 million Americans kicked the habit, and an estimated 95 percent of them did it on their own without undergoing counseling or attending programs. We recommend that you read *Progress Report on a Nation Kicking the Habit,* 1977, available from the Office of Cancer Communications, National Cancer Institute, Building 31, Room 10A16, Bethesda, Maryland 20014. It is enlightening reading, well referenced and indexed, and it is especially helpful in dealing with such methods and techniques as group therapy, self-help, gradual cessation filters, hypnosis, positive reinforcement, and aversion.

Whether you kick the habit on your own or do it with the help of a group program, one of the most difficult aspects is to stay "smoke free." Having supportive friends and relatives helps. Call your local Lung Association or American Cancer Society office. You'll find them eager to help you stop smoking or prevent you from starting again.

Alcohol. As discussed in chapter 9, there is little evidence that alcohol is itself a carcinogen. But the use of alcohol along with cigarette smoking increases one's risk of cancer of the mouth and esophagus significantly. The mechanism of action of alcohol is unknown. Perhaps it acts as an irritant, making cells more susceptible to the carcinogens in smoke, or perhaps it is related to nutritional deficiencies that are common in heavy drinkers and smokers. Excessive use of alcohol should be avoided, and those who smoke should be particularly careful.

Sunbathing. Once a sign of the overworked peasant, the sun tan bestows beauty and status in America; but ultraviolet rays from the sun (or sun lamps) can cause skin cancer, especially in persons with fair complexions. A slight tan can be protective, however. As the melanin pigment in the skin darkens, it prevents the ultraviolet rays from damaging the sensitive layers beneath. To minimize risk, avoid sunbathing between ten in the morning and two in the afternoon, when the sun's rays are most direct. Work on a tan very gradually, fifteen or twenty minutes the first day out and five minutes more each subsequent day. Don't use a reflector—it concentrates the rays. Use a lotion with a sunscreen. The FDA is currently considering labeling provisions for over-the-counter sunscreen products. These products include chemical and physical blocking agents. Among those ingredients found by the FDA to be "safe and effective" when used as directed include aminobenzoic acid (para-aminobenzoic acid or PABA), padimate A and padimate O, red petrolatum, and titanium dioxide. These solutions must usually be reapplied after sweating or swimming. To protect yourself further, wear light clothing and a hat and be sure to use a beach umbrella. Watch out for reflection off water, sand, and snow; reflection can be as harmful as direct rays. Remember that ultraviolet rays can pierce haze and clouds and are especially potent at high altitudes.

Skin cancer, when treated early, is often curable. Early warning signs include sores that don't heal; visible size or color changes in warts or moles; development of unusual pigmented areas like scaly patches; red sensitive areas with a crusty center; red, brown, or black lesions and nodules; and white or yellow lumpy patches on the lips.

X rays. Diagnostic X rays hold a valid place in medical science, but too many of us get too many X rays. To minimize the risk of cancer from X rays, we recommend the following:

Discourage precautionary chest X rays. Most people do not need a yearly chest X ray, used extensively in the 1960s to screen the population for tuberculosis. The requirement of an annual chest X ray to maintain employment should be challenged as needlessly increasing one's cancer risk. Skin tuberculin tests are the best initial screening procedure.

Dental X rays need not be taken on a regular basis or as a standard part of every dental examination. They should be taken only when diagnostic procedure demands. If you move or change dentists, request copies of your X rays so that they need not be repeated. Do the same if you change physicians.

Avoid X rays during pregnancy, especially during the first three months, unless a life-saving procedure for the mother indicates that X rays are needed.

A lead apron or shield, particularly for the gonad area (pelvis and scrotum), should be used to prevent reproductive damage in both men and women and to protect against X-ray scatter.

Mammography is not usually used in women under the age of thirty-five, since the breast tissue of young women is too dense for the procedure to be effective. The NCI now recommends that women aged thirty-five to thirty-nine have mammographic exams only if they have a *personal* history of breast cancer, and that women aged forty to forty-nine have mammographic exams only if there is a *personal or family* history of breast cancer. For women over fifty, mammography appears to have a proven benefit in breast cancer detection and should be used routinely. Unfortunately, the NCI has not determined how often "routinely" is.

Finally don't request unnecessary X rays.

Cosmetics. At present there are no regulations requiring that cosmetics ingredients—whether you put them on your face, rub them into your skin, or apply them under your arm—be tested for safety. Until laws to protect the consumer from hazardous chemicals in cosmetics products are enacted by Congress, the following knowledge can be helpful.

Known carcinogens which may be present in hair dye products are 4-methoxy-m-phenylenediamine, 4-methoxy-m-phenylenediamine sulfate, 2-nitro-p-phenylenediamine and its sulfate, 4-amino-2-nitrophenol, direct black 38, and direct blue 6.* Most of these are found in permanent hair dyes, not tints or rinses. Unfortunately other ingredients in tints, rinses, and semipermanent and permanent dyes have not been properly tested, and the extent of their toxicity is unknown. The ingredients in question should be listed on the product labels. If they are not, or if your beautician dyes your hair, write to the manufacturer and request ingredient information for the specific shade you use.

A plant product called henna may be a wise alternative to dyeing for people with medium-dark and dark hair. It coats the hair shaft in tones ranging from transparent to red and black and lasts several weeks. Some salons are experimenting with henna mixed with or alternated with semipermanent dyes.

Processes variously called frosting, tipping, streaking, highlighting, sun lighting, and tortoise shelling involve the selection and dyeing of relatively few hairs, and the chemical used rarely touches the scalp. Therefore, hazardous chemicals will not be absorbed through the skin as they are during the full dyeing process, and the risks should be low or nonexistent.

Oral Contraceptives and Synthetic Hormones. Oral contraceptives and synthetic hormones used routinely during and after

---

* As discussed in chapter 9, many manufacturers began to formulate their products to remove these carcinogens.

menopause are cancer risks that you can probably eliminate from your life. Many doctors agree that the mild discomforts of menopause may be borne without the aid of routinely prescribed artificial hormones.

Other contraceptive methods, although possibly less convenient, approach the pill in effectiveness but do not put the user at the risk of cancer. If the pill is chosen, minimal estrogen content is advised.

Cooking over an Open Fire. The charring of foods by fire results in the formation of carcinogenic compounds. Polynuclear aromatic hydrocarbons, described briefly in chapter 7, are formed any time meat is burned during cooking. Therefore, although it is wise to cook meats well to eliminate as much fat as possible, the cooking should not involve charcoal broiling, panfrying, or any other method likely to burn the meat. Broiling foods is a good alternative.

Cooking with Microwave Ovens. There is no conclusive evidence showing that the use of microwave ovens will increase one's risk of cancer. However, there is no conclusive evidence showing that they are safe, and there are some signs that exposure to microwaves may pose a cancer risk.

Microwave ovens can leak nonionizing radiation if the door interlock system, which turns off the oven when the door is open, is poorly adjusted. Dealers, service organizations, and some federal, state, or local programs may test ovens for leakage. The FDA has issued a leakage standard of 5 microwatts/cm^2 at 5 centimeters from the oven surface for the lifetime of ovens manufactured after October 6, 1971, but we do not know if this standard is safe. The FDA does recommend the following safety precautions:

—Follow manufacturer's directions for oven operation.
—Check to make sure that the oven was not damaged in shipping.
—Never insert objects through the door grill or around the seal.

—Don't tamper with or inactivate the door interlock.

—Don't operate an empty oven.

—Clean the oven with water and a mild detergent. Don't use abrasives.

—Have the oven serviced regularly by qualified service technicians for signs of wear, damage, or tampering.

—Don't watch the food cooking through the grill.

—For oven models made before the October 1971 standard, turn the oven off before opening the door and stay at least two feet away from the oven when it is on.

Diet. Diet is one of the most significant ways in which you can reduce your risk of exposure to carcinogens. You can make decisions at the supermarket, in the kitchen, and at the table that eliminate a number of cancer risks and still provide a well-balanced diet.

Although they are a necessary part of the diet, fats can be double jeopardy, possibly by facilitating the action of carcinogens or by carrying residues of cancer-causing agents. For most Americans, decreasing the amount of fat in the diet will be a positive measure for weight control and prevention of cardiovascular disease and cancer.

One of the easiest ways to reduce dietary fat is to eat less red meat. It is not necessary to eliminate meat. Cutting down will help. So will selecting cuts of meat without excess fat, trimming visible fat before cooking, and carefully removing cooking fat.

Most pesticide, hormone, and industrial residues are found in the fat portion of food. Grain-fed beef and pork and milk-fed veal generally have the most residues, while grass-fed animals have the least residues.

Poultry has comparatively little fat, and virtually all of it can be removed before cooking.

Avoid all organ meats, such as liver and pancreas (sweetbreads). Carcinogenic feed additives, such as DES, concentrate in such organs.

Fish is an excellent source of low-fat protein, but unfortunately many waters of the U.S. are contaminated by PCBs and other chemicals. Indeed, if the FDA goes to a PCB action level of 2 parts per million, many fish from inland or estuarine waters will be unmarketable in interstate commerce. Any species of fish that frequent polluted waters, such as Lake Michigan, the James River, Lake Ontario, and the Hudson River, should be avoided, but there are numerous other waterways with unpublicized problems, so it would be wise to check on local conditions before you consume fish taken from them. As a general rule eat only freshwater fish taken from uncontaminated upland streams and ponds and saltwater fish, such as cod, halibut, and pollack, that are found offshore and do not frequent the inshore coast or estuaries.

Dairy products are a source of dietary fats. Whole milk, cream, butter, creamed cottage cheese, ice cream, and high-fat yogurt and cheeses can easily be replaced by skim milk, margarine, uncreamed cottage cheese, ice milk, low-fat yogurt, and low-fat cheeses. Vegetable oils and vegetable oil margarine contain very high percentages of fat but fewer chemical residues than meats, since the contaminants concentrate as they move up the food chain into animals. Corn oil generally has fewer pesticide residues than soybean or cottonseed oil. It is therefore best to buy pure corn oil margarine.

Fruits and vegetables are very low in fats, with levels generally less than 1 percent. But pesticide residues on the edible skins can be a problem, so be sure to peel or wash them (with soapy warm water) carefully. Fruits and vegetables labeled "organically grown" may have been raised without added pesticides, but there is no assurance that they were. Legumes such as soybeans can be used to replace meat protein in the diet. Nuts are good sources of protein, but they are high in fat. The FDA rarely checks for pesticide residues in nuts, unfortunately. Your local heart association will be very helpful in providing guidelines for dietary fat.

Besides accidental additives harbored in fat, you can go a long way toward eliminating deliberate chemical additives from the diet. Prepared foods such as frozen pizzas, TV dinners, and dessert mixes have the most additives, and ingredients should be listed on the label. Some labels may only say "artificial flavor" or "artificial color." Fortunately manufacturers are beginning to realize that a large segment of the population will buy so-called natural foods processed without chemical colors, flavors, and preservatives. Become a label reader. It may mean switching brands, and that may mean a decreased risk. The Center for Science in the Public Interest has compiled a list of safe, unsafe, and status-undetermined additives, which is given in appendix A.

It is very easy to increase the amount of fiber in the diet. More raw or cooked fruits and vegetables will add fiber and nutrients. Peas, beans, and potatoes are also good fiber sources. Fruits with seeds (strawberries, raspberries, figs) are high in fiber. Switching from refined to unrefined grains (whole wheat, bran, brown rice, unbleached white flour) is beneficial. Other good grain products are oat and corn meal, wheat germ, bulgur, millet, bran flakes, and barley.

Breast Feeding. If you plan to breast-feed your child, you'll want to minimize the chemical residues in your fat tissue, which will be incorporated into milk fat. The "prudent" diet described above should be initiated as far in advance of nursing as possible.

Parents who are concerned about breast milk contaminants should consider nursing for a shorter time or supplementing breast feeding with bottle feeding. Choose a formula whose contents most nearly approximate human breast milk. When preparing powdered formulas, use water filtered through activated carbon, as described in the next section.

Drinking Water. Home filtration of drinking water with activated carbon to remove contaminating carcinogenic chemicals is not entirely satisfactory because the consumer has no way of measuring the chemicals that might still remain in the finished water or the bacteria that might be growing on the carbon and contaminate the water. However, activated carbon filtration can be an effective method, and if care is taken to change the carbon at least once every three weeks and to boil the water before use, most problems can be largely overcome. Until carbon filters are installed in municipal drinking water treatment plants, the consumer who wants clean water to drink, use in cooking, or prepare infant formulas with has no choice but to use home filtration. Three methods are described in appendix B.

Children's Sleepwear. The hazards associated with the use of chemical flame retardants in children's sleepwear have been detailed in chapter 9. As a result of private and governmental action the use of chemical flame retardants for this purpose will be significantly minimized or eliminated in the future. However, chemically treated sleepwear is still available for sale, and many families own children's sleepwear treated with Tris or other chemicals. Since most of the chemicals that have been used to flame-retard children's sleepwear have not been adequately tested for safety, we recommend the following:

Buy only children's sleepwear made of materials that are inherently flame resistant or those that specifically state on the label that no chemicals have been used to meet the flammability requirements. The following common fabrics do not contain chemical flame retardants: Modacrylic, SEF, Kanecaron, Cordelan, Vinal/Vinyon, and Leavil. Usually blends of these materials with polyester and/or nylon do not have any chemicals added. Therefore, they are generally considered safe. In addition, certain 100 percent polyester fabrics do not contain flame-retardant additives. But unless this is stated on the label, it is best to avoid these.

All of the foregoing materials are available in sleepwear or children's sections at most department and specialty stores. The way to check for the materials is to look at the label on the sleepwear.

Any fabric not listed here (including acetate, triacetate, nylon, cotton, and blends with polyester) may have a chemical additive to meet government regulations for fire retardancy. Sleepwear larger than children's size 14 does not have to be treated with a flame retardant but, to be sure, check the package and the label on the garment. Children's sizes 0 to 6X have been treated with flame retardants since mid-1972, and sizes 7 to 14 since mid-1975.

Based on information available to us on the effects of washing Tris-treated sleepwear, we do not believe that washing adequately reduces the risk from chemically treated polyester garments. The usual labeled recommendation of using detergents rather than soap has nothing to do with removal of chemical flame retardants. Soap can leave deposits on the fabric that increase its flammability. Therefore, to be absolutely safe, *chemically treated garments of polyesters and polyester blended with acetate or triacetate should be discarded and not used.* Don't pass on old polyester (blended or not blended with acetate or triacetate) sleepwear to younger siblings or your friends' children.

Home Use of Pesticides. As noted in chapter 6, the manufacture and use of a number of carcinogenic pesticides have been severely restricted or eliminated. These include DDT, aldrin, dieldrin, chlordane, and heptachlor. However, existing supplies of some of these may still be available for sale, and sale for specific uses may continue indefinitely. For example, while the use of chlordane for some citrus crops and other fruits has been prohibited, it remains on the market for use in controlling termites. It is best not to use these pesticides at all. If you choose to use such hazardous pesticides, use them only for their limited approved purposes. All other uses have been eliminated because they pose an imminent hazard to human health. Before using any of these pesticides or others about which you have doubts, consult books such as *Grow It Safely* and *Household Pest Control,* by Stephanie Harris, available from the Health Research Group, 2000 P Street N.W., Washington, D.C. 20036, and see the bibliographical essay in chapter 6 for sources on nonhazardous alternative methods of pest control.

Cleaning Solutions and Solvents. Many cleaners, solvents, paints, spot removers, cements, and other household products contain carcinogenic chemicals that are released into the air and inhaled during their normal use. It is best not to use any product that contains known volatile carcinogens such as benzene, carbon tetrachloride, or perchloroethylene. If you choose to use such products, be sure that your work area is very well ventilated.

Asbestos. As described in chapter 5, exposure to asbestos may come from a wide variety of sources. Although action to prevent such exposure may in many cases require state or federal regulations, several instances exist in which both individuals and local authorities can take steps to avert asbestos exposure.

Where asbestos-containing rock has been used in road resurfacing, roadways can be sealed by the local governments responsible for road maintenance. Where asbestos-containing crushed rock has been used to fill in driveways or playgrounds, this rock should be carefully removed and replaced.

Where asbestos-containing material has been used either to fireproof or to decorate ceilings in buildings such as public schools, local school boards can determine the extent of asbestos use, seal ceilings that are not yet damaged or decaying, and replace those showing wear and deterioration.

Personal Involvement in the Regulatory Process. Speaking of the need for public involvement in the democratic process, Ralph Nader once wrote, "A citizenship of wholesale delegation and abdication to public and private power systems, such as prevails now, makes such periodic checks as elections little more than rituals." In exactly the same way our current failure as individuals to take part in the regulatory process at the local, state, and national levels allows an unchecked public power system to make decisions, many times influenced only by private corporate interests. Most citizens see no way to influence what state and federal governments do, and they often despair over decisions that they find incomprehensible or incorrect. However, unless individuals make the effort to be actively involved, the regulatory process so important to achieving effective cancer prevention will continue to be ineffective. In a democratic society this process seeks public comment and review of its decisions as a means of providing a system of checks and balances. When citizens fail to provide that review, only those interests directly affected spend the time and effort to be involved—often with the result that necessary regulations are weakened or completely eliminated. Though people can control personal habits such as smoking, diet, and the home use of pesticides, a person can do only so much alone. "The most effective preventive measures seem to be those that require the least individual effort, such as the public health management of water, air, sewage, and food, [and] regulation of drugs," Drs. Ernest Seward and Andrew Sorensen, of the University of Rochester School of Medicine and Dentistry, have observed. What can be done?

Become an active member of a local or national public interest group that is working to articulate goals and values you agree with. Many of these groups, such as the Environmental Defense Fund, have full-time professional staffs working daily to provide an effective public voice. Have local private interest groups of which you are a member make an effort to speak out on issues important to you. For example, both the Bass Anglers Sportsman's Society and the La Leche League have recently been involved in efforts to control the further use and disposal of PCBs. Clearly, overseeing governmental regulation is not the focus of these organizations. But each has realized that decisions being made to regulate PCBs will impact on their specific interests. The longer PCBs go on being discharged into our rivers and streams, the longer it will be before bass fishermen can safely enjoy eating the fish they catch. And if the disposal of PCBs currently in use in the environment is not controlled properly, the levels of PCBs in mothers' milk will remain dangerously high. Without such efforts by individuals and citizen groups the governmental steps necessary for proper regulation will not occur.

Historically, state governments have done little to combat cancer, but in 1975, following the public outcry in New Jersey over publication of the National Cancer Institute's *Atlases* showing the high rate of cancer incidence in the state, Governor Brendan Byrne created a Cabinet Committee on Cancer Control. This committee, which consists of the heads of various state departments, coordinates investigations, research, and information on cancer in New Jersey. Thus far the Department of Environmental Protection (DEP) has been the most aggressive agency. The DEP has drawn up its own Program on Environmental Cancer and Toxic Substances, aimed at monitoring air, groundwater, surface water, and other drinking water sources for carcinogens and other toxic compounds, on a statewide basis. The program is also planning to utilize short-term biological tests such as the Ames test to measure the cancer-causing potential of air and water effluents.

The DEP will use the information gained from monitoring to map areas of the state that are contaminated and to identify those populations that may be exposed to carcinogens. The DEP will relate the monitoring information to cancer mortality rates in an effort to determine if the geographical distribution of cancer is related to environmental contamination.

As for the federal authorities, it appears that they are at last beginning to awaken to the realization that cancer control must be accomplished through systematic, broad-based regulation that does not permit data to remain buried until a public interest group files a petition or a disaster occurs. The record of control and regulation has not been good, to say the least. Dr. Sidney M. Wolfe, of Ralph Nader's Health Research Group, has prepared tables (see appendix C) indicating which carcinogenic chemicals have been regulated by the federal government, the date when evidence became available that the chemical was carcinogenic, the date of final governmental regulatory action, and the stimulus for this action. Wolfe's research makes it all too clear that action has been irregular, slow in coming, and largely in response to outside pressure. Indeed, the impetus for control of twenty-two out of twenty-six carcinogens finally regulated by the government originated with public interest or union groups.

In 1977 the Occupational Safety and Health Administration proposed a completely new plan to regulate carcinogens in the workplace. Before October 1976 OSHA had proposed standards for only seventeen carcinogens, and every time it or any other regulatory agency had attempted to regulate a carcinogen, it faced a lengthy court battle. Instead of regulating carcinogens on a one-by-one, case-by-case basis in court, OSHA proposes to use a systematic approach that involves dividing chemicals into four generic categories and specifying what regulatory action will automatically result when a chemical is classified in a particular category. The judgment by OSHA as to the appropriateness of the category chosen will be subject to review for each chemical, but the lengthy and costly debate over what regulatory steps should result will not have to be repeatedly reviewed and debated on an individual-chemical basis.

Category I—proven carcinogens—would be so designated by OSHA on the basis of two positive animal tests or one positive animal test and positive evidence from short-term assays such as the Ames test. Protocols for animal tests have developed to the point where valid results can be achieved. To keep arguing about the significance of such results is pointless, an unnecessary waste of taxpayers' monies, and the cause of delay in taking necessary protective actions. As Judge Harold Leventhal, of the U.S. Court of Appeals, D.C. Circuit, wrote in his decision in the aldrin/dieldrin case, "Although extrapolation of data from mice to men may be qualitatively imprecise, it is sufficient to establish a 'substantial likelihood' that harm will result."

For chemicals designated Category I an emergency temporary standard would be issued to offer workers immediate protection. Subsequently a permanent standard would be established. These standards could involve both the use of personal safety equipment, such as respirators, and changes in design technologies to minimize as much as possible or eliminate, where feasible, worker exposure to the hazardous chemical.

Category II—suspect carcinogens—would be so classified from the result of a single positive animal test and would require further testing before possible classification as a Category I chemical. In the interim, until further data are developed, control of worker exposure would be based on the other known hazardous properties of the chemical, such as acute toxicity.

Category III—noncarcinogens—would be so classified because no data existed showing that these chemicals caused cancer in animals or humans. Regulation of exposure to these chemicals in the workplace would be based on other toxicological effects they might pose.

Category IV is a designation for chemicals not used in the U.S. and therefore currently not the direct concern of OSHA.

Although the proposed OSHA regulations are a step in the right direction, they are not a final solution by any means. They need modification to ensure that, where sufficient data do not currently exist to classify a chemical with certainty, such as in Category II or III, the necessary data *will* be developed. Classification in Category II, suspect carcinogens, does not require nearly as strict a regulation as Category I. Therefore, while this is appropriate for the short term until more is known, it is not acceptable as a final classification. Unless testing to resolve the issue of carcinogenicity is mandated, chemicals may sit for years in Category II and potentially harmful worker exposure be allowed to continue.

Characteristically, the chemical industry "categorically" opposes the OSHA plan. The American Industrial Health Council, an industry and trade organization, has been especially vociferous. It argues that the plan is inflexible and allows little in the way of discretionary judgment. Manufacturers and processors claim that excessive testing will be an economic hardship and that animal tests and short-term screens are unreliable indicators. Richard Fleming, vice-president of Air Products, Inc., told *Chemical Week* magazine that the OSHA proposal is "scientifically unsupportable, administratively unsound, legally wrong and economically unfeasible."

Despite the protests of industry, the old chemical-by-chemical approach to regulation has been not only inadequate but dangerous to the public and the environment. The fiascos with pesticides, food additives, and industrial pollutants demonstrate this beyond question. A systematic approach, such as that proposed by OSHA, is absolutely essential. In 1977 the Environmental Defense Fund petitioned the Environmental Protection Agency to start a program for airborne carcinogens modeled on the OSHA plan. Even the lackluster Consumer Product Safety Commission has prepared a policy paper for dealing with carcinogens on a systematic generic basis; the Manufacturing Chemists Association, however, has had the policy enjoined in District Court in Louisiana, on procedural grounds.

The generic approach to carcinogen regulation must also be coordinated. In 1978 the Consumer Product Safety Commission proposed a standard to limit the amount of benzene in home-use consumer products, but the EPA has yet to promulgate an emission standard for this volatile carcinogen after decades of highly suggestive evidence. Meanwhile, in 1978 OSHA set benzene standards of 1 ppm for an eight-hour day.* Three different approaches by three different agencies to one of the most widely used and widely dispersed organic solvents.

Systematic generic regulation of a hazard, it is hoped, will automatically elicit appropriate government response. This approach should also assist industry because it provides an incentive for early testing of chemicals and allows advance planning for production. It is to the benefit of all—government, industry, labor, scientist, and citizen—to institute generic regulation so that carcinogens can be dealt with expediently and safely.

In 1976, after more than five years of drafting legislation, Congress passed the Toxic Substances Control Act (TSCA) to allow the EPA to regulate those hazardous chemicals that do not fall under the jurisdiction of other agencies or acts. It is the first major law that can require health and environmental safety testing on a chemical or product (other than drugs, pesticides, and food additives) before it is manufactured and marketed. The regulatory machinery has been slow and, in part, overburdened in the implementation of this broad law. At best the TSCA can be expected to give the EPA an in-depth look at

---

* In October 1978 the American Petroleum Institute persuaded the 5th Circuit Court of Appeals to stay the enactment of OSHA's workplace benzene standard on the grounds that the agency had failed to properly consider the regulation's economic impact.

the chemical industry in this country and to catch a few of the PCB or kepone incidents *before* they become tragedies.*

The Office of Toxic Substances at the EPA, which administers both the TSCA and the Federal Insecticide, Fungicide and Rodenticide Act, increased its personnel from 45 in 1976 to 150 in 1978, requesting 573 for 1979, with a budgetary allotment that rose from 8 million dollars to 57 million dollars. But many areas are woefully understaffed. The Bureau of Cosmetics at the FDA employs only 45 people, including field officers, and has a yearly budget of less than 2 million dollars. Compare this to the 254.7 million dollars that the cigarette industry spent to *advertise* the top twenty brands in 1975, or the estimated 200 million dollars that Clairol alone sells in hair dye products annually.

The uses of pollution control technology are also aspects of societal response to carcinogens in the environment. In many cases human exposure to carcinogens cannot be eliminated totally or instantaneously because appropriate control technology is unavailable. But there is a mechanism that, if employed correctly, could provide protection from carcinogens in accordance with the most advanced control technology of the day. This system would incorporate continual revision of regulations for the hazardous material, so that in cases where control technology improves, industry is required to adjust its level of pollutants accordingly. The ultimate goal is one of zero emissions of the carcinogen, but there would be no forced closure of industries that could not meet the standard until better control technologies were available. This mode of gradual removal of toxins would be applied only as a last resort, when all other manners of protection had failed.

It is obvious that future efforts to regulate the manufacture, use, and disposal of carcinogenic chemicals must be vastly improved to avoid both the continued pollution of our environment and the PCB-type tragedies of the past. Without such efforts the cancer epidemic we face today may be considered

---

* Unfortunately, two-and-a-half years have passed since the enactment of this law, and EPA's timid and laborious approach offers little hope that major chemical disasters will be averted in the future.

small by the standards of the future. Because of our past failures we have all been exposed unnecessarily to carcinogenic hazards. Although early detection and treatment of cancer are not preventive steps, they are no less important, especially for those who already harbor the disease.

Screening tests, such as a Pap smear for cervical cancer, a pelvic examination for uterine cancer, proctosigmoidoscopy for colon cancer, self-examination of breasts in women for breast cancer, and laryngoscopy for cancer of the larynx can detect cancers at an early stage. For many cancers such early detection can greatly affect the chances for "cure" and survival.

Populations at High Risk. Special efforts are needed to identify and monitor the health of those individuals known to be at high risk. Many of these people have been occupationally exposed to carcinogens, and their risks of contracting cancer are higher than those for the normal population.

Recently we have begun to identify high-risk populations. There are far more than ten million Americans who have been exposed to asbestos as a result of past employment. Their risk of mesothelioma, lung cancer, and other forms of cancer is increased, and these individuals should be screened throughout their lives for early detection of disease. There are approximately two million American women who took the hormone DES during pregnancy and who, along with their offspring, may suffer an increased risk of cancer. There are perhaps a million people who received X-ray treatment of the head and neck region who face an increased risk of thyroid cancer.

It is not enough simply to publicize the fact that high-risk groups exist. Concerted efforts must be made to find individuals in such groups and to provide them with the necessary screening procedures. Social Security records can be used to help identify individuals previously exposed through occupation to carcinogenic risks.

While certain populations are at high risk, everyone should know the seven warning signals of cancer. They are:

—change in bowel or bladder habits;
—a sore that does not heal;

—any unusual bleeding or discharge;
—a thickening or lump, especially in the breast;
—indigestion or difficulty in swallowing;
—an obvious change in a wart or mole;
—nagging cough or hoarseness.

But all our efforts will be successful only if we as individuals take steps both to make personal changes and to support necessary governmental regulation. If we are not convinced that the cancer problem can be solved, it won't be. Not everything causes cancer. We can win the battle if we choose to fight.

APPENDIXES
BIBLIOGRAPHICAL ESSAY
INDEX

COMMON FOOD ADDITIVES

AVOID

All artificial colorings should be avoided. Most are synthetic chemicals not found in nature. Some are safer than others, but names of colorings are not listed on label. Used mostly in foods of low nutritional value, usually indicating that fruit or natural ingredient omitted.

Additive	Use	Comment
Blue No. 1	In beverages, candy, baked goods.	Very poorly tested.
Blue No. 2	Pet food, beverages, candy.	Very poorly tested.
Citrus Red No. 2	Skin of some Florida oranges.	May cause cancer. Does not seep through into pulp.
Green No. 3	Candy, beverages.	Needs better testing.
Orange B	Hot dogs.	Causes cancer in animals.
Red No. 3	Cherries in fruit cocktail, candy, baked goods.	May cause cancer.
Red No. 40	Soda, candy, gelatin desserts, pastry, pet food, sausage.	Causes cancer in mice. Widely used.
Yellow No. 5	Gelatin desserts, candy, pet food, baked goods.	Poorly tested; might cause cancer. Some people allergic to it. Widely used.
Brominated Vegetable Oil (BVO)	Emulsifier, clouding agent. Citrus-flavored soft drinks.	Residue found in body fat; safer substitutes available.
Butylated Hydroxytoluene (BHT)	Antioxidant. Cereals, chewing gum, potato chips, oils, etc.	May cause cancer; stored in body fat; can cause allergic reaction. Safer alternatives.

AVOID

Additive	Use	Comment
Caffeine	Stimulant. Naturally in coffee, tea, cocoa; added to soft drinks.	Causes sleeplessness; may cause miscarriages or birth defects.
Quinine	Flavoring. Tonic water, quinine water, bitter lemon.	Poorly tested; some possibility that may cause birth defects.
Saccharin	Noncaloric sweetener. "Diet" products.	Causes cancer in animals.
Sodium Nitrite, Sodium Nitrate	Preservative, coloring, flavoring. Bacon, ham, frankfurters, luncheon meats, smoked fish, corned beef.	Prevents growth of botulism bacteria, but can lead to formation of small amounts of cancer-causing nitrosamines, particularly in fried bacon.

CAUTION

Additive	Use	Comment
Artificial Coloring Yellow No. 6	Beverages, sausage, baked goods, candy, gelatin.	Appears safe, but can cause allergic reactions.
Artificial Flavoring	Soda, candy, breakfast cereals, gelatin desserts, etc.	Hundreds of chemicals used to mimic natural flavors, almost exclusively in "junk" foods, indicates "real thing" is left out. May cause hyperactivity in some children.
Butylated Hydroxyanisole (BHA)	Antioxidant. Cereals, chewing gum, potato chips, oils.	Appears safer than BHT but needs better testing. Safer substitutes available.
Gums: Locust Bean, Guar, Furcelleran, Arabic, Karaya, Tragacanth, Ghatti	Thickening, stabilizing agents. Beverages, ice cream, frozen pudding, salad dressing, dough, cottage cheese, candy, drink mixes.	Derived from bushes, trees or seaweed; poorly tested but probably safe.
Heptyl Paraben	Preservative. Beer.	Probably safe, has not been tested in presence of alcohol.

CAUTION

Additive	Use	Comment
Monosodium Glutamate (MSG)	Flavor enhancer. Soup, seafood, poultry, cheese, sauces, stews, etc.	Damages brain cells in infant mice; causes "Chinese restaurant syndrome" (headache and burning or tightness in head, neck, arms) in some sensitive adults.
Phosphoric Acid; Phosphates	Acidifier, chelating agent, buffer, emulsifier, nutrient, discoloration inhibitor. Baked goods, cheese, powdered foods, cured meat, soda, breakfast cereals, dried potatoes.	Useful chemicals that are not toxic, but their widespread use creates dietary imbalance that may be causing osteoporosis.
Propyl Gallate	Antioxidant. Oil, meat products, potato sticks, chicken soup base, chewing gum.	Not adequately tested; use is frequently unnecessary.
Sulfur Dioxide, Sodium Bisulfite	Preservative, bleach. Sliced fruit, wine, grape juice, dried potatoes, dried fruit.	Can destroy vitamin B-1, but otherwise safe.

SAFE

Additive	Use	Comment
Alginate, Propylene Glycol Alginate	Thickening agent, foam stabilizer. Ice cream, cheese, candy, yogurt.	Derived from seaweed.
Alpha Tocopherol	Antioxidant, nutrient. Vegetable oil.	Vitamin E.
Ascorbic Acid, Erythorbic Acid	Antioxidant, nutrient, color stabilizer. Oily foods, cereals, soft drinks, cured meats.	Ascorbic acid and its salt, sodium ascorbate, provide nutrient vitamin C; erythorbic acid has no value as vitamin. All help prevent formation of cancer-causing nitrosamines.
Beta Carotene	Coloring, nutrient. Margarine, shortening, non-dairy creamers, butter.	Body converts it to vitamin A.

SAFE

Additive	Use	Comment
Calcium (or Sodium) Propionate	Preservative. Bread, rolls, pies, cakes.	Prevents mold growth; calcium a nutrient.
Calcium (or Sodium) Stearoyl Lactylate	Dough conditioner, whipping agent. Bread dough, cake fillings, artificial whipped cream, processed egg white.	Sodium stearoyl fumarate, also safe, serves same function.
Carrageenan	Thickening and whitening agent. Ice cream, jelly, chocolate milk, infant formula.	From "Irish moss" seaweed.
Casein, Sodium Caseinate	Thickening and whitening agent. Ice cream, ice milk, sherbet, coffee creamers.	Nutritious, the principal protein in milk.
Citric Acid, Sodium Citrate	Acid, flavoring, chelating agent. Ice cream, sherbet, fruit drinks, candy, carbonated beverages, instant potatoes.	Citric acid is abundant in citrus fruits and berries; an important metabolite.
EDTA	Chelating agent. Salad dressing, margarine, sandwich spreads, mayonnaise, processed fruits and vegetables, canned shellfish, soft drinks.	Traps metallic impurities that would otherwise cause rancidity and discoloration.
Ferrous Gluconate	Coloring, nutrient. Black olives.	A source of nutrient iron.
Fumaric Acid	Tartness agent. Powdered drinks, puddings, pie fillings, gelatin desserts.	Safe, but to enhance solution in cold water, DSS added, a poorly tested, detergentlike additive.
Gelatin	Thickening, gelling agent. Powdered dessert mix, yogurt, ice cream, cheese spread, beverages.	From animal bones, hooves and other parts. Little nutritional value as protein.
Glycerin (Glycerol)	Maintains water content. Marshmallow, candy, fudge, baked goods.	Natural backbone of fat molecules. Used as energy or to build complex molecules.
Hydrolyzed Vegetable Protein (HVP)	Flavor enhancer. Instant soups, frankfurters, sauce mixers, beef stew.	Vegetable (usually soybean) protein, chemically broken down into constituent amino acids.
Lactic Acid	Acidity regulator. Spanish olives, cheese, frozen desserts, carbonated beverages.	Naturally occurring in almost all living organisms.

SAFE

Additive	Use	Comment
Lactose	Sweetener. Whipped topping mix, breakfast pastry.	Slightly sweet carbohydrate from milk.
Lecithin	Emulsifier, antioxidant. Baked goods, margarine, chocolate, ice cream.	Common in animals and plants; a source of the nutrient choline.
Mannitol	Sweetener. Chewing gum, low-calorie foods.	Less sweet than sugar but because it is poorly absorbed by body, has only half the calories of sugar.
Mono- and Diglycerides	Emulsifiers. Baked goods, margarine, candy, peanut butter.	Safe, but used mostly in foods that are high in sugar or fat.
Polysorbate 60, 65 and 80	Emulsifiers. Baked goods, frozen desserts, imitation dairy products.	Synthetic but appear to be safe.
Sodium Benzoate	Preservative. Fruit juice, carbonated drinks, pickles, preserves.	Used more than 70 years to prevent growth of microorganisms.
Sodium Carboxymethylcellulose (CMC)	Thickening, stabilizing agent, prevents sugar from crystallizing. Ice cream, beer, pie fillings, icings, diet foods, candy.	Made by reacting cellulose with acetic acid (vinegar); studies indicate safety.
Sorbic Acid, Potassium Sorbate	Prevents mold, bacterial growth. Cheese, syrup, jelly, cake, wine, dried fruits.	From berries of mountain ash. Sorbate may be safe substitute for sodium nitrite in bacon.
Sorbitan Monostearate	Emulsifier. Cakes, candy, frozen pudding, icing.	Keeps oil and water mixed.
Sorbitol	Sweetener, thickening agent, moisturizer. Dietetic drinks and foods; candy, shredded coconut, chewing gum.	From fruits and berries, half as sweet as sugar; slowly absorbed, thus safe for diabetics.
Starch, Modified Starch	Thickening agent. Soup, gravy, baby foods.	From flour, potatoes, corn; modified chemically to improve solution in cold water. Used to make foods look thicker and richer.
Vanillin, Ethyl Vanillin	Substitute for vanilla flavoring. Ice cream, baked goods, beverages, chocolate, candy, gelatin desserts.	Vanillin, synthetic version of main flavor in vanilla bean, is safe; ethyl vanillin has more authentic taste but needs more testing.

SPECIAL CONSIDERATIONS

Additive	Use	Comment
Salt (Sodium chloride)	Flavoring. Most processed foods: soup, potato chips, crackers, cured meat, etc.	Large amounts of sodium may cause high blood pressure in susceptible people and increase risk of heart attack and stroke.
Sugars: Corn Syrup, Dextrose, Glucose, Invert Sugar, Sugar	Sweeteners. Candy, soft drinks, cookies, syrups, toppings, sweetened cereals and many other foods.	Mostly in foods with low, if any, nutritional value. Excess sugars may promote tooth decay and precipitate diabetes in susceptible persons; condensed source of calories.

Based on "Chemical Cuisine," a poster prepared by Nutrition Action, a project of Center for Science in the Public Interest. From the *New York Times,* July 12, 1978.

APPENDIX B
HOME WATER
FILTRATION METHODS

The first two methods shown here are less efficient than the third, primarily because the water does not stay in contact with the carbon for as long a time. Method III was tested by scientists at the U.S. Environmental Protection Agency and was found to result in the production of a high-quality water when used to treat drinking water drawn from the Ohio River at Cincinnati, one of the most heavily polluted water supplies in the U.S.

METHOD I

Materials: Standard glass bulb baster (8¼″ × ¾″), block of wood, rubber band, 1-quart glass jar, plug of cotton, activated carbon granules. (See diagram 1.)

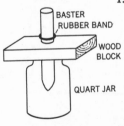

1. To construct the filter: Drill a hole in the block of wood ¾″ or slightly larger to allow the glass bulb baster (without the bulb) to slide through. Place the rubber band on the glass baster just above the wood in order to prevent the column from sliding all the way through the wood. Rest the block of wood on the mouth of the quart jar in order to suspend it. Put a plug of cotton in the bottom of the baster.
2. If the granular activated carbon has not been prewashed, place the carbon in another glass jar. Fill with water, cover, and shake. Let the carbon settle to the bottom. If any fine black particles are present in the water above the settled carbon, pour off the water and repeat the procedure until the water is clear. The use of prewashed carbon should eliminate most of the carbon dust; in that case this step can be shortened to just one wash, in order to check cleanliness.
3. Now fill the baster half full with granular activated carbon. Pour tap water through the column.

4. Pour the water from the filled jar into a pan and bring it to a boil, then reduce the heat and simmer it as slowly as possible for 15 to 20 minutes. (The latter procedure is to avoid evaporation and hence concentration of the salts.) Boiling will both sterilize the water and further remove certain volatile organics like chloroform.
5. Store in the refrigerator until used.
6. Change carbon every 3 weeks, or after 20 gallons of water have been filtered.

METHOD II

Materials: Large funnel (e.g., Melitta coffee filter), filter paper (Melitta coffee filter paper), glass collecting jar (1 quart or larger) with lid, granular activated carbon. (See diagram 2.)

1. Place filter paper in funnel.
2. Follow step 2, method I.
3. Holding the funnel over the sink, pour the water with carbon through the funnel. Enough carbon should be used to fill the funnel to approximately ¼ full.
4. Place a clean collecting jar under the funnel and begin slowly pouring water through the funnel. A piece of clean filter paper can be placed on top of the carbon so as not to disturb the carbon while pouring the water into the funnel.
5. Follow steps 4, 5, and 6, method I.

METHOD III

Materials: ¼" copper tubing, ¼" tubing tee, 36" × ¾"-inside-diameter copper or galvanized steel pipe (a shorter column may be used if there are space limitations), ice maker saddle valve, reducing union for ¾" pipe to ¼" tubing, funnel, filter paper, 1-gallon glass bottle, plastic pan, plug of cotton, activated carbon granules. (See diagram 3.)

1. Construct the filter as illustrated in diagram 3.
2. Disinfect the empty column with a 5% solution of laundry bleach by filling the column and letting it stand for a couple of minutes.
3. Rinse the column thoroughly.
4. Put a plug of cotton in the bottom of the column.
5. Fill the column with water and add previously wetted (2 hours) washed carbon to a depth of 26".
6. Maintain the water level above the carbon by placing the ¼" tubing tee above the surface of the carbon as illustrated.
7. Operate the carbon column continuously, 24 hours a day, at a flow rate of 1 gallon per day, using the saddle valve to adjust the flow rate.
8. Follow steps 4, 5, and 6 in method I.

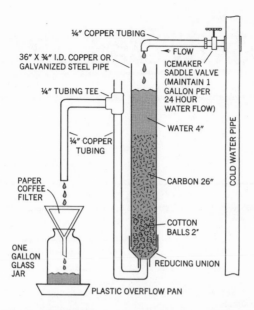

¼" COPPER TUBING

FLOW

ICEMAKER SADDLE VALVE (MAINTAIN 1 GALLON PER 24 HOUR WATER FLOW)

36" X ¾" I.D. COPPER OR GALVANIZED STEEL PIPE

¼" TUBING TEE

¼" COPPER TUBING

WATER 4"

CARBON 26"

PAPER COFFEE FILTER

COTTON BALLS 2"

ONE GALLON GLASS JAR

REDUCING UNION

COLD WATER PIPE

PLASTIC OVERFLOW PAN

Granular activated carbon particularly prepared for use in treating drinking water can be purchased in one-pound bags from Walnut Acres, Penns Creek, Pennsylvania 17862.

TABLE 1
Lag in Federal Regulatory Action on Carcinogens—Workplace Carcinogens
a = animal
h = human

Carcinogen	Earliest evidence of cancer
4-dimethylaminoazobenzene	1936 (a)
Beta-naphthylamine	1938 (a)
	1952 (h)
2-acetylaminofluorene	1941 (a)
Chromates	1948 (h)
Benzidine	1950 (a)
	1952 (h)
4-aminodiphenyl	1952 (a)
	1955 (h)
Beta-propiolactone	1955 (a)
Asbestos	1955 (h)
	1957 (a)
4-nitrodiphenyl	1955 (h)
	1958 (a)
Alpha-naphthylamine (ANA)	1956 (a)
N-nitrosodimethylamine	1956 (a)
Dichlorobenzidine	1959 (a)
Bis (chloromethyl) ether	1968 (a)
	1972 (h)
Methylene (bis) chloroaniline (MOCA)	1969 (a)
Ethyleneimine (EI)	1969 (a)
Methyl chloromethyl ether	1969 (a)
Benzene	1974 (h)

* Abbreviations: AFL-CIO, American Federation of Labor & Congress of Industrial Organizations; ETS, Emergency Temporary Standard; HRG, Health Research Group; OCAW, Oil, Chemical and Atomic Workers; OSHA, Occupational

Action initiated by public interest group or labor union *	Final regulatory action *
January 1973—OCAW, HRG: petition to OSHA	1973—OSHA: ETS
January 1973—OCAW, HRG: petition to OSHA	1973—OSHA: ETS
January 1973—OCAW, HRG: petition to OSHA	1973—OSHA: ETS
1975—USW: petition to OSHA	none
January 1973—OCAW, HRG: petition to OSHA	1973—OSHA: ETS
1973—OCAW, HRG: petition to OSHA	1973—OSHA: ETS
1973—OCAW, HRG: petition to OSHA	1973—OSHA: ETS
1972—AFL-CIO: petition to OSHA	1972—OSHA: standard
January 1973—OCAW, HRG: petition to OSHA	1973—OSHA: ETS
	1973—OSHA: ETS
January 1973—OCAW, HRG: petition to OSHA	1973—OSHA: ETS
January 1973—OCAW, HRG: petition to OSHA	1973—OSHA: ETS
January 1973—OCAW, HRG: petition to OSHA	1973—OSHA: ETS
	1974—court: vacated standard of 1973
	1973—OSHA: ETS
	1973—OSHA: ETS
Summer 1976—URW: petition to OSHA	1976—OSHA: petition denied

Safety and Health Administration; URW, United Rubber Workers; USW, United Steel Workers.

TABLE 2
Lag in Federal Regulatory Action on Carcinogens—Pesticides
a = animal
h = human

Carcinogen	Earliest evidence of cancer	Action initiated by public interest group or labor union *
Endrin	1958 (a)	1975—EDF: petition to EPA
Heptachlor/chlordane	1959 (a)	1974—EDF: petition to EPA
Aramite	1960 (a)	
Kepone	1961 (a)	
Aldrin/dieldrin	1962 (a)	December 1970—EDF: petition to EPA
Mirex	1969 (a)	
1,1,1-trichloro-2,2-di (4-chlorophenyl) ethane (DDT)	1969 (a)	1969—EDF: petition to EPA
Strobane	1969 (a)	
Avadex	1969 (a)	
Bis (2-chloroethyl) ether	1969 (a)	
N-(2-hydroxyethyl) hydrazine	1969 (a)	
pentachloronitrobenzene (PCNB)	1969 (a)	
Piperonyl butoxide	1969 (a)	
2-chloroethyltrimethylammonium chloride (CCC)	1969 (a)	
Chloranil	1969 (a)	
Cyanamide	1969 (a)	
Zectran	1969 (a)	
Captan	1969 (a)	
Chlorobenzilate	1969 (a)	
Perthane	1969 (a)	
Ethylene dibromide (EDB)	1973 (a)	1975—EDF: petition to EPA

* Abbreviations: EDF, Environmental Defense Fund; EPA, Environmental Protection Agency; RPAR, Rebuttable Presumption Against Registration. (A notice issued by the EPA to the manufacturer of any pesticide found to induce tumors in animals. Manufacturer is given a period of time following issuance of notice within which to prove that the chemical is safe. Failure to prove safety results in EPA issuance of intent to cancel license, within 180 days.)
    Candidate on May 1, 1976, RPAR list—The May 1, 1976, RPAR list indicates *projected* time schedules and "candidates" for RPAR, with toxicity characteristics indicated. *No action has been taken* on these chemicals by the EPA.

Preliminary action by EPA *	Final regulatory action by EPA
RPAR—1976	none †
March 1971—EPA announces intent to investigate	1975—EPA: suspended
1973 EPA secret list; high priority candidate on May 1, 1976, RPAR list	none †
RPAR—1976	none †
March 1971—EPA announces intent to investigate	1974—EPA: suspended
investigational hearing still underway (1971–?)	none †
November 1969: EPA announces intent to investigate	1972—EPA: canceled
candidate on May 1, 1976, RPAR list	none †
1973 EPA secret list; high priority	none
1973 EPA secret list; high priority	none
1973 EPA secret list; high priority	none
1973 EPA secret list; high priority	none †
candidate on May 1, 1976, RPAR list	
candidate on May 1, 1976, RPAR list	none
1973 EPA secret list; high priority	none
candidate on May 1, 1976, RPAR list	none †
	1972—EPA: canceled for most predator uses
1973 EPA secret list; high priority	none
1973 EPA secret list; high priority	none
1973 EPA secret list; high priority	none †
RPAR 1976	
candidate on May 1, 1976, RPAR list	none
candidate on May 1, 1976, RPAR list	none †

1973 secret EPA list—List of harmful pesticides, compiled in 1973 and circulated only within the EPA. Includes summary of toxicity characteristics and priority levels designated by the EPA (low to high) for each chemical. (We list only "high-priority" pesticides.)

† Since the publication of Dr. Wolfe's chart, action on the following pesticides has taken place: endrin, RPAR 1976; aramite, voluntary cancellation; kepone, voluntary cancellation; mirex, voluntary cancellation; strobane, voluntary cancellation; pentachloronitrobenzene (PCNB), RPAR 1977; chloranil, voluntary cancellation; chlorobenzilate, RPAR 1976; ethylene dibromide (EDB), RPAR 1977.

TABLE 3

Lag in Federal Regulatory Action on Carcinogens—Ubiquitous Exposure
a = animal
h = human

Carcinogen	Earliest evidence of cancer
Diethylstilbestrol (DES)	1941 (a)
	1971 (h)
FD & C Red No. 2	1970 (a)
FD & C Violet No. 1	1962 (a)
Vinyl chloride	1969 (a)
	1974 (h)
Polychlorinated biphenyls (PCBs)	1972 (a)
	1976 (h)
Trichloroethylene	1975 (a)
Chloroform	1976 (a)

* Abbreviations: AFL-CIO, American Federation of Labor & Congress of Industrial Organizations; CPSC, Consumer Product Safety Commission; CSPI, Center for Science in the Public Interest; EDF, Environmental Defense Fund; EPA,

Action initiated by public interest group or labor union *	Final regulatory action
1971—EDF: petition to FDA on DES as feed additive	FDA: none
1971—HRG: petition to FDA	1976—FDA: ban
1971—CSPI: petition to FDA	1973—FDA: ban
1974—URW, IUD/AFL-CIO, OCAW: petition to OSHA	1974—OSHA: occupational standard
1974—HRG: petition to EPA, FDA, CPSC on aerosols	1974—EPA, FDA, CPSC: aerosols
1975—HRG: petition to FDA on food packaging	none—FDA: food packaging
1976—EDF: petition to EPA	none—FDA none—OSHA
1975—HRG: petition to FDA	1976—FDA none—OSHA: occupational standard
1976—HRG: petition to FDA	1976—FDA: drugs

Environmental Protection Agency; FDA, Food and Drug Administration; HRG, Health Research Group; IUD, Industrial Union Department; OCAW, Oil, Chemical and Atomic Workers; OSHA, Occupational Safety and Health Administration.

BIBLIOGRAPHICAL ESSAY

We suggest the following books and papers, many of which we have used for sources, to readers who wish to pursue a particular aspect of environmental carcinogenesis.

CHAPTER 1: THE NATURE AND SCOPE OF THE PROBLEM

A most basic, but highly technical, reference is H. H. Hiatt, J. D. Watson, and J. A. Winsten, eds., *Origins of Human Cancer* (Cold Spring Harbor, N.Y.: Cold Spring Harbor Laboratory, 1977), which consists of the papers presented at the international conference held in September 1976 at the Cold Spring Harbor Laboratory on Long Island. Published in three volumes totaling almost 1,900 pages, the books deal with the incidence of cancer in humans, mechanisms of carcinogenesis, and human-risk assessment. The editors note that "more papers were presented than in any meeting yet held at Cold Spring Harbor. Also exceptional were the breadth of disciplines represented, including epidemiologists, clinical oncologists, animal oncologists, molecular biologists, virologists, immunologists, toxicologists, policy analysts, government regulators, scientists from industry, and representatives of the news media. Participants were asked to discuss the state-of-the-art in order to promote a better understanding of each other's research and policy problems, languages, and methods of pursuing the common goal."

Also of value is Joseph F. Fraumeni, Jr., ed., *Persons at High Risk of Cancer* (New York: Academic Press, 1975), which comprises the proceedings of a conference sponsored in December 1974 by the National Cancer Institute and the American Cancer Society. Among other subjects individual papers deal with such environmental factors as tobacco, radiation, occupation, drugs, diet, and air pollution. For the distribution of various forms of cancer in the United States and abroad, plus factors associated with high or low risks, see David L. Levin, Susan S. Devesa, J. David Godwin II, and Debra R. Silverman, *Cancer Rates and Risks*, 2d ed., Department of Health, Education and Welfare Publication no. (NIH) 76-691 (Washington, D.C., 1974). Michael B. Shimkin has written two books in popular language: *Science and Cancer*,

DHEW Publication no. (NIH) 77-568 (Washington, D.C., 1973), an account of the nature of cancer and the efforts of science and medicine to control it; and *Contrary to Nature,* DHEW Publication no. (NIH) 76-720 (Washington, D.C., 1977), an illustrated commentary on the medical history of cancer from Graeco-Roman times to the present day.

Cancer distribution in the U.S. is dealt with visually in Thomas J. Mason, Frank W. McKay, Robert Hoover, W. J. Blot, and Joseph F. Fraumeni, Jr., *Atlas of Cancer Mortality for U.S. Counties: 1950–1969,* DHEW Publication no. (NIH) 75-780 (Washington, D.C.: U.S. Government Printing Office, 1975); *Atlas of Cancer Mortality Among U.S. Nonwhites,* by the same authors, DHEW Publication no. (NIH) 76-1204 (Washington, D.C.: U.S. Government Printing Office, 1976); Robert Hoover and Joseph F. Fraumeni, Jr., "Cancer Mortality in U.S. Counties with Chemical Industries," *Environmental Research* 9 (1975): 196–207; and Robert Hoover, T. J. Mason, F. W. McKay, and J. F. Fraumeni, Jr., "Cancer by County: New Sources for Etiologic Clues," *Science* 189 (19 September 1975): 1,005–1,007.

Thanks to Dr. Glenn Paulson, Assistant Commissioner for Science of the Department of Environmental Protection in Trenton, New Jersey, we were able to consult a draft copy of Michael R. Greenberg's *The Spatial Distribution of Cancer Mortality and of High and Low Risk Factors in the New Jersey–New York–Philadelphia Metropolitan Regions, 1950–1969.*

We are grateful to Dr. Wilhelm C. Hueper, author of more than three hundred papers and books on the occupational and environmental causes of cancer, for letting us read his untitled and unpublished reminiscences, which permitted us to go back into time and to realize the difficulties that faced the pioneering oncologist. Hueper's *Occupational Tumors and Allied Diseases* (Springfield, Ill.: Charles C. Thomas, 1942) remains a landmark.

Hazards of the workplace are dealt with at length in Umberto Saffiotti and Joseph K. Wagoner, eds., *Occupational Carcinogenesis* (New York: New York Academy of Sciences, 1976), which consists of papers presented at a conference of the same name in 1975. The New York Academy of Sciences has since adapted and published the papers as a popularly written book, *Cancer and the Worker* (New York: New York Academy of Sciences, 1977).

Popularly written books on occupational cancer include Paul Brodeur's *Expendable Americans* (New York: The Viking Press, 1974), which is largely an account of asbestosis and is unfortunately not indexed; and Willard S. Randall and Stephen D. Solomon's *Building Six* (Boston: Little, Brown & Company, 1975), which deals with the cancer incidence among workers handling bis(chloromethyl)ether at the Rohm and Haas plant in Bridesburg, Pennsylvania. See also Rachel Scott, *Muscle & Blood* (New York: E. P. Dutton & Company, Inc., 1974), which covers a wide range of industrial hazards; and the helpful volume by Erik P. Eckholm, *The Picture of Health, Environmental Sources of Disease* (New York: W. W. Norton & Company, Inc., 1977).

"Carcinogens in the Environment," reprinted from *The Sixth Annual Report of the Council on Environmental Quality* (December 1975) and available from the U.S. Government Printing Office, Washington, D.C., Stock no. 041–011–00030–1, is a handy booklet. Far more detailed and of great worth in defining the spread of environmental pollution in recent decades is *Effects of Chronic Exposure to Low-Level Pollutants in the Environment,* prepared by the Congressional Research Service of the Library of Congress for the Subcommittee on the Environment and the Atmosphere, Committee on Science and Technology, House of Representatives, 94th Cong., 1st sess., November 1975, Serial no. 0.

The International Agency for Research on Cancer, an autonomous body within the World Health Organization, published *Environmental Pollution and Carcinogenic Risks,* IARC Publications no. 13 (Lyon, France, 1976), which contains a number of stimulating papers, such as Cesare Maltoni, "Occupational Chemical Carcinogenesis: New Facts, Priorities and Perspectives"; L. M. Shabad and G. A. Smirnov, "Aviation and Environmental Benzo(a)pyrene Pollution"; H. F. Stich, A. B. Acton, and B. P. Dunn, "Carcinogens in Estuaries, Their Monitoring and Possible Hazard to Man"; and John Higginson, "The Importance of Environmental Factors in Cancer." In 1972 the IARC, which is in Lyon, France, began a monograph series entitled Evaluation of the Carcinogenic Risk of Chemicals to Man. As of this writing, sixteen volumes have appeared in the series, dealing with chlorinated hydrocarbons, sex hormones, asbestos, the herbicides 2,4-D and 2,4,5-T, and numerous other chemicals. In the U.S., IARC publications may be obtained from Q Corporation, 49 Sheridan Avenue, Albany, New York 12210. The American Chemical Society has published *Chemical Carcinogens,* ACS Monograph 173 (Washington, D.C., 1976), which contains papers entitled "Bioassays and Tests for Chemical Carcinogens," "Polynuclear Aromatic Carcinogens," "Soots, Tars and Oils as Causes of Occupational Cancer," and "Carcinogens in Food," among other subjects.

Among general works, Pat McGrady's *The Savage Cell* (New York: Basic Books, Inc., 1964) remains valuable, even though much of the information has been superseded by developments in cancer research. Among other works we have consulted are Joseph C. Maroon, *What You Can Do About Cancer* (Garden City, N.Y.: Doubleday & Company, Inc., 1969); June Goodfield, *The Siege of Cancer* (New York: Random House, 1975), an account of various researches into cancer but unfortunately not indexed; and Ronald Glasser, *The Greatest Battle* (New York: Random House, 1976), an account by a physician of the environmental causes of cancer. Larry Agran's *The Cancer Connection, and What We Can Do About It* (Boston: Houghton Mifflin Company, 1977) is a muckraking work about the environmental causation of cancer. It offers a very interesting account of chemical contamination of the Little Elk Valley in Maryland, among other case histories. Jane E. Brody, of the *New York Times,* and Arthur I. Holleb, of the American Cancer Society, have written *You Can Fight Cancer and Win* (New York: Quadrangle, 1977). This book pays court to the theme of prevention and as such conveys some helpful information, but it tends to gloss over the role of government in confronting carcinogens in the environment.

Two recent books address the carcinogenesis problem from the preventive point of view: Dr. Elizabeth Whelan's *Preventing Cancer* (New York: W. W. Norton and Co., 1978) relies heavily on the personal aspects such as cigarette smoking and occupation, and questions the significance of the effects of chemicals in the environment. *The Politics of Cancer* by Dr. Samuel Epstein is an authoritative description of the relation of cancer to public policy, and the personal and societal requirements for effective cancer prevention (San Francisco: Sierra Club Books, 1978).

Articles in the *New York Times* and the Washington *Post,* especially as reflected by the reporting of Richard Severo and David Burnham for the former and Morton Mintz for the latter, have been helpful; and *Environment* magazine and *Columbia Journalism Review* have published articles of pertinence. *Environment* has always been in the forefront. For examples of the *CJR,* see Wade Roberts, "Phosvel: A Tale of Missed Cues," July–August 1977, which deals with the "Phosvel zombies," workers at the Velsicol Chemical Corporation plant near Houston who suffered from exposure to the pesticide Phosvel; and Betty Medsger, "Asbestos, the California Story," September–October 1977.

CHAPTER 2: THE BIOLOGY OF CANCER

Armin C. Braun, of the Rockefeller University, wrote *The Cancer Problem* (New York: Columbia University Press, 1969) as a basic exploration of the genetic and molecular regulation of cellular processes. Braun's *The Biology of Cancer* (Reading, Mass.: Addison-Wesley, 1974) furthered the same inquiries, and we regard this as perhaps the best general book to describe the differences between normal cells and tumor cells. It is written in a clear, direct manner for those who know a little about life sciences but nothing about cancer.

Among the other general sources available, Kirk and McCollough have edited a handy volume called *Cancer Today* (Acton, Australia: John Curtin School of Medical Research, 1975), which reads easily and describes not only the biology of the disease but also the factors likely to influence cancer rates and the mechanisms of chemical carcinogenesis. Victor Richards's *The Wayward Cell* (Berkeley: University of California Press, 1972) presents a general discussion of the origin, nature, and treatment of cancer. Henry Lynch's *Cancer and You* (Springfield, Ill.: Charles C. Thomas, 1971) is a source of factual information on the primary types of cancer affecting man, with background material to aid the reader's understanding of the disease.

A number of books approach carcinogenesis from a historical perspective, or else are interesting historically because of developments that have taken place since they were written. A good example of the latter is George Wolf's *Chemical Induction of Cancer* (Cambridge, Mass.: Harvard University Press, 1952). It describes the biological aspects of tumor initiation as they were perceived twenty-five years ago. D. W. Smithers, *On the Nature of Neoplasia in Man* (London: E. & S. Livingstone, Ltd., 1964), collects some of the important papers from lectures on cancer research.

Two of the best historical treatises on cancer were written by Isaac Berenblum, a pioneer in carcinogenesis research. The earlier, *Man Against Cancer* (Baltimore: The Johns Hopkins University Press, 1952), relates both the nature of cancer and the research efforts to elucidate mechanisms and etiology, while his *Carcinogenesis as a Biological Problem* (Amsterdam and New York: North-Holland/American Elsevier, 1974) is among the best and most up-to-date books. It traces the historical development of our understanding of the biochemical mechanisms of carcinogenesis, in addition to outlining principles for cancer prevention.

Technical literature on cancer pours forth from the research world at an extremely high rate. A good number of journals, *Cancer, Cancer Letters, Cancer Research, Journal of the National Cancer Institute,* and *British Journal of Cancer,* devote themselves entirely to the topic. To examine the biochemical nature of carcinogenesis, see Harris Busch, *An Introduction to the Biochemistry of the Cancer Cell* (New York: Academic Press, 1962), which describes the genetic nature and appearance of the cancer cell; and Oscar Bodansky, *The Biochemistry of Human Cancer* (New York: Academic Press, 1975), which discusses the biochemistry of various specific neoplasms and some general aspects of enzymes in cancer.

Cancer research itself is a fascinating story. Harris Busch has edited a thirteen-volume series entitled *Methods of Cancer Research* (New York: Academic Press, most recent volume 1976), which covers a wide range of material, from research on specific drugs to broad discussions of the various cellular components of the carcinogenic process. E. J. Ambrose, D. M. Easty, and J. A. H. Wylie's *The Cancer Cell in Vitro* (London: Butterworths, 1967) describes tissue culture techniques for cell and organ culture study. Busch also edited *The Molecular Biology of Cancer* (New York: Academic Press, 1974), which deals with the science of the disease at the molecular level. Busch covers such areas as protein synthesis and the role of nuclear proteins in carcinogenic mechanisms. For a highly specific look at information of this nature, *The Molecular Basis of Neoplasia* (Austin: University of Texas Press, 1961) is a good place to begin. Collected by the M. D. Anderson Hospital and Tumor Institute, these papers were presented at conferences on cancer biochemistry. Their subjects range from nucleic acid, enzyme, and protein synthesis in carcinogenesis to the synthesis of histidine, a nucleic acid, by the *Salmonella typhimurium* bacterium. This latter paper, by Bruce Ames and Philip Hartman, discusses the basic work leading to the development of the so-called Ames test for mutagenesis/carcinogenesis. Each year a series of these symposia are published. Others include *The Proliferation and Spread of Neoplastic Cells* (1967), *Environment and Cancer* (1971), and *Cellular Membranes and Tumor Cell Behavior* (1975).

Two other recent series round out our list of technical source materials. Frederick F. Beeker, ed., *Cancer 1, A Comprehensive Treatise* (New York: Plenum Press, 1975), is the first in a four-volume series. This volume specifically focuses on the etiology of cancer, with sections on the interactions and metabolism of chemical carcinogens. Phillipe Shubik is general editor of a series entitled *The Physiopathology of Cancer*. The initial volume, edited by F. Homburger, *Biology and Biochemistry* (Basel: S. Karger, 1974), deals not only with the biochemical mechanisms of chemical carcinogens but also with the roles of modifying agents, promoting agents, and viruses.

CHAPTER 3: PCBS: A CASE IN POINT

The literature on this contaminant has become a growth industry. The paper that prompted worldwide investigation and concern is Sören Jensen, "Report of a New Chemical Hazard," *New Scientist* 32 (1966): 612. Jensen's description of how he isolated and identified the contaminant is to be found in his article, "The PCB Story," *Ambio* 1, no. 4 (August 1972): 123–131. The same issue of *Ambio* contains Gensyu Umeda's "PCB Poisoning in Japan" on pp. 132–134. Barry Commoner, "Workplace Burden," *Environment* 15, no. 6 (July–August 1973): 15–20, raised anew old questions about PCBs as a hazard to human health by citing J. W. Jones and H. S. Alden, "Acneform Dermatergosis," *Archives of Dermatology and Syphilology* 33, no. 6 (1936): 1,022–1,034; and Leonard Greenburg, "Chlorinated Naphthalenes and Diphenyls," *Industrial Medicine* 12, no. 8 (August 1943): 520–521. Robert Risebrough, with Virginia Brodine, brought PCBs to public attention in the U.S. in "More Letters in the Wind," *Environment* 12, no. 1 (January–February 1970): 16–27.

The testimony of James H. Wright of Westinghouse and Edward L. Simons of General Electric is to be found in "Transcript of Proceedings,

United States of America, Environmental Protection Agency, In the Matter of: Toxic Pollutant Effluent Standards, Docket no. 1" (Arlington, Virginia, 8 May 1974). The decision of Abraham D. Sofaer on GE's pollution of the Hudson River is entitled "State of New York Department of Environmental Conservation, In the Matter of Alleged Violations of Sections 17-0501, 17-0511 and 11-0503 of the Environmental Conservation Law of the State of New York by: General Electric Company, Respondent; Interim Opinion and Order, File no. 2833" (Albany, N.Y., 9 February 1976).

The volume entitled *National Conference on Polychlorinated Biphenyls*, Chicago, 19–21 November 1975, Report no. EPA-560/6-75-004 (Washington, D.C.: Office of Toxic Substances, EPA, March 1976), contains a wealth of papers on all aspects of PCBs. Among them are Masanori Kuratsune, Yoshito Masuda, and Junya Nagayama, "Some of the Recent Findings Concerning Yusho"; Renate Kimbrough, "Pathological Findings Associated with Chronic Experimental Exposure to PCBs"; James R. Allen and D. H. Norback, "Pathobiological Responses of Primates to Polychlorinated Biphenyl Exposure"; Frederick W. Kutz and S. C. Strassman, "Residues of Polychlorinated Biphenyls in the General Population of the United States"; and Charles R. Walker, "The Occurrence of PCBs in the National Fish and Wildlife Monitoring Program."

Doris J. Finlay, Frederick H. Siff, and Vincent J. DeCarlo, *Review of PCB Levels in the Environment*, Report no. EPA-560/7-76-001 (Washington, D.C.: Office of Toxic Substances, EPA, January 1976), contains information of value that has, in some instances at least, failed to reach the public, for example, the data showing PCB contamination to be "both widespread and at high levels" throughout the state of Connecticut.

Versar, Inc., prepared *PCBs in the United States Industrial Use and Environmental Distribution*, Report no. EPA-560/6-76-005 (Washington, D.C.: Office of Toxic Substances, EPA, 25 February 1976), which offers a history of the production, usage, and distribution of PCBs, dating back to Theodore Swann's efforts in the 1920s. The U.S. Government Printing Office published *Polychlorinated Biphenyls (PCB)*, Hearings Before the Subcommittee on Fisheries and Wildlife Conservation and the Environment, Committee on Merchant Marine and Fisheries, House of Representatives, 94th Cong., 2d sess., 28–30 January 1976, Serial no. 94-24, in which various witnesses, such as Representative Richard Ottinger and John Harris-Cronin, a Hudson River conservationist, had at the EPA for its "scandalous and deplorable episode of inaction and ineffectiveness." PCB contamination of Canadian fish, wildlife, and humans is documented in *Background to the Regulations of Polychlorinated Biphenyls (PCB) in Canada*, Technical Report no. 76-1, Environment Canada, 1 April 1976. Perhaps the most comprehensive work summarizing the physical and biological properties of PCBs is to be found in Dr. Ian T. C. Nesbit's Criteria Document on PCBs, written for the EPA in 1976.

In June 1978 the New York Academy of Sciences held an International Conference on Health Effects of Halogenated Aromatic Hydrocarbons. Among the papers presented were Marcus and Dora Wasserman, "World PCB Map—Storage in Man and His Biologic Environment in the Seventies"; Harukuni Urabe and Masakazu Asahi, "Present State of Yusho Patients"; S. Alf Fischbein, Mary Snow Wolff, Ruth Lillis, Irving J. Selikoff, and John Thornton, "Clinical Findings Among PCB-Exposed Workers in a Capacitor Manufacturing Facility"; and Albert Miller, Raphael Warshaw, S. Alf Fischbein, and John Thornton, "Decrease in Vital Capacity in PCB-Exposed Workers in a Capacitor Manufacturing Facility."

CHAPTER 4: DRINKING WATER AND CANCER

For descriptions of the drinking water problems before the passage of the Safe Drinking Water Act in 1974, see Robert Harris and Ed Brecher's "Is the Water Safe to Drink?" published in *Consumer Reports* in a three-part series (June, July, August 1974). These articles were among the first to focus national attention on the problem of organics in drinking water and to offer a number of potential solutions. For a historical perspective on water pollution (not including cancer) see M. N. Baker's *The Quest for Pure Water* (Lancaster, Pa.: Lancaster Press, 1948). A Nader report, David Zwick and Marcy Benstock's *Water Wasteland* (New York: Grossman Publishers, Inc., 1971), was one of the early popular books to look at water. Few have appeared since.

Among the technical publications addressing the organic contamination of drinking water and adverse health effects are *Drinking Water and Health,* a 1977 report by the National Academy of Sciences ordered by Congress. It assesses the health effects of contaminants identified in drinking water at that time. A more summary assessment appears in the lengthy preamble to the EPA's proposed regulations to control organic chemicals in drinking water, *Federal Register* 43, no. 28 (9 February 1978): 5,755 ff. The epidemiological evidence linking chemically contaminated drinking water to increased cancer mortality is discussed by Ken Cantor in a forthcoming article in the *Journal of the National Cancer Institute.* Examples of particular epidemiological studies demonstrating this correlation include R. H. Harris, T. Page, and N. A. Reiches, "Carcinogens in Drinking Water," in *Origins of Human Cancer* (Cold Spring Harbor, N.Y.: Cold Spring Harbor Laboratory, 1977), vol. A.

A recent broad survey of many of the issues raised by chemical contaminations of drinking water, including adverse health effects, costs of treatment, and current European practice, is contained in the report of a conference entitled "Safe Drinking Water: Current and Future Problems" held in March 1978 by Resources for the Future, Washington, D.C. (in press).

Finally, there are numerous documents (many published by the EPA) available on the extent of chemical contamination of the nation's drinking water supplies: J. M. Symons et al., "National Organics Reconnaissance Survey for Halogenated Organics," *Journal of the American Water Works Association* 67 (1975): 634; "National Organics Monitoring Survey," EPA Office of Water Supply, 1977; and "Report to Congress: Preliminary Assessment of Suspected Carcinogens in Drinking Water," E.P.A. 1975. In addition there are guides for treatment: "Interim Treatment Guide for the Control of Chloroform and Other Trihalomethanes," EPA Water Supply Research Division, MERL, 1976; "Interim Treatment Guide for Controlling Organic Contaminants in Drinking Water Using Granular Activated Carbon," EPA Water Supply Research Division, MERL, 1978. Cost estimates are available for installing activated carbon filtration: "The Economic Impact of a Trihalomethane Regulation for Drinking Water," prepared by Temple, Barker and Sloane, Inc., EPA Office of Water Supply, August 1977; "Revised Economic Impact Analysis of Proposed Regulations on Organic Contaminants in Drinking Water," prepared by Temple, Barker and Sloane, Inc., EPA Office of Drinking Water, July 1978. The EPA also publishes pamphlets describing the Safe Drinking Water Act and how it works, for example, "Is Your Drinking Water Safe?" March 1977.

CHAPTER 5: AIRBORNE CARCINOGENS

The few books that have been written deal with the health effects of air pollutants in general, rather than carcinogens in particular. A good, relatively early treatment of the subject is Ronald G. Ridker's *Economic Costs of Air Pollution: Studies in Measurement* (New York: Frederick A. Praeger, 1967). Although the book does not contain detailed studies of individual pollutants, it does provide the first comprehensive estimate of the health care costs imposed by various air pollutants. *Environmental Factors in Respiratory Disease* (New York: Academic Press, 1972), edited by Douglas H. K. Lee, contains papers on the relationship between respiratory disease and air pollution. Several papers discuss the relationship between air pollutants and cancer.

Undoubtedly the best overall study of the health effects of air pollution is Lester B. Lane and Eugene P. Sesken's *Air Pollution and Human Health* (Baltimore: The Johns Hopkins University Press, 1977). This work contains the most recent and comprehensive compilation of health effects studies on various air pollutants and the most recent estimate of the costs and benefits of controlling air pollution. It also provides an overview of the effects of air pollution on cancer rates. Much shorter but very useful is *The Health Costs of Air Pollution* (New York: American Lung Association, 1977). It contains a very readable summary of the major studies performed during the period and provides an excellent comparative analysis for use by laymen.

One of the few works that focuses almost exclusively on carcinogenic air pollutants is the *Proceedings of the Specialty Conference on Toxic Substances in the Air and Environment,* conducted by the New England Section of the Air Pollution Control Association in November 1976 (Pittsburgh: APCA, 1977). This volume contains summaries of a number of papers on individual pollutants, such as arsenic and vinyl chloride, that have been linked to cancer in humans. The National Academy of Sciences has also done a series of detailed monographs on individual pollutants that may pose a carcinogenic hazard to man. Among them are *Chromium* (Washington, D.C.: NAS, 1974), *Particulate Polycyclic Organic Matter* (Washington, D.C.: NAS, 1972), and *Vanadium* (Washington, D.C.: NAS, 1974). These are probably the most detailed studies available on individual pollutants, although they cover only a fraction of those suspected of causing cancer in man.

Much of the more recent research on airborne carcinogens has been performed by independent research organizations under contract to the Environmental Protection Agency, such as the GCA Corporation and the Mitre Corporation, which studied "high volume" chemicals. For GCA, see volumes 1–14, Contract no. 68-02-1337 (Bedford, Mass.: GCA/Technology Division, 1976). These reports contain information on the health effects of each pollutant, production sources, and potential control measures. The Mitre report covers additional organic pollutants. The Mitre reports, all prepared pursuant to EPA Contract no. 68-02-1495, are available from either Mitre or the Environmental Protection Agency. The Mitre Corporation has also completed a study entitled "A Preliminary Assessment of the Problems of Carcinogens in the Atmosphere," MTR-6874 (Mitre Corporation, 1975), which is an excellent summary of the relationship between cancer and air pollution as well as a discussion of the prospects for controlling carcinogens in the atmosphere.

CHAPTER 6: PESTICIDES

The most comprehensive description of pesticides and their effects is found in the U.S. Department of HEW's *Report of the Secretary's Commission on Pesticides and Their Relationship to Environmental Health*

(December 1969), more often called the Mrak Commission Report, after its chairman. This review of five thousand scientific references surveys the uses and benefits of pesticides; the routes of environmental contamination, including air, water, soil, and food; the manufacture and use of pesticides; accidents; and alternatives for pest control.

A report by the House Committee on Government Operations in 1969 (H. Rept. 91–637, 91st Cong., 1st sess.), *Deficiencies in the Administration of the Federal Insecticide, Fungicide and Rodenticide Act,* investigated charges by the General Accounting Office that the Department of Agriculture was inefficient at enforcing health and safety procedures involving pesticides.

The manner in which American agricultural practice has become deeply enmeshed in pesticide use is explored in a report prepared for the Council on Environmental Quality and the EPA in July 1974, *Farmers' Pesticide Use Decisions and Attitudes on Alternate Crop Protection Methods,* by R. von Rümker and F. Horay. The study outlines farmers' reasons for using pesticides, their knowledge of alternative crop protection methodology, and sources of information on chemical and non-chemical crop protection.

A sixty-member committee of the NAS National Research Council spent three years putting together a report on pesticide use; *Contemporary Pest Control Practices and Prospects* (Washington, D.C.: NAS, 1975) is an extensive and comprehensive five-volume treatise that found that chemical insecticides were losing their effectiveness and recommended replacement of many of them within the next ten years.

The April 1976 "Oversight Hearings" of the House Committee on Interstate and Foreign Commerce (94th Cong., 2d sess.) chaired by Congressman John Moss also addressed the pesticide problem from a critical point of view—this time *after* the jurisdiction for pesticide regulation had been switched to the EPA. It suggested that programs under FIFRA must be changed to reduce hazardous use of pesticides. The hearings concentrated on the lack of a sound cancer policy at the EPA, determination of benefits and risks, and difficulties with data assimilation and interpretation. Data problems in pesticide safety were also the subject of hearings before the Subcommittee on Conservation, Energy and Natural Resources of the House Committee on Government Operations (94th Cong., 2d sess., 11 February and 5 March 1976).

A number of Government Accounting Office reports have assessed the EPA pesticide program. Key reports are *EPA Efforts to Remove Hazardous Pesticides from the Channels of Trade* (26 April 1973), *Pesticides: Actions Needed to Protect the Consumer from Defective Products* (23 May 1974), and *Federal Pesticide Registration Program: Is It Protecting the Public and the Environment Adequately from Pesticide Hazards?* (4 December 1975).

The pesticide problem came alive, of course, not in the technical or governmental literature but with publication of Rachel Carson's *Silent Spring* (Boston: Houghton Mifflin Company, 1962). The evolution of the book and a description of its social, political, and scientific impact can be found in Frank Graham, Jr.'s *Since Silent Spring* (Boston: Houghton Mifflin Company, 1970).

Integrated pest management (IPM), the science of biological and limited chemical pest control is no longer a subject known only to entomologists. Several practical guides describe alternatives for the home gardener. These include *How to Control Garden Pests Without Killing Almost Everything Else,* by Helga and William Olkowski, available for $1.50 from the Rachel Carson Trust for the Living Environment, Inc., 8940 Jones Hill Road, Washington, D.C. 20014. Dr. and Mrs. Olkowski have written extensively on the subject of IPM. You might want to request reprints of articles by them from the John Muir Institute, 1307 Acton Street, Berkeley, California 94706. *Pesticide Dos and Don'ts,* a pamphlet by Dr. Ian T. C. Nisbet, is published by the National Audubon Society, 950 Third Avenue, New York, New York 10022.

The National Wildlife Federation (1412 16th Street, NW, Washington, D.C. 20036) has a pamphlet called *Pesticides and Your Environment,* by John Cary Stone, which suggests pesticide alternatives and ranks pesticides for home use in terms of safest to most dangerous. A very recent book on IPM is *Least Is Best—A Guide to Putting Integrated Pest Management into Action,* edited by Jerome Goldstein (J.G. Press, Box 351, Emmaus, Pennsylvania 18049, 1978, $6.95). Chapters and sections include "De-Spraying America," "Farmers' Motivation for Using . . . and for Not Using Pesticides," "Research in IPM," "IPM for Consumers and Policy Makers," and "The New IPM Industry," which is an assessment of employment as agricultural practice shifts to less reliance on chemical pesticides.

CHAPTER 7: DIET

Among the most useful books is Harrison Wellford's *Sowing the Wind* (New York: Grossman Publishers, Inc., 1972), a Nader report on the Department of Agriculture, food safety, and the chemical harvest, which identifies the major problems with pesticide use, additives in animal feed, and government meat programs. Another Nader report is *The Chemical Feast,* by James S. Turner (New York: Grossman Publishers, Inc., 1970), an exposé on the food industry, the FDA, and the food safety laws. Also in the muckraking vein is Jacqueline Verrett and Jean Carper's *Eating May Be Hazardous to Your Health* (New York: Simon and Schuster, 1974), which is a dated description of how and why the FDA fails to regulate hazardous food additives. Beatrice Trum Hunter has written *Food Additives and Federal Policy: The Mirage of Safety* (New York: Charles Scribner's Sons, 1975). For the person who wants to know what's in food and what's safe, we recommend Michael F. Jacobson's *Eaters Digest: The Consumer's Factbook of Food Additives* (Garden City, N.Y.: Doubleday and Company, Inc., 1972), which describes major additives in detail.

The U.S. Congress's Office of Technology Assessment published an excellent volume called *Cancer Testing Technology and Saccharin* (1977), which details the available evidence on saccharin's risks and benefits. The origins of the food additives law and the Delaney Clause are summarized in the *Report of the Select Committee to Investigate the Use of Chemicals in Foods and Cosmetics* (Rept. 2356, 82d Cong., 2d sess., June 1952). The "Color Additive" hearings before the House Interstate and Foreign Commerce Committee (1960) contain a lively debate on the pros and cons of extending the Delaney Clause to the color additives law that immediately preceded the 1958 Food Additives Amendment. A collection of papers by scientists for and against the Delaney Clause as a science-based law appears in *Preventive Medicine* 2 (1973).

Technical and scientific evaluations of the link between diet and cancer abound. *Cancer Research* 35, no. 11, pt. 2 (November 1975), presents the results of a symposium on the role of nutrition in the causation of cancer. The entire volume is a valuable reference, describing epidemiological clues, dietary factors in association with hormone-dependent cancers, alcoholism and nutritional imbalance, and the various dietary factors and affected sites. For a more recent view of hormone-dependent cancers and nutrition see *Preventive Medicine* 7, no. 5 (June 1978). It contains a series of papers from an American-Japanese conference on breast cancer and diet. A good review of nutritional aspects is found in John W. Berg's "Diet" chapter in Joseph F. Fraumeni, Jr., ed., *Persons at High Risk of Cancer* (New York: Academic Press, 1975). It contains more than 150 references and short discussions of the various sources of carcinogens in the food supply. "Diet and Gastrointestinal Cancer," by Ernst L. Wynder and his colleagues at the American Health Foundation, *Clinics in Gastroenterology* 5, no. 3 (1976): 463 ff., represents one of the reviews and investigations of the diet/cancer link by this group.

For aflatoxin chronic toxicity, see articles by Gerald Wogan in *Food and Cosmetics Toxicology* 12 (1974) and in *Federation Proceedings* 27, no. 3 (1978). The National Academy of Sciences in 1973 published a volume entitled *Toxicants Occurring Naturally in Foods,* including chapters on natural estrogens, mycotoxins, and so on. A review paper by Wogan, "Naturally Occurring Carcinogens in Food," is found in *Tumor Research* 11 (1969), pp. 134–162.

An excellent survey of international epidemiology and nutritional carcinogenesis is found in K. K. Carroll and H. T. Khor's "Dietary Fat in Relation to Tumorigenesis" in *Progress in Biochemical Pharmacology* 10 (1975): 308–353. Dietary fat and its role in the etiology of cancer are discussed by E. L. Wynder and K. Mabuchi in "Etiological and Preventive Aspects of Human Cancer," *Preventive Medicine* 1 (1972): 300–334; and in Wynder's "Nutrition and Cancer," *Federation Proceedings* 35, no. 6 (1976): 1,309–1,315. The advocacy of high-fiber diets as a preventive measure is seen in Denis Burkitt's "Some Neglected Leads to Cancer Causation," *Journal of the National Cancer Institute* 47, no. 5 (1971): 913–919; and Burkitt, Walker, and Painter, "Effect of Dietary Fiber on Stools and Transit-Times and Its Role in the Causation of Disease," *The Lancet* 2 (1972): 1,408. For information regarding the role of intestinal bacteria valuable sources are M. Hill et al., "Bacteria and Aetiology of Cancer of the Large Bowel," *The Lancet*, 16 January 1971: 95–100; Hill, "Bacteria and the Etiology of Colonic Cancer," *Cancer* 34 (1974): 815–818; and Reddy et al., "Effect of High Risk and Low Risk Diets for Colon Carcinogenesis on Fecal Microflora and Steroids in Man," *The Journal of Nutrition* 105, no. 7 (July 1975): 878.

A recent book summarizes much of the current knowledge on dietary aspects of carcinogenesis. Edited by Myron Winick, *Nutrition and Cancer*, Current Concepts in Nutrition Series, vol. 6 (New York: John Wiley & Sons, Inc., 1977), is a good collection of papers on dietary factors, nutritional deficiencies, prevention, and therapy. The articles are of a highly technical nature.

CHAPTER 8: RADIATION

Literature on the health effects of ionizing radiation is vast both in scope and in volume. The standard reference is *The Effects on Populations of Exposure to Low Levels of Ionizing Radiation* (Washington, D.C.: National Academy of Sciences and the National Research Council, 1972). Also known as the BEIR (Biological Effects of Ionizing Radiations) Report, it concisely describes the various sources of exposure, the environmental effects, and the health hazards of radiation, including genetic, developmental, and somatic effects. A new version, responding to new knowledge in the field, is forthcoming.

The Environmental Protection Agency Office of Radiation Programs has recently published *Radiological Quality of the Environment in the United States*, Rept. no. EPA-520/1–77–009 (Washington, D.C.: EPA, 1977). It offers a compilation of radiation sources, with an evaluation of each source for its potential contribution to health effects. Although not indexed, it contains a glossary and helpful bibliography after each chapter.

The Bureau of Radiological Health at the Food and Drug Administration has an enormous list of free consumer and technical publications available. The topics include medical devices, medical diagnosis and treatment, and home-use products (TVs, microwave ovens, etc.). To obtain information on specific topics, write to Bureau of Radiological Health, HFX-28, FDA, Rockville, Maryland 20857. Ralph Nader's Health Research Group has published *Consumer's Guide to Medical and Dental X-rays*. It can be obtained for $3 from HRG, Suite 708, 2000 P Street, NW, Washington, D.C. 20036.

The Energy Research and Development Administration also offers informational pamphlets on the various energy sources. Some are free, others are less than $1. For a booklet list or specific information write to ERDA-Technical Information Center, P.O. Box 62, Oak Ridge, Tennessee 37830.

Radiation has been a persistent topic in the popular literature, although most of the material has focused on nuclear power generation. A good overview of radiation topics can be derived from *Silent Slaughter*, by Joel Griffiths and Richard Ballantine (Chicago: Henry Regnery Co., 1972). Paul Brodeur deals with microwaves in *The Zapping of America* (New York: W. W. Norton & Company, Inc., 1977). He has since written an article on microwave ovens and one on public response to the microwave and radio frequency wave problem in the *APF Reporter* 1, nos. 1 and 2, pp. 3 and 14, respectively (Alicia Patterson Foundation, 1978).

CHAPTER 9: CONSUMER PRODUCTS

General sources on carcinogenic or otherwise harmful aspects of consumer products are not readily available. Samuel Epstein and Richard Grundy edited *The Legislation of Product Safety* (Cambridge, Mass.: MIT Press, 1974), which is one place to start. They describe efforts (and failure) to protect the public from hazards in electronic products, drugs, chemicals, pesticides, food additives, and cosmetics. Evaluation of risk/benefit approaches and case studies of legislative and administrative responses make interesting reading.

One compendium of information on product hazards that we have found very useful is Robert E. Gosselin et al., *Clinical Toxicology of Commercial Products*, 4th ed. (Baltimore: The Williams and Wilkins Company, 1976). This volume, found in medical school libraries, is essentially an acute-poisoning desk reference for physicians. However, it lists a great number of consumer products (from nail polish to pet shampoo to paint stripper) and their chemical components. Manufacturers' addresses are included, as are historical descriptions of known toxic effects of widely used ingredients.

The FDA publishes a monthly magazine called *FDA Consumer,* which naturally devotes considerable space to describing what the agency is doing to protect consumers, such as listing seizure and complaint actions taken under the Food, Drug and Cosmetic Act. There are, however, general articles on food contaminants, drugs (laetrile and estrogen are particularly well represented), X rays, cosmetics, and medical technology. The magazine (HEW Pub. no. [FDA] 78–1001) is available from U.S. Government Printing Office, Division of Public Documents, Washington, D.C. 20402.

There is no dearth of information on the health effects of smoking. The Public Health Service Office on Smoking and Health (5600 Fishers Lane, Park Building 1–58, Rockville, Maryland 20857) provides a clearinghouse for such information. Available are two helpful source books. One, *The Health Consequences of Smoking,* 1975, offers summaries of reports on cardiovascular disease, cancer, nonneoplastic bronchopulmonary disease, and the effects of smoking on nonsmokers. Topics such as pregnancy, allergy, and peptic ulcer disease are referenced in the previous volumes in this series. The other, a most readable and informative summary, was produced by the Office of Cancer Communications at the National Cancer Institute. *The Smoking Digest, Progress Report on a Nation Kicking the Habit,* 1977, profiles smokers and attitudes and beliefs about smoking, lists information and education sources, describes cessation techniques and programs, outlines legislation and regulation, and examines the tobacco industry. The *Digest* provides some limited health effects information. The section on attitudes toward smoking was largely derived from a government survey entitled "Adult Use of Tobacco—1975." The Office on Smoking and Health supplies these and other assessments of smoking.

For a discussion of tobacco and its international health and economic consequences see Erik Eckholm's *Cutting Tobacco's Toll,* Worldwatch Paper 18, March 1978, available from the Worldwatch Institute, 1776 Massachusetts Avenue, NW, Washington, D.C. 20036. Action on Smoking and Health (ASH), a nonprofit organization at 2000 H Street, NW, Washington, D.C. 20006, publishes a newsletter on efforts to curtail smoking through legal and educational pathways.

The National Clearinghouse for Alcohol Information, part of the National Institute on Alcohol Abuse and Alcoholism, publishes a summary of health effects. *Alcohol and Health—New Knowledge* (1974, currently being updated) has a section on alcohol and cancer that is concise and extensively referenced. Copies may be obtained from the Clearinghouse at P.O. Box 2345, Rockville, Maryland 20852. Three more recent papers on alcohol and cancer are I. D. J. Bross and J. Coombs, "Early Onset of Oral Cancer Among Women Who Drink and Smoke," *Oncology* 23 (1976): 136–139; Roger Williams and John Harm, "Association of Cancer Sites with Tobacco and Alcohol Consumption and Socioeconomic Status of Patients: Interview from the

Third National Cancer Survey," *Journal of the National Cancer Institute* 58, no. 3 (March 1977): 525–547; and E. Yamasaki and Bruce Ames, "Concentration of Mutagens from Urine by Adsorption with the Non-Polar Resin XAD-2: Cigarette Smokers Have Mutagenic Urine," *Proceedings of the National Academy of Sciences* 74, no. 8 (August 1977): 3,555.

Discussions of hormonal influence on cancer rates can be found in virtually any medical journal and especially in cancer, obstetrics, and gynecology journals. Jean Marx wrote an objective review article in *Science,* 27 February 1976, pp. 838–841, entitled "Estrogen Drugs: Do They Increase the Risk of Cancer?" Arthur Herbst updates the DES file in "Summary of the Changes in the Human Female Genital Tract as a Consequence of Maternal Diethylstilbestrol Therapy," *Journal of Toxicology and Environmental Health* (supplement) 1 (1976): 13–20. The association of liver tumors and the Pill is described in Nissen and Vent, "Liver Tumors and Oral Contraceptives," *Obstetrics and Gynecology* 46, no. 460 (1975): 309–310.

A review of the side effects of oral contraceptives is found in the FDA's "Notice and Proposal of Revised Physician and Patient Labeling" in *Federal Register* 41, no. 236 (7 December 1976): 53,630 ff. Revisions for labeling estrogens for general use, outlining the uses and dangers, can also be found in *Federal Register* 42, no. 141 (22 July 1977): 37,645 ff. FDA Commissioner Donald Kennedy's remarks on estrogen drug labeling (17 October 1977) are enlightening. The Office of Cancer Communications of the National Cancer Institute has a number of informative pamphlets on cancer at various sites, as well as on cancer treatment, DES, and other hormone/cancer connections. The address is Office of Cancer Communications, National Cancer Institute, Bethesda, Maryland 20014.

For an excellent legal analysis of the safety issues involved with cosmetics see Joseph A. Page and Kathleen A. Blackburn, "Behind the Looking Glass: Administrative, Legislative and Private Approaches to Cosmetic Safety Regulation," *UCLA Law Review* 24 (1977): 795. The most complete review of the scientific evidence is found in the Testimony of the Environmental Defense Fund Before the Subcommittee on Oversight and Investigation of the House Committee on Interstate and Foreign Commerce on the Subject of Cosmetic Safety (2 February 1978). The "Proposed Warning Statement," published by the FDA's Bureau of Cosmetics in *Federal Register* 43, no. 4 (6 January 1978): 1,101 ff., also describes the evidence linking hair dye ingredients to cancer. The paper by Bruce Ames et al. that served as the early warning on hair dye toxicity is "Hair Dyes Are Mutagenic: Identification of a Variety of Mutagenic Ingredients," *Proceedings of the National Academy of Sciences* 72, no. 6 (June 1975): 2,423. *Cancer and Coal Tar Hair Dyes: An Unregulated Hazard to Consumers* is the title of a General Accounting

Office Report (HRD 78–22, 6 December 1977) that summarizes the hazards of hair dyes.

A recent, more technical review is F. N. Marzulli et al., "Hair Dye Toxicity: A Review," *Journal of Environmental Pathology and Toxicology* 1, no. 4 (March 1978).

The most informative and complete description of the Tris case can be found in the Environmental Defense Fund's Petitions to the Consumer Product Safety Commission (24 March 1976 and 8 February 1977).

CHAPTER 10: CHILDREN AND CANCER

There is little literature on environmental etiology of cancer in children. Most medical emphasis in childhood cancer has been on treatment, cure, and family management. Genetics and childhood cancer are described in John J. Mulvill, Robert W. Miller, and Joseph F. Fraumeni, Jr., *Progress in Cancer Research,* vol. 3 (New York: Raven Press, 1977). Each article is extremely well referenced. The discussions are of necessity technical, but the review nature of the articles makes them accessible to a reader with some science background. Subjects range from "Childhood Tumors and Birth Defects" to "A Statistician's Viewpoint of Familial Cancer."

A related book is *Cancer and Genetics* (New York: Alan R. Liss, Inc., 1976), edited by Daniel Bergsma, from the 1975 National Foundation–March of Dimes and University of Kansas Medical Center Birth Defects Conference. Genetic factors and immunodeficiency disease are described as they relate to carcinogenesis.

James G. Wilson's *Environment and Birth Defects* (New York: Academic Press, 1973) is helpful for understanding the nature of the processes that inhibit fetal development. The known causes of developmental abnormality and evaluation of human teratogenic risks are described in clear language.

For a technical review of transplacental carcinogenesis see the International Agency for Research on Cancer (IARC) Scientific Publication no. 4, *Transplacental Carcinogenesis,* edited by L. Tomatis and U. Mohr (Lyon, France: IARC, 1973).

In June 1976 a number of organizations including the Society for Occupational and Environmental Health (SOEH), NIOSH, and the National Foundation–March of Dimes held a two-day conference entitled "Women and the Workplace." Edited by Eula Bingham, the *Proceedings* were published in 1977 by SOEH (1714 Massachusetts Avenue, NW, Washington, D.C. 20036). They provide a valuable dialogue among working women, labor and government officials, and environmental health specialists—and the topic generating the most discussion is that of fetal health.

Dorothy Noyes Kane's "Bad Air for Children," *Environment* 18, no. 9 (November 1976): 26–34, has been particularly helpful in its consideration of the distinctions between children and adults in respiratory capacity and daily activity rates.

We have relied on Stephanie Harris and Joseph Highland's *Birthright Denied: The Risks and Benefits of Breastfeeding*, 2d ed. rev. (1977), available for $1.50 from the Environmental Defense Fund, 1525 18th Street, NW, Washington, D.C. 20036, for information on the contamination of human breast milk by agricultural and industrial chemicals. This is probably the only source material to evaluate this topic and to compare breast milk and infant formula nutritionally. In addition it contains an assessment of the literature to date on the advantages of breastfeeding. The pamphlet is not indexed but has a valuable bibliography, glossary, and appendices.

Sources on the effects of environmental chemicals and radiation on children include A. Stewart and G. W. Kneale, "Radiation Dose Effects in Relation to Obstetric X-rays and Childhood Cancers," *The Lancet* 1 (1970): 1,185–1,188; W. M. Court Brown and Richard Doll, "Leukemia and Aplastic Anemia in Patients Irradiated for Ankylosing Spondylitis" (London: Her Majesty's Stationery Office, 1957); A. L. Herbst et al., "Adenocarcinoma of the Vagina: Association of Maternal Stilbestrol Therapy with Tumor Appearance in Young Women," *New England Journal of Medicine* 284 (1971): 878–881; J. J. Nora and A. H. Nora, "Birth Defects and Oral Contraceptives," *The Lancet* 1 (1973): 941; A. Yamaguchi et al., "Survey on Pregnant Women Having Consumed Rice Oil Contaminated with Chlorobiphenyls and Their Babies," *Acta Fukuoka Medicine* 62 (1971): 117; and M. L. Newhouse and H. Thompson, "Mesothelioma of Pleura and Peritoneum Following Exposure to Asbestos in London Area," *British Journal of Industrial Medicine* 22 (1965): 261.

INDEX

A NOTE ON THE TYPE

The text of this book was set in a face called Times Roman, designed by STANLEY MORISON for *The Times* (London), and first introduced by that newspaper in 1932.

Among typographers and designers of the twentieth century, Stanley Morison has been a strong forming influence, as typographical adviser to the English Monotype Corporation, as a director of two distinguished English publishing houses, and as a writer of sensibility, erudition, and keen practical sense.

Composed by Fuller Typesetting of Lancaster, Pennsylvania.
Printed and bound by The Book Press, Inc., Brattleboro, Vermont.
Typography and binding design by Karolina Harris.